# MORE THAN A HOSPITAL

# MORE THAN A HOSPITAL

## University of Alberta Hospitals 1906 – 1986

*J. Ross Vant & Tony Cashman*

ISBN 0-9692654-0-9

Acknowledgements

In connection with Book One the authors wish to recognize the research of Mrs. Muriel Krysko and enthusiastic participation by staff of the Archives of the City of Edmonton. Without their interest and skill, Book One would have been a mere shadow of itself.

Through Books Two and Three the authors have enjoyed the encouragement and companionship of many wise and generous people. To them this history is dedicated.

The Board of the University of Alberta Hospitals wish to make public knowledge the interest and support of the University of Alberta Hospitals Foundation in bringing this chronicle to reality.


Credits

Cover and book design: Susan Colberg
Printing and binding: The Jasper Printing Group Limited
Photography: University of Alberta Archives: pages 26, 27, 33, 46, 70, 81, 89, 98, 130, 132, 136
Archives of the City of Edmonton: pages 18, 19, 23, 29, 32, 34, 37, 42, 45
Provincial Archives of Alberta: pages 51, 80, 84, 111, 116
Glenbow-Alberta Institute: pages 174, 186, 187
Lauren Dale: pages 366, 372, 378, 379

Other photos were contributed by photography and illustration, Media Services, University of Alberta Hospitals, or graciously lent by individuals.

8440 112 Street
Edmonton, Alberta
Canada T6G 2B7

# Contents

*Foreword — Dr. Bernard Snell*

# Foreword

*Dr. Bernard Snell*

Peter Owen's apt appraisal "more than a hospital" has the wonderful quality of being true of the University of Alberta Hospitals at every step of the way. To the founders it was certainly more than a hospital. It was an expression of civic pride bound up in the ambitions of Strathcona to be "The University City."

Since 1906 it has been cause for pride, and controversy. It has been the last resort of victims of cataclysms such as the polio epidemics and the world wars. It has been a centre for those tireless questings which underlie the advance of medicine as science and healing art.

When the Walter C. Mackenzie Health Sciences Centre began to take physical shape, giving promise of a new dimension, it became clear that the Hospitals possessed a history demanding to be written. Someone must bring together all the forces which made the University of Alberta Hospitals what it is today, and breathe life and humanity again into events dehydrated for annual reports, and growing drier with each passing year. The message was clear. The point remaining to be clarified was who could do it. I thought of two people, both of whom I met shortly after my own arrival on the scene in 1957.

The first was Dr. J. Ross Vant, a leading personality in the Hospitals and the community for half a century.

Ross Vant grew up in rural Saskatchewan. He obtained his arts degree from the University of Saskatchewan, taught in prairie schools, earned his medical degree from the University of Manitoba, and came to our hospital as senior resident in 1929. Here he found much to interest him including the therapeutic dietitian, Margaret Malone, who he persuaded to become Mrs. Vant. After his residency at Montreal's Royal Victoria Hospital in obstetrics and gynaecology he returned to our hospital staff and to private practice, in the course of which, over many years, he delivered some 25,000 new residents for Edmonton. In 1940, when war service took many hospital staff away, Ross was asked to serve for six months as medical superintendent. In 1942 he was named professor and head of the Department of Obstetrics and Gynaecology and held that post for twenty years.

Ross is an inventive chap. In the catalogue of Down Bros., Mayer and Phelps, a British firm which supplies instruments for the medical profession, are obstetrical instruments identified as Dr. Vant Model. They originated in the mind of Ross, who described to the firm's Canadian representative exactly what he needed. They were designed and manufactured to his specifications.

Since retirement Ross has been busy. In season he can be found golfing at the Mayfair Club. He may also be found holding court at the Faculty Club. He keeps in touch with developments in the profession and in the hospital. The Vants' daughter is the wife of our Vice-president (Finance). He is active with the Family Planning Council, to which his experience and wisdom are freely available. In connection with this, I may re-tell, with Dr. Vant's permission, a story he tells on himself. Not long ago he went down one dark and stormy night to give a lecture at the Council office. As he hung up his coat he was amused to hear a young woman's voice whisper: "I think that old geezer has wandered into the wrong place."

I also quote a favourite story of my successor, Donald Cramp, who took over as President on August 1 1984. He mailed out to interested parties a document showing a new administrative structure. Reflecting the hospital's current status as a large corporation it listed what seemed a large number of people. From Dr. Vant he received back a brief note saying: "Young man, when I ran the hospital I had *three* assistants."

So Ross Vant was the first person who came to mind. The second was someone to do the writing and search the missing pieces in our history. Our records went back only to 1922 when we took the hospital back from the Canadian army. The second person I thought of was Tony Cashman, whom I had met in the Air Force reserves shortly after my arrival from the United Kingdom. He was then writing short stories about colourful characters and events in Edmonton's past. Later on he wrote histories of Alberta and western Canada, and of institutions — such as the Alberta Motor Association, Alberta Government Telephones and the Edmonton Exhibition Association.

To restore humanity to the official records interviews were sought with some 200 people who had contributed to the making of the records, some as early as in the mid-'20s. And the personal recollections were so warm they compelled a rethinking of the format.

Our original concept was the traditional "objective" chronicle. This approach was necessary for the earliest years and was admirably suited to the post-1961 era when the hospital grew very large and complex. But for the middle period it was seen that the true personality of the institution would be lost if told from an impersonal "objective" view. The staff was a small family group, in which everyone knew everyone else, in which strong personalities dominated and shy ones were appreciated. It seemed that the hospital of this period should be seen from a personal viewpoint, and who had a better view than Dr. Vant?

There was some reluctance on the part of the doctor, who numbers modesty among his fine qualities. We are all grateful that he gave consent, followed by enthusiastic participation.

This is to explain the structure of the narrative which follows. It's unusual, but the same may be said of the University of Alberta Hospitals.

# Book I

*Tony Cashman*

1901—1918

# Chapter 1

# 1901—1911
*The Good Old Days*

The University of Alberta, and the University of Alberta Hospitals, have their roots in the brief but exuberant career of the city of Strathcona.

From 1899 to 1912 Strathcona made an independent stand on the south bank of the river, determined to outshine older, larger, Edmonton across the valley. Beneath the bright banner of boosterism Strathcona enjoyed its own charter, its own crest which won the designer a $10 prize, its own ambitions, and its own member of the first Alberta legislature, who happened as well to be first premier of the province.

As premier, A.C. Rutherford brought Strathcona the provincial University. He was able to brush aside the pretensions of lesser communities, in particular those of Calgary, and lodge the provincial seat of higher learning in a pleasant woodland grove at the end of Whyte Avenue, the broad main thoroughfare on which stood the law offices of Rutherford and Jamieson.

The hospital was founded in 1906, the university in 1908. Their destinies were fused permanently in the clear flame of civic pride.

It was in 1901 that the villagers of Strathcona, for such they were then, had their first brush with running a hospital. The health officer of the Northwest Territories said a "pest house" was needed in the district for epidemics, and they agreed with their civic rivals across the river to share the cost on a population basis, Edmonton claiming 3,000 adventurous souls and Strathcona 1,500. The Hudson's Bay Company offered a large building which was no longer of any value, though thousands of visitors to Fort Edmonton Park now tour a replica of this building each summer. Offered for a "pest house" was the historic "big house" of the chief factors. It was also being used as a clubhouse by the forerunner of the Edmonton Golf and Country Club. Its career as "pest house" was mercifully brief. After a smallpox epidemic a few months later it was burned to the ground.

But the idea took hold. On January 20 1903 "the council heard the medical men of the town with regard to the matter of establishing a hospital in Strathcona."

The medical men came to council armed with a petition which was weighty — literally and figuratively. The pages were headed:

"We the undersigned ratepayers of the town of Strathcona request that you may be pleased to submit a bylaw to raise the sum of $10,000 for the purpose of purchasing land and erection of an hospital . . ."

The undersigned numbered 96 and their autographs, some in pencil, constituted a veritable guest book of the strong personalities of young Strathcona. Robert Ritchie, founder of the historic mill which still stands on Saskatchewan Drive. Robert Ochsner, founder of the brewery which stood till recently on the Drive. Thomas Bennett, the first mayor of Strathcona, who had boasted that grass would grow in the streets of Edmonton. J. Hamilton McDonald, editor of The Plain-Dealer. Frank Cowles, founder of the drugstore. Will Ross, also a druggist and proprietor of Ross Hall, centre of lively social activity. John Jackson of the foundry. W.H. Bedard of the tannery. John Pollard of the brick yard in Walterdale. John Walter, founder of Walterdale. And the property owners included seven ladies — Mrs. McRae who ran a boardinghouse and Mrs. Kennedy and Miss Ord who were dressmakers. The signature of "J. Gainer" represented an achievement. Growing up in rural Ireland the founder of the packing plant never learned to read or write and signed with x's when he arrived on the first passenger train into south Edmonton in 1891. But with stubborn purpose he learned to write his name and was always proud to attach his signature to a document, especially one promoting the stature of Strathcona.

It was a ladies auxiliary which raised the first money for the project. And while it did not proceed at once it was not forgotten and the amount collected was not to be dismissed with a titter. Safe in the bank, $160 represented the cost of a bed when the hospital came to be. Though the cost of a bed in the Mackenzie Centre eighty years later was to be $400,000, what of it?

But start-up cost, then as now, was not the real problem. It was operating money afterwards. Many centres depended for hospitals on Catholic sisters, as Edmonton did with the Grey Nuns at the General. Though it took him three years the problem was solved by one of the medical men who had addressed the council, Dr. Seymour Archibald. A graduate of the Bellevue Medical College in New York he came to the south-bank community in 1898 as surgeon to the Canadian Pacific Railway, and at the incorporation of Strathcona became municipal health officer. The CPR had a large presence in the community — originally owning half of the townsite. Dr. Archibald kept a grand idea under his two hats and waited for his chance to engineer the crucial financial support for starting a hospital.

The scheme received a nudge-and-wink of support at the highest level on February 20 1906 when no less a personage than Premier Rutherford, only six months in office, came to town council with other citizens of Strathcona, proposing that a public meeting be called to consider buying a site for a hospital. This suggestion, coming from whom it did in the way it did, must mean that Mr. Rutherford had in mind an arm of the provincial university which was to be his monument.

Meanwhile the opportunity Dr. Archibald had been waiting for came a couple of weeks later with the visit of two CPR dignitaries — Jamieson the general superintendent and Niblock the divisional superintendent. The company doctor sold his CPR chiefs on what was in effect a hospital insurance scheme for employees of the railroad. They agreed that each employee in the division east to Wainwright would be assessed 50 cents a month for support of the hospital and would receive treatment as needed.

Dr. Archibald brought the good news to council on the evening of March 20 1906, where he anticipated vigorous support from George Elliott.

Mr. Elliott, general merchant on Whyte Avenue, had been elected to council a few months earlier and wasn't very happy when he came home from his first meeting, telling his wife angrily that his fellow aldermen had voted him chairman of the Health and Relief Committee, whose chief responsibility was sewers. The town was putting in a sewer system and the work was lagging. He announced that he would resign from the committee the new morning. However, as Mrs. Elliott observed, "a bedtime snack and a good sleep often helps to settle our turmoils." So Mr. Elliott did not resign but turned the attention of the health committee to the need for a hospital.

It was obvious that the health of any of Strathcona's 2,927 residents was put at risk by a journey to hospital. There were two in Edmonton, population 11,534, but for a person sick or injured the trip was at best tedious and at worst traumatic. Down the long Scona Hill, across the one bridge, up McDougall Hill to the public hospital on Boyle Street, (forerunner of the Royal Alex) or the General run by the Grey Nuns at 112th Street.

Alderman Elliott was all attention on the night of March 20 1906 when Dr. Archibald brought the fateful news from the CPR. So was the entire community. At the end of it Mr. Elliott's Health and Relief Committee was appointed "to take the initiative in the formation and maintenance of a hospital," though Alderman J.I. McFarland, a member of the three-man group, regretted that he wouldn't be able to attend to the formation because he'd be out of town on business for a month. To a person who laboured on the Walter C. Mackenzie Health Sciences Centre of the present University Hospitals it might seem strange that a month's absence would cause Mr. McFarland to miss the action entirely, but it was true. Mr. Elliott and J.J. McKenzie had the hospital open in exactly seventeen days!

The building was ready to occupy, which helped of course. It was at the corner of the 78th Avenue and 105th Street, the northeast corner. It had been put up as a house by Luc Barry of St. Albert, who, with his son Thomas, had whipsawed the lumber, hauled it to the site and built the house — two storeys with an attic. Mr. Barry was willing to rent for $50 a month.

The hospital opened its doors on April 6 1906 — after the first patient had come through a window. It happened when the workmen had gone away for lunch leaving the place locked. A young man injured in an accident in the CPR yards had to be boosted through a window, presumably the first railroad man to realize on his 50 cent investment.

The telephone was connected next day, and the date, April 7, was noted some months later in a tart note from the secretary-treasurer of the city of Edmonton to his counterpart in Strathcona, stating that the connection charge of $4.50 was not unreasonable, and furthermore had not been paid.

A press report of April 14 said: "Six rooms have been furnished and up-to-date furnishings for a first-class operating room will soon be here." There were to be 15 beds altogether at a start-up cost of about $100 each. The men's public ward was in the attic, the women's public ward and two private rooms on the second floor. On the ground floor, and it was very much a ground floor flush with the prairie, were the operating room, kitchen and matron's office.

The first matron, and first chief executive of the hospital, was Florence Tofield. She came from Montreal at $45 a month and brought Miss Vance to assist her at $35 a month. B.W. Johnston, the first orderly, made $25.

The hectic start-up was observed at close hand by Mrs. George Elliott, wife of the chairman of the health committee. Forty years later she wrote from sunny retirement in California a long breezy letter which has become "one of the books of the Old Testament" in the history of the University of Alberta Hospitals.

Of the frenetic weeks when her husband was taking a hand with hammer and saw and helping bring in electricity and plumbing to convert the Barry house to a haven for the sick, she wrote:

"Furnishing progressed rapidly — all but pillows for the comfort of the suffering. Only wool pillows could be found on either side of the river — they harden. Wholesale supplies had to come from Winnipeg, and then only when a wholesale house had orders for a full car load which would be sorted out after reaching Edmonton and dear knows when that would be. I suggested to Mr. Elliott (for I was doing what I could to help — both physically and vocally) that I take the best of our two feather beds and make it into pillows. That problem was solved."

She also wrote: "Mr. Elliott was one of the head officers of the Oddfellows Lodge and they asked permission to furnish one bedroom, to be at the service of any Oddfellow who might need it, but for general use at other times. This offer was gratefully accepted and another room furnished. For this room, when making those pillow ticks, I sewed in the Oddfellows symbol. I sometimes wonder if those pillows are still in existence. The feathers were good."

The pace was apparently too hectic for the first matron, whose vision of hospital routine had been shaped in sedate Montreal. In July Miss Tofield retreated to the more placid life of private duty nurse but the institution had the good fortune to attract Jessie Dickson. Miss Dickson knew what to expect. At age 30 she was in fact an old-timer of Strathcona, having come from Scotland in the '90s with the family of William Durrand, a carpenter and contractor who helped sign the first hospital petition. Of the two professions easily accessible to young women of her time she opted for nursing and went to train at the Brandon General under the famous Miss Birtles. She received her diploma in April 1900 and worked at a community hospital in Ymir, British Columbia, a Kootenay mining town where there were certainly emergency admissions on Saturday nights. When Jessie moved to the Calgary General she participated in the Scottish rite of laundering the sheets on New Year's Eve so Hogmanay revels could begin free of any unfinished business from the old year. Montreal was never like this, or if it was, so long ago that the first matron had no such

A photographer was not on hand to record the admission of the first patient on April 6 1906, possibly because an injured railway worker was brought in before the locks were removed from the doors of the hospital. An artist's conception was sought, and because of the unique circumstances of the event a cartoonist seemed the appropriate choice. The commission was accepted by Yardley Jones

experience to warn her what to expect in Strathcona. Jessie Dickson did and served the cause with sparkling dedication for five remarkable years.

In the hospital's first year editors watched developments with appropriate booster spirit.

In June 1906 one wrote: "The physicians of the town visit the institution monthly in rotation." The medical staff were all the doctors practicing in Strathcona. They took turns being "house surgeon."

On September 15 1906 the *Strathcona Plain Dealer* reported that to date the hospital had received 99 patients, six had died, and cash collected from patients

*Matron of many honours. Jessie Dickson, lady superintendent of Strathcona Hospital, July 1906 — April 1911*

totalled $894.30.

On October 1 there were 20 patients.

On November 23 the *Edmonton Bulletin* reported: "For the first time in some months the Strathcona General Hospital is not at present taxed to capacity, there now being only 13 patients while the building will contain 15 without crowding. There are four typhoid patients but all are recovering."

In December a *Bulletin* editorial commented on the success of the municipally-run hospital and the efficient work being done by Miss Dickson and her four assistant nurses. At the first of December the institution had received 141 patients, of whom nine had died, and it was within $500 of being self-supporting.

On December 24 this editorial drew a letter — a rather testy letter — from Dr. Archibald. The CPR's chief surgeon complained that the contribution of the Canadian Pacific Railway had not been recognized. He said hospital revenue had been $2,129 with $1,300 coming from the payroll deductions of divisional employees. Total expense for 1906 was $4,148.66 — an amount which in 1986 was being expended every 12 minutes.

The proud city fathers took responsibility for the deficit left when all fees and contributions were counted and the gifts were substantial. The baseball club put on a benefit game and presented the matron with a heavy-duty sewing machine. Miss Wainwright, a relative of the undertaker, raised $90 with a variety concert. And E.L. Crumb, the sign painter, made a highly visible contribution. He hand-painted *Hospital* on one of those electric globes which hung above the front doors of public buildings such as police and fire stations. By night it was a beacon guiding the afflicted to the centre for healing, and threw considerable light in a community where the power plant shut down on Christmas Day to give workers the holiday at home.

In Miss Dickson's tenure as matron all contributions were acknowledged through the press.

---

*Mr. and Mrs. A. McPhee — three night shirts*
*Mrs. Durrand — bushel of tomatoes and other vegetables*
*A Friend — 13 oxtails*
*Presbyterian Christian Endeavour — flowers*
*Judge and Mrs. Tipton — two bottles of wine*
*John Gainer — box of oranges*
*P. Burns & Co. — one turkey*
*Mr. Vogel — six wild ducks*
*Mr. Tranter — dozen pair of slippers*
*A.G. Baalim — two-storey fruitcake and holly*
*for the Christmas tree*
*George Thomson — perfume for the staff*
*Frank Cowles — fancy cup and saucer for each nurse*

While the hospital counted on help from friends and the CPR, for constant unwavering support — financial, psychological and every-day practical — in the short term and the long term — for richer or poorer — it looked to the ladies aid. In all communities of the frontier the dependency was the same. Over in Edmonton the auxiliary raised funds for the public hospital with grand balls at the Thistle Rink and rallies at Diamond baseball park. Edmonton's first IODE chapter was formed that year to provide the community with modern ambulance service. The Westward Ho! Chapter raised money to buy a fine ambulance but it was based at the firehall and when suffering humanity required a fast trip it was hooked to a pair of firehorses who knew how to run only at a thunderous gallop which increased the suffering of the occupant. So the Imperial Order of the Daughters of the Empire pitched in again and bought a team of ambulance horses, handsome dignified blacks trained in Toronto to run in soothing synchronization.

On the south side the feminine force began to gather on August 3 1906. There was a meeting at the town hall after which the *Plain Dealer* announced: "The town ladies are now canvassing for funds to aid them in holding a monster picnic in the near future in aid of the town hospital." The picnic must have been a monster indeed, bringing in $708.75. Obviously the organization created for the public deserved to be formalized and this announcement appeared: "A meeting of the Ladies Hospital Aid Society will be held on Monday afternoon, October 1st at 3 o'clock in the town hall."

Their fund-raising added to the quality of social life south of the river, as shown by these news reports of 1909:

"The ladies aid of the Strathcona hospital have decided upon February 12 as the date of their annual ball. This big social event is looked forward to as one of the main attractions of the year."

"The ladies in charge of the arrangements have had the floor (of Odd-fellows Hall) scrubbed and polished to a finish. Richardson's orchestra will be in attendance."

"It is expected that there will be a large attendance from Edmonton as well as Strathcona at the annual charity ball tonight in aid of the Strathcona hospital. A special street car will be run to Edmonton at the close of the ball."

The electric light department added to the brightness by contributing free light, a custom begun with the ball of 1907. That glittering occasion raised $529.

The hospital's governing body took a new name into 1907. The Health and Relief Committee was restyled Hospital, Sanitation and Relief Committee in recognition of its revised priorities and had a new chairman as well. George Elliott had declined to run again for council and the man in the chair was Alderman William E. Rankin, with R.A. Hulbert and J.J. McKenzie. This trio took on a major expansion program. Laundry was an urgent problem and was solved by remodelling a stable at the back of the lot. With running water and a $25 stove it was converted to a laundry, and to run it the committee was able to hire Mah Tay at $40 a month, five dollars less than they were paying their chief executive officer, Miss Dickson. A nurses residence was also urgent so they bought a prefabricated hut known as a Canada Cottage and set it up beside the house. But that still wasn't enough so a tent went up beside the hut.

Though Mr. Elliott was no longer on the committee he still felt involved, as Mrs. Elliott recounted: "Bedding was hard to get, especially sheets and pillow cases. George came home with a whole bolt of cotton. Could I make it up into sheets? I was busy washing clothes but they could wait. So I pulled out my machine and made up that bolt." The ladies aid made a major project of furnishing the nurses residence, also a maternity ward which opened in February, and with spring coming mounted a successful campaign to have a sidewalk extended along 78th Avenue to the hospital.

Official volunteer efforts had assembled so much equipment for care of the sick that it seemed prudent to insure it against loss, so action was taken on March 7. One policy covered the contents of the house for $1,000, another the nurses cabin and contents for $500, total premium $18.75. However no immediate action was taken to pay the hospital's first insurance premium and seven months later the agent was still writing the council trying to wangle a remittance.

Two days after the insurance was taken medical history was made. On March 9 "an operation for appendicitis was performed on Alfred Harris, the eleven-year-old son of Officer Harris, who has been ill for the past six weeks. This operation is the first of its kind to have taken place in the hospital. The little lad had been in too delicate a condition to undertake the operation at an earlier date but grew worse on Saturday and it was decided to operate as last resort. (The patient went home a month later much improved.) Officer Harris is very grateful to the hospital staff for their skilful and tender attention to his son."

On April 9 occurred a council meeting with two events of historical significance, only one of which was on the agenda. It had been decided that fiscal efficiency would rise if drugs for the hospital were ordered on a yearly contract rather than day to day, and Frank Cowles got the business with a low bid of $203.50 — three percent of the annual hospital budget. (In 1986 the University Hospital pharmacy was issuing contracts for $5½ million, still three percent.) The drug contract was on the agenda, then came startling news from the hospital which disrupted the normal order of business. A doctor had brought a man to the hospital with delirium tremens and the man was terrorizing the patients. Miss Dickson the matron had refused strongly to admit him because he was drunk, but the doctor maintained he was sober but in a fever of delirium tremens, and as a fever case, could not be refused admission. So the doctor had the man carried in and laid on the linoleum. Even Miss Dickson's impressive equanimity was shattered. The orderly was away on a night out. Several nurses were off duty. The place was in an uproar. Grasping their civic responsibilities by the horns the councillors suspended the meeting and went to intervene. On the spot they hired an emergency orderly to sit with the cause of the disturbance and authorized the house surgeon, Dr. L.W. May, to make an official diagnosis and decide whether the man was medically drunk or feverish. Regular business then resumed and a curtain of mystery closed over the aftermath but the incident is a significant glimpse into life at the first Strathcona hospital.

At this stage the municipal level of government was the only one involved in the fortunes of the institution. Not for another year did the Strathcona Hospital show up under "grants" in the Public Accounts of Alberta. The province had left in effect the Hospitals Ordinance of the Northwest Territories, dated 1901, and offered a grant of 25 cents per patient day to "designated" institutions. In November 1908 Strathcona joined an uprising led from Fort Macleod, urging all hospitals to unite in demanding that the government pay 50 cents a day, the same as Saskatchewan. "We consider the present method paying 50 cents for non-paying patients and 25 cents for paying patients is not at all satisfactory," wrote the secretary of the Macleod hospital board. "(We suggest) that delegates from each hospital meet on a certain date at Edmonton and lay our claim before the minister of agriculture. . ."

The mayor of Strathcona joined the delegation but they were unable to move the minister responsible for health care and the rate remained at 25 cents for all the years the hospital was in Luc Barry's house. Epidemics of typhoid fever put the greatest strains on hospitals, the disease spreading through primitive water supplies, and the "typhoid" years show up in the provincial grants like growth rings in a tree stump.

| | |
|---|---|
| 1908 | $1,388.50 |
| 1909 | $353.23 |
| 1910 | $2,003.00 |
| 1911 | $963.75 |
| 1912 | $1,969.75 |

In 1908 there was an indication that the federal level of government would become involved as well. Miss Dickson received a nice letter from the nation's capital saying Ottawa would pay hospitalization for immigrant paupers — a dollar a day. It sounded sincere but there is no record of any grants ever being paid and small wonder. There was a catch, a Catch-28. Clause 28 of the Immigration Act stated that an immigrant who became a charge on public funds at any level could be deported. What newcomer would admit to being a pauper and risk deportation?

Government grants were helpful in financing a hospital but the most sought-after funding was the service provided by student nurses under the apprenticeship system and the Strathcona hospital achieved a school of nursing late in 1908. On the evening of November 17 there were two important gatherings in town. "In Baalim's hall a fair sized audience were present by invitation to hear the concert given by Mr. Tees of Winnipeg who is exhibiting the new Victor records on a large concert phonograph." Meanwhile, in the council chamber the hospital committee recommended "a training school for nurses be proceeded with at once, according to the course of lectures furnished by the Brandon General Hospital, and that a meeting of a medical board be called at once to ascertain what subject each doctor will teach."

It followed that the program would be that of the Brandon General. Miss Dickson had trained there and alumni were expected to go forth into the world as missionaries for their alma mater's viewpoint on folding sheets and any other aspect of nursing.

Miss Dickson's first recruit was a Camrose girl, Cora McWhirter, whose future husband Dr. Isaac Whitney McEachern was then busy with his pioneer practice at Bawlf and in years ahead would be on the medical staff of the University Hospital. Cora went home and recruited her townsmate Sigrid Hoyme (Magee) and they formed the first class, and became the first of that very small group to earn the Maltese Cross pin identifying a graduate of the Strathcona Hospital. They earned four dollars a month — earned is certainly an understatement — out of which they paid for books and uniforms. They also earned room and board but the room was in the tent.

By the standards of the time a hospital with a training school should have had 36 beds. The Strathcona approached that size only during typhoid epidemics when cots were pitched in corridors and nurses themselves were often stricken. Miss Hoyme caught typhoid in one epidemic and was out four months.

The institution was so pinched for money that students were sent on private duty with the hospital keeping the fee. Miss Hoyme was once sent to a maternity case at Wolf Creek — on the Grand Trunk Pacific grade through the mountains. The rails had been laid only to Stony Plain so she rode the rest of the way on the grade — in an open buggy with the company surgeon — trying not to look down into the horrifying depths at river crossings.

Half a century later she recalled that the second class to graduate consisted of Miss Foulls and Miss Collinson, and the third the Thompson (or possibly Townsend) sisters.

On one occasion the nurses installed new linoleum and were warned by the doctors: "If you keep on doing that you'll never get a new hospital."

Staff nurses came and went. One of these ladies, Miss Rant of Victoria, made such an impression on Major Marriott the manager of the Bank of Commerce that he offered his hand in marriage, and this was a good connection for the hospital because in the years immediately ahead the Major was to play a dominant role in the erection of the first unit of the hospital on the campus of the university.

For a brief period in 1907 and '08 the institution was under nominal control of a City Hospitals Board, created through Bylaw 196. The council persuaded some estimable citizens to serve on the board — John Walter, J.J. Duggan, William Weeks the real estate man and Harry Wilson, former postmaster. However, although the board was given control of management of all Strathcona hospitals it couldn't spend any money — only funds previously authorized by council. So on February 10 1908 the board formally self-destructed because it wasn't doing anything useful, a precedent which has seldom been honoured in the observance, and the hospital continued to be run as usual by council's committee.

This agency was renamed Hospital and Relief Committee (sanitation being dropped) in 1908 and the chairman was William F. Cameron the real estate man. The next year George Elliott was back on council and took a second turn running the hospital committee. In 1910 the chairman was Hugh Calder, whose farm is now the district of Lansdowne, and in 1911 it was Billy Vogel the

The Strathcona cottage hospital on a nice day in 1909 or 1910, nice enough for a patient to sit out on the upper veranda, facing the sun from 78th Avenue and 105th Street, northeast corner. The sun-taker was identified by Dr. Evan Greene, one of the local doctors who served the hospital, as his patient Mr. Hurlburt. He named the gentleman of Napoleonic stance as Dr. L. W. May, and pointed out the large window left of the front door as the source of light for the operating room. Sigrid Hoyme Magee identified the nurses as herself (on railing), Miss V. Collinson and Arletta Foulls. Off behind to the left is the Oddfellows Hall, which served in 1912 as a temporary hospital, bridging the gap between cottage and campus

butcher. A prize exhibit in Mr. Vogel's shop was an eagle he'd had mounted after a Sunday stroll along Mill Creek. The eagle was so full of Mill Creek rodents it couldn't get airborne and Mr. Vogel ran it down in a footrace.

In the summer of 1909 committee members observed with pride the first paving on Whyte Avenue — two blocks either side of the CPR station — and observed as well that the tent being used for an extra nurses residence wouldn't last another winter so they rented the house next door for $15 a month. In 1910 chairman Hugh Calder took office with a pledge to improve safety in the hospital. An outside fire escape was built from the second storey and the coal furnace was enclosed in a sheet of asbestos plaster. The front veranda was also made safer, in some manner not specified.

Satisfaction over safety was shattered when the CPR announced a change in its financial arrangement. Instead of employees contributing 50 cents a month to the upkeep of the hospital the railroad would keep the money and pay a dollar a day for workers actually receiving treatment. This unilateral action caused a fresh outbreak of that prairie saying: "Damn the CPR!" The furious committee ruled that railroad workers could be received in the public ward "provided there are vacancies."

By this time the hospital had settled into fiscal routines. Twice a year Miss Dickson made up two neat hand-written lists for the government grants — one of paying patients, another of non-paying. Her lists for July-December 1910 have survived, and reveal that the average stay was 27.6 days. Explaining the reduction to 9.7 days in 1986 will take a book.

The state of accounts led to some irritation in council. Alderman Cameron protested one day that with some exceptions all the good-paying patients were going to Edmonton while the hoboes went to Strathcona and big bills were run up which were never paid. And Alderman Tipton complained: " I learned something today that appalled me — that there are $8,000 outstanding on the books against paitents who have been treated and have never done anything to pay their debts."

In fact, bad debts of 1909 totalled $826, but the hospital was doing its best to collect through proper channels. Unpaid accounts were referred to the city's solicitors — the firm of Rutherford and Jamieson. The Strathcona hospital was perhaps the only one anywhere to have a law firm headed by the premier of a province dunning its debtors.

Complaints were more common than in the euphoric start-up period and in April 1911 Mr. Sanford of Salisbury appeared before council to object to the conditions faced by visitors. There was a cross dog to contend with and the visiting hour was restricted to the afternoon so people with jobs to hold couldn't see friends and relatives. What was done about the dog is not known but it's clear that no action was taken on Mr. Sanford's other complaint. The afternoon visiting hour was an article of faith, writ in stone, cast in concrete, which stayed in force for many long years.

But council had more pressing problems in April 1911 when Mr. Sanford came to lodge his rather reasonable objection. Matrimony was breaking up the beautiful relationship between the hospital and Jessie Dickson. After five keystone years she was to marry Dr. L.L. Fuller, a remarkable dentist whose license had been issued by the Northwest Territories in 1903. He conducted his practice travelling out to country towns on the railroads and years later, when bush pilots opened up the north, he decided they'd opened it for dentistry as well. To show the appreciation of the community the council presented Miss Dickson with the handsome hand-crafted scroll reproduced on the opposite page. And to show that it harboured no ill will towards Dr. Fuller for stealing the popular matron the council listened favourably when he asked for a civic grant of

*The front veranda of the hospital, 1910. Matron Jessie Dickson throws up her hands (she often had cause to). The unidentified lady with the large hat is probably with the auxiliary. Left rear is Miss Joffries possibly a housekeeper. Seated left is Miss Rant, the staff nurse who married one of Strathcona's most eligible bachelors, Major Marriott the bank manager. Next, the entire first nursing class: Cora McWhirter (McEachern) and Sigrid Hoyme (Magee)*

$300 to provide hospitality at a bonspiel he was arranging for a dental convention. Hospitality remained a central element of Jessie Dickson's personality. She lived in the community another half century and her home was a popular dining spot for servicemen of two world wars.

Her departure marked the end of the beginning for the institution which became the University of Alberta Hospitals. The converted house had served admirably for the day but always in the imaginary shadow of a grand pile of brick and stone with "tomorrow" inscribed above the impressive entrance. Like hospital boards of the 1960s, '70s and '80s the Strathcona committees worked

> ## City of Strathcona, Alta.
>
> Whereas for several years past Miss Jessie M. Dickson has served the City of Strathcona as Matron of the Municipal Hospital. And Whereas it is learned that she is about to Vacate the said office of Matron; Now Therefore Be it Resolved by the Council of the City of Strathcona, that we regret very much to lose the services of a lady who has served the City so long and faithfully, and we Commend her many Womanly qualities, And would assure her that in her future life she has the Warmest and most heartfelt good wishes of the Citizens of this entire City for her future Welfare and happiness.
>
> 25 April 1911
>
> Arthur Davies　Mayor
>
> Chas Earl Cox　Secretary

with two hospitals in mind — the one they had to keep going and the grand state-of-the-art monument they were trying to build for the future. By spring of 1911 it seemed that something might be just about to happen.

# Chapter 2

# 1907—1912

*Enter the University*

The big hospital had been on the agenda a long time, ever since January 1907. In that historic month it was one of three major issues confronted by elected representatives of the people, others being the city charter and the gas franchise. Strathcona was about to shed its status of town and bloom as a city and messages were going to the provincial government about contents of the charter. The men of council went on record in favour of votes for women — as long as they were married and presumably had husbands to instruct them. However this provision was left out of the city charter presented to the legislature, amid angry charges that the councillors had sent secret messages urging the government to disregard their own resolution.

The gas franchise was awarded to a young enterpriser named Cyrus Eaton, who hailed from the Maritimes and Cleveland, and had a scheme to make heating gas from wheat straw. He'd demonstrated the process at a pilot plant in Strathcona but when district farmers discovered what he was up to the price of wheat straw skyrocketed and the system was no longer economically viable. So Cyrus Eaton went back to Cleveland and made millions and millions of dollars anyway.

The site for the big hospital was conceived on a suitable scale. Council decided that an entire city block should be reserved for it and looked for land to pioneer boat builder and lumber-and-coal magnate John Walter. Mr. Walter owned an entire river lot, stretching nearly three blocks wide from the river down to University Avenue. He offered Block 172 for $10,000. Block 172 is easily identified though no hospital was ever built there. It's now Tipton Park, bounded by 80th and 81st Avenues and 108th and 109th Streets, and the name is somehow appropriate. It commemorates J.G. "Judge" Tipton, who among other distinctions became in 1907 the first known resident of Strathcona to journey to the Mayo Clinic in Rochester, Minnesota.

Council took an option on Block 172 pending a plebiscite and listened to the doctors. The physicians thought 60 beds would constitute a big hospital and on May 29 1907 the scheme went to a vote: Should the city float a bond issue for $70,000 to purchase Block 172 and build a hospital? Interest in the matter brought a large turnout at Polling Station Number One (the only station) and the vote was an overwhelming "yea" — 286 in favour opposed by six knockers who didn't deserve to be citizens of Strathcona. Council announced a contest for the best design. Local architects responded with 11 entries and the prize and the contract went to the firm of Magoon, Hopkins and James.

The foundation was dug. Nurses from the rented house liked to stop and admire the excavation on their walks. But then the project lagged. A brief business recession was a factor. Fiscal caution dictated that just enough of the authorized bonds be sold to pay John Walter for the land. Then a new factor entered into the delay, a factor of immense historical significance to the institution. It was described delightfully by Mrs. George Elliott in her famous epistle from California: "Courage had crept into the hearts of those council men, and they decided to buy some property near the University grounds and build. The ground was procured but before anything more could be done President Tory of the Alberta University came to our home one evening with a proposition from the provincial government, that if the hospital were built on the university grounds (that splendid educational centre that the government had procured for educational purposes) about 160 acres, if I remember rightly, with its abundance of pure clean air and magnificent scenery, which in itself would almost cure some diseases, that if the hospital were built on the provincial government university grounds, they would pay half the expenses, and that they would just as soon as development warranted, build a medical school of the best."

Henry Marshall Tory entered the scenario in January 1908 with a mandate to found the University of Alberta. His "Idea of a University" was limitless as the woods which stretched to all horizons and glowed evergreen and gold in the brief autumn, making so vivid an impression on Marion Alexander, wife of the first professor of classics, that they became the official colours.

Dr. Tory had a knack for founding universities. He had already established McGill College of the West which became UBC; in the first world war he set up "Khaki College" for Canadian troops overseas; and in retirement founded Carleton in Ottawa.

He was everything a founding president had to be including an adroit political showman, as he demonstrated in staging the first convocation. It occurred on October 13 1908, a happening which fairly vibrated with the unique booster spirit of the age, and in which the ladies aid of the hospital played a prominent part in fusing the destinies of two great institutions.

This headline captures the moment:

---

*Convocation a Brilliant Event*
**First Convocation of the University of Alberta**
**a Memorable Occasion — A Great Assemblage**
*Triumphantly Strathcona participated yesterday*
*in the greatest civic, social and*
*educational event in its history*

---

The University's five professors had begun lectures on the top floor of Queen Alexandra School, and to ensure success for the prize Premier Rutherford had brought the city, all grade 11 students had been promoted to higher learning. The University of Alberta had no graduates to receive degrees so Dr. Tory called a convocation of anyone in northern Alberta who had a degree from any university anywhere. And a great assemblage of no less than 40 came in their robes to bask in the brilliance of a memorable occasion.

At noon in the Strathcona Hotel the city tendered a civic luncheon. Then to the Oddfellows Hall for the convocation, at which a thousand people heard

"Strathcona young ladies prettily costumed as Red Cross nurses" help fuse the destinies of hospital and university. With costumes and refreshments supplied by the hospital auxiliary they serve guests of the first convocation of the university, staged October 13 1908, and described by the press as "the greatest civic, social and educational event in [Strathcona's] history." Marion Lavell (fourth from the left) is destined to become a real nurse, Jennie Carmichael (eighth) to become first secretary to Dr. Tory, mastermind of the unique convocation

the undergraduates shout campus yells composed for the occasion by E.K. Broadus the professor of English, and Dr. Tory outlined his idea of a university. In the evening there was a dinner at the Oddfellows Hall with more speeches, and after that a reception upstairs staged by the Ladies Hospital Aid Society. "Refreshments were served to the guests seated around the room by Strathcona young ladies prettily costumed as Red Cross nurses."

The photograph does the duty of 10,000 words in conveying the poise and charm of Strathcona's young society women, one of whom actually became a nurse, though alas in Calgary. Marion Lavell pioneered the well-baby clinic. And Jennie Carmichael became Dr. Tory's first secretary. Truly this entertainment helped fuse the destinies of hospital and university.

Early the next year Dr. Tory advanced his "idea of a hospital." There were plans afoot for big ones on either side of the river, and even though the cities of Edmonton and Strathcona had collaborated on a promotional map entitled *Future Hub of the Universe — Joint Population 25,000* — Dr. Tory didn't think that was enough to sustain two major centres of healing. Edmonton, he said, should give up its plan for what eventually became the Royal Alexandra, and support a Union Hospital, which would be built, logically, on his campus. To this institution the University would contribute two scientific laboratories. "In these laboratories I propose to place at least two men of recognized scientific training who would devote their time to solution of such medical problems as might arise in the province and at the same time carry on research upon the scientific problems which confront us in connection with public and private health."

Citizens of Strathcona took the broad view of the Tory plan. On April 4 1909 city council came out in favour and said it was "prepared to make a liberal grant towards same."

The next day the board of trade met and drafted a highly positive resolution for council to consider:

"That this city is now prepared to join with the University of Alberta to the extent of contributing $100,000 towards the immediate providing of a Union Hospital Building and laboratories at the university ground, to conform with the architectural plans of the university that will meet the present needs and form a nucleus of the institution that will be needed to fulfill the future requirements of the university and the province."

There couldn't be a view broader than that, but over in Edmonton, alas, they took the narrow view. That the Union Hospital was a scheme to do them out of the Royal Alex. A partisan editor called the president of the university "a visionary who is out to grab everything in sight." So nothing happened.

In fact Dr. Tory had trouble getting anything to happen in 1909. In September there was a much-photographed ceremony as Premier Rutherford broke prairie sod for the Arts Building which was supposed to be the first on campus, but Dr. Tory didn't like the design supplied by the provincial architect — some said it looked like a prison, others said it wasn't that bad, more like a factory — and stalled construction till he could design one he liked better. In 1910 he lost his chief ally when Premier Rutherford resigned in a commotion over railway bonds, prompting some opportunist Calgarians to attempt to hijack the campus to the foothills city. Fortunately St. Stephen's College, a church-affiliated residence, rose that year to solidify the grip of Strathcona and by 1911 Dr. Tory was advancing on a broad front. In April, as Strathcona bade reluctant godspeed to Miss Dickson the faithful matron, he welcomed the first occupant of the first university building. Athabasca Hall was only half-complete but the basement was enough for the provincial laboratory, one of the facilities he had promised in a health sciences centre to serve all Alberta.

The man in charge was Dr. D.G. Revell, who was to be a beloved figure on

*Spring 1911 — a plank walk provides dry passage through the woods to Athabasca Hall, first building on campus. The first tenant is the provincial laboratory, historically the original component of the medical school*

campus for four decades. "Daddy" Revell had earned his MD in Toronto in 1900 and progressed to the University of Chicago where he spent seven years on a fellowship. He was then offered a choice of California or Alberta and took Alberta of course, arriving with an appointment as director of the provincial lab. The first government showed how important it regarded the lab by putting it in the original Terrace Building on the legislature grounds where the 25 MLAs met. But it was in the basement, with steam radiators overhead and icy floors underfoot, a combination which impelled Dr. Revell to a unique scientist's uniform of straw hat and heavy overshoes.

*These gentlemen help fuse the destinies of hospital and university*

After setting up his equipment on campus he and Dr. Tory became extremely active on the Strathcona hospital committee, even though they didn't happen to be members. The chairman for 1911 was Billy Vogel the butcher, who took a brief sabbatical to run the power plant when the electrical manager quit without notice. The other official members were Valentine E. Richards the merchant and John T. Radford the moving man, whose big horses had pulled the plough for Premier Rutherford at the sod-breaking for the Arts Building. After listening to Tory and Revell the committee recommended that council ask the ratepayers for more hospital money, another $50,000 to go with

*Henry Marshall Tory (right), President of the University 1908—1928, and D.G. "Daddy" Revell, Director of the Provincial Laboratory, Professor of Anatomy, 1907—1938. Both are extremely active in affairs of the hospital committee of Strathcona's city council though neither happens to be a member*

the $70,000 voted in 1907.

The vote was called for May 10, and on the eve a Strathcona tradition was observed. Ratepayers were invited to a town meeting at which they could quiz their elected representatives about the money bylaws over which they had the power of yea or nay. Fifty citizens showed up and one observed, to applause: "We have been so long delayed in this work that we begin to feel dubious about hospital schemes." The agreement with the university drew interest for two hours with many hard questions but really no hard answers. The two parties had agreed to agree and that's as far as they'd got. Mayor Davies conceded that only the money of Strathcona taxpayers would go into the hospital, with no contribution from the provincial government, but if Dr. Tory achieved his ambition of a medical school the government would be "expected" to pay the bills. But as ex-mayor J.J. Duggan said: "The ratepayers can rest assured that the interests of the university are also the interests of Strathcona." And the next day the bylaw passed on a vote of 252 to 15.

Mayor Davies said construction could begin in three weeks. Chairman Vogel said the sick would be "under a new roof before the snow flies." However events couldn't move that quickly because of circumstances — circumstances which recurred 60 years later when the Centennial Hospital proposal was judged inadequate and a difficult process precipitated and that led to the Walter C. Mackenzie Health Sciences Centre. The delays were problems of scale and site.

The 1911 committee still had the plan bought from Magoon and Hopkins four years earlier but there was evident feeling that the concept was not broad enough, providing 60 beds where 96 now seemed necessary for needs of community and university. Sixty years later the board decided the Mackenzie Centre should be designed by a consortium of local architects led by a man of international renown. Tory and Revell had a similar idea and were authorized by the committee to follow up correspondence they'd begun with Meyer J. Sturm of Chicago. Mr. Sturm, a graduate of the Massachusetts Institute of Technology, began a practice in 1896 which endured half a century and as late as the second world war found him designing wartime housing for a chemical company. He agreed to be consulting architect for one-and-a-half percent of the total cost, supplying designs to be executed by the Strathcona firm of Wilson and Herrald, who were to earn two-and-a-half percent. Meyer Sturm was to exert a long long influence. His arrangement of floor-to-ceiling heights and central corridors was adhered to with every addition through to 1957.

Negotiations with the architect took several months. In the meantime, on June 9, council approved Bylaw 402, authorizing the hospital committee to execute an agreement with the University board of governors. Both parties were agreed in principle that the site should be three-and-a-half acres, expandable to nine as required. But they were several blocks apart on the location. Dr. Tory favoured 89th Avenue so patients could enjoy the view of the river valley, but the boosters held out for 112th Street near 85th Avenue so citizens could enjoy the view of the hospital.

There was public grumbling about the lack of progress. Then, on September 27 a new impetus entered the scenario and all hospital decisions were marked "urgent." On that day the twin cities of Edmonton and Strathcona voted to amalgamate — by a majority of seven-to-one north of the river, only three-to-one on the south. And both sides united in outrage at the Dominion census commissioner. This egregious official claimed that the population of Edmonton was a paltry 24,882 and Strathcona an even paltrier 6,182. However there was no time to worry about him. The province accepted the desire for union. Legislation would be introduced. The rival cities would become one on February 1 1912, and the ubiquitous Dr. Tory had created cause for firm decisions on the

*The big three — from the left, farmer Hugh Calder, the Chairman of council's Hospital Committee in 1910, William Vogel, Chairman till December 15 1911 when the committee is replaced by the Strathcona Hospital Board, a body set up to survive the coming amalgamation with Edmonton, chaired by bank manager Guy Marriott*

hospital. He'd been a member of the committee which negotiated terms of amalgamation and Clause 15 stated that the obligations of the Strathcona Hospital would be assumed by the extended city.

Time was running out. Strathcona might be dying but was going to do so with its boots on. With only six weeks remaining council abolished its hospital *committee* and created a *board* which would survive the demise of the independent city and nurture the dreams of Strathcona in the afterlife.

The Strathcona Hospital Board (created through Bylaw 433) comprised six committed boosters of south bank causes. Dr. Revell was one. Billy Vogel and Hugh Calder, former chairmen of the hospital committee, were two more. So were Fred Jamieson, law partner of Premier Rutherford, and Thomas Walsh, soon to be elected a south side representative on the council of the amalgamated cities. So was the chairman, Guy Marriott. Major Marriott was manager of the Bank of Commerce on Whyte Avenue. He had taken his first interest in hospital matters when he spotted Miss Rant, the nurse from Victoria, and persuaded her to give up $30 a month to be Mrs. Marriott. He was commanding officer of the Strathcona Squadron of the 19th Alberta Mounted Rifles, and a mover in all causes bearing the quality label of Strathcona: the Strathcona Board of Trade, the Strathcona Club, the Strathcona Curling Club, the Strathcona Shooting Club. He belonged to the Edmonton Club as well, but then he had to know what went on in the camp of the enemy.

With two weeks remaining the agreement with the university had not been signed. Major Marriott and the boosters were still holding out for a further improvement in the site. The governors had agreed to 112th Street at 85th Avenue but the boosters wanted more. They wanted a move a short distance to the south so the main entrance would face east along 85th Avenue. A five-storey building, viewed through an archway of trees, would be an important tonic to civic psyche.

The governors caved in and on January 31 1912, Strathcona's last day, civic officials kept busy signing documents which the amalgamated city was obliged to honour, one being the agreement with the University of Alberta. The city would cause a hospital to be built on campus and when the university achieved a faculty of medicine it would take over the hospital and assume the debenture debt.

# Chapter 3

# 1912—1914

*On to the Campus*

It wasn't long before the council of the amalgamated cities, dominated by Edmonton, showed some muscle in the matter. The name Strathcona was dropped, the body was retitled City Hospital Board, and two north side residents replaced south bank boosters. Billy Vogel and Fred Jamieson were supplanted by Allan Fraser and Kenneth McKenzie, but the two strong men were left in office to carry the project to reality on campus — Major Marriott and Dr. Revell.

With visions of impressive facades dancing in their heads they went prospecting for money. Block 172 was no longer required, so it was offered to the amalgamated city for $35,000 — a profit of $25,000 — and eventually became Tipton Park. The secretary was instructed to write some possible benefactors, none of which was the provincial government. The Hospital Ordinance of the Northwest Territories was still conveniently in effect, limiting provincial generosity to operating grants only — of 25 cents per patient day.

The secretary tried the CPR and the Grand Trunk Pacific Railway without success but Lord Strathcona, whose name had been on the city and would be on the hospital, responded handsomely. This titan among pioneer entrepreneurs wrote from London that "it would accord (him) much pleasure to contribute to the extent of $25,000" and his "cheque would be forthcoming at any time as may be required."

Heartened by this and other omens the boosters pressed on. On April 18 they journeyed overtown for the official opening of the Royal Alexandra Hospital, which was also replacing a converted house. A week later they awarded a contract for excavation of their own site, and chose Eben Wilson, whose low bid offered to dig the hole for 35 cents a cubic yard, and for five dollars extra to haul away the uprooted trees of the forest primeval.

Eben's dig was preceded by pomp and circumstance. Guests were invited to a sod-turning but it was more than that. It was a first-breaking of the wild prairie to the gentling effects of civilization and conducted with the élan which accompanied Premier Rutherford's symbolic ploughing exhibition on the site of the Arts Building. The ceremony graced a sunny day in early spring, when the leaves of Garneau were still tightly furled, and the ploughing party had an honour guard of nurses in professional white.

The architectural drawings came from Meyer Sturm and went out for tender — a main building of 96 beds which he thought could be had for $118,000 and a boiler-laundry house at $18,000. On the afternoon of July 17 the board gathered to open the bids. They came, they saw, they were staggered. The lowest was $233,708.

This set off a small flurry of spending. A little earlier the board had declined to put out $150 to bring Mr. Sturm from Saskatoon where he'd been superintending another project, but in the emergency they voted to spend the same amount to send local architect Easton Herrald all the way to Chicago to work personally with the head man and "suggest where material changes could be made in the cost of the building without affecting the value."

*Copy of Lord Strathcona's Letter,*

No H677

28 Grosvenor Sq, W
London 3 Feb 1912

Dear Sir,

In your letter of the 19th Jany last you inform me that the City of Strathcona in 1907 passed a by-law to raise $70,000⁰⁰ for the purpose of buying a site and erecting a City Hospital and that last year a by-law for a further $50,000⁰⁰ was passed, and that the University of Alberta have given a site of about eight acres on their Campus for its erection.

You further intimate that there is a sum of about $100,000⁰⁰ available for the building, and that the Hospital Board who have been appointed to carry out the scheme are desirous of securing donations for the furnishing and equipment in a suitable manner so that the entire sum may be devoted to the building which is planned for about 70 or 80 beds.

It will afford me much pleasure to contribute to the extent of $25,000⁰⁰ (Twenty five thousand dollars) to the building fund of the Hospital, and my cheque for that amount will be forthcoming at any time as may be required.

Believe me,
Very truly yours

(Signed) Strathcona

Charles E Cox Esq
Say Treasurer
Strathcona General Hospital
Strathcona Alta
Canada.

Months of irksome delay set in. The excavation filled with water and ducks floated there. Not till mid-October could Mr. Herrald report with changes which he and Mr. Sturm felt should bring the cost down to the original estimate without sacrifice of beds or efficiency.

But by this time the board had other ideas. The amalgamated city was bubbling with exciting evidence of metropolitan growth. The mammoth piers of the High Level Bridge were rising from the valley floor. The dome of the legislature was taking shape. The excavation was done for the Macdonald Hotel. The Strathcona Public Library was open. Athabasca Hall was joined by As-

*1913 — late April or early May. A crowd gathers to cheer the breaking of the sod for the campus hospital. Nurses form an honour guard for the ploughing party. A pile of new gravel makes a backdrop. Concrete mixers will soon be moving in to start the foundation. A sunny day for the ceremony, but off behind, towards the northeast, the leaves on the trees of Garneau are still tightly furled*

siniboia. Why not think bigger? Why not twice the hospital? Dr. Revell and Major Marriott were sent to the city council as a delegation to seek $300,000 — to build a hospital with 200 beds and a nurses' home.

We can be sure that Dr. Revell made an arresting presentation on October 15. In long years that lay ahead medical students would note his power to make them sit up and listen with rapt attention to lectures on subjects which seemed to guarantee a good snooze.

However, at the same meeting the Royal Alex and Misericordia Hospitals were asking for construction grants and the councillors formed themselves into a

*Street scene in Strathcona 1913 — a crowd gathers for an auction of horses. One side of Whyte Avenue is blocked off for the event. Visible on the right is the Dominion Hotel*

committee of the whole to meet the onslaught.

As a committee, in several sessions, they decided the city must have control in exchange for grants. The Misericordia was offered $50,000 on condition that it be managed by a public board — a condition which the Sisters flatly rejected. To Strathcona $150,000 was offered — but only on the basis of a new agreement with the university, "recommending rearrangement of the board and making the hospital a civic institution."

This produced some intense bargaining with Dr. Tory and the university governors, in which the university made concessions, but preserved the goal of a teaching institution. The lease of the site was transferred from the hospital board to the city for five dollars a year. The city would make the construction grant. When medical teaching began the university would take over but would treat city patients at 25 cents per day, and for each "pauper" patient — 50 cents per day.

The future was thus assured. In a year a handsome facility with a handsome facade would grace the end of 85th Avenue. But that was in a year. In the meantime the board was leading the double life of the board of the 1970s — maintaining an outdated hospital while planning a new one. The future was rosy but there was the present to deal with — a whole year of it — and the present was decidedly murky.

The rented house was too small to meet the needs of the community through 1913 and things weren't going too well there anyway. Since Miss Dickson's departure two matrons had come and gone. A third was filling in until a permanent replacement could be found but she really didn't want the job and was able to charge the board $25 a week in the emergency.

The answer to the board's prayer was found in the unlikely centre of Blackwater Junction, Ontario. Annie Baird was her name. She was a graduate of Toronto General and came so highly regarded that the board agreed to incur the cost of her move to the west — a sum of $73.40.

This move provided a permanent matron but still needed was a temporary hospital to see the community through 1913. The building was found readily enough, just two blocks away. The Oddfellows Hall, scene of many gala occasions including the first convocation of the university, stood empty. It was on 80th Avenue, the south side, east of 105th Street. The building was easy enough to find, the owner was a different proposition. He lived in England and his agent lived in Saskatoon. The agent was agreeable to a lease and proposed arranging details by post, with appropriate documents travelling by rail and sea. However, so great was the public need that the board threw its usual fiscal caution to the wind and authorized a cablegram. The absentee landlord accepted $2,500 for the year and the boosters addressed the problems of giving the community two distinct but equally necessary hospitals, one coming, one going.

In this period they relied heavily on Miss Baird. Older, larger hospitals of the east were run by gentleman medical superintendents with MD's, but on the local scene the lady superintendent was still chief executive officer, combining in her busy person the functions of the entire administrative staff of today's

University Hospitals, except in the matter of cheques. Signing of cheques was reserved to the board.

The board's attutude toward Miss Baird was one of referral and deferral, a relationship neatly illustrated by the following resolution:

"In regard to fees to be charged at the Oddfellows Hall it was decided to ask the lady superintendent if she considered the following schedule equitable and if not to suggest such amendments as she considered desirable. Public ward $1.00 per day, semi-private $1.50 per day, private $2.50 per day."

She was also entrusted with standardizing hospital equipment for the future. She chose the beds, tables, chairs and all the etceteras, which were ordered for the Oddfellows Hall and eventually the campus. Although Miss Baird couldn't sign cheques the grateful board was willing to sign any she requested, for recruiting a class of six student nurses or offering a bonus to Tom Smith, the devoted orderly. Tom lived in the hospital. He had worked beyond the call of duty caring for a man who came in with typhoid and then developed erysipelas. Tom's salary of $25 a month was augmented by a gratuity of $15. Miss Baird was given the go-ahead to choose the linoleum and cork-carpet for the floors and the burlap for the walls. And the ladies aid rose handsomely to the need as always. The ladies raised $1,850 to buy furnishings for a women's ward of 13 beds and a maternity ward of eight, all of which would go eventually into the big hospital. Dr. Revell spoke so compellingly of the value of a clinical labora-tory that he was authorized to spend $500 on the project. Though he never figured out how to do it an icehouse was a more urgent need. On the grounds of the Oddfellows Hall was a frame shack. For $130 contractor James McKibben agreed to take it apart and reconstruct it as an icehouse, 26 feet by 15.

The Oddfellows Hall was occupied on January 20 1913, and although the city of Strathcona belonged to history its soul went marching on. Civic let-terheads were being used up on hospital reports which could bring nothing but satisfaction to founders of the once independent city.

By the spring of 1913 the big hospital was beginning to show at the end of 85th Avenue but the first impression was a distinct letdown. The facing bricks lacked the class the boosters hoped for. All agreed it was "very desirable that the appearance of the building should be in keeping with the general standard of buildings on the (university) grounds." Other buildings on campus numbered three: Athabasca Hall, Assiniboia Hall, and St. Stephen's College — with Pembina Hall and the Arts Building underway. Keeping up appearances required an investment of $1,450 in pressed bricks from Redcliff, Alberta. The rejected local products were not wasted, however. They went into the service building at the rear, housing the boiler, laundry and kitchen. The contract for that unit was awarded also to Olson and Johnson — for $51,985.

June 25 1913 was a day to remember. That was the day the crowd gathered beneath the walls of the brick hospital to witness the laying of the cornerstone. There were speeches — extravagant speeches appropriate to the day and to the age — from Mayor Short, from Jimmy Douglas the member of parliament, and Major Marriott the chairman, but no member of the ladies aid could be prevailed upon to speak so the chairman observed gracefully that the ladies were "doers not talkers" and reminded the crowd that the board had $10,000 worth of furnishings to move into the handsome structure being dedicated that day, thanks in large part to the fund-raising of the silent partners. Even statistics on illness were presented as joyful evidence of community progress. The rented house had treated 156 patients in 1910, 160 in 1911, 300 in 1912. And in case of misgivings about the new building being on campus the crowd was assured it would be "a truly public hospital where all citizens could come when sick or injured."

*June 25 1913 — a day of sunny satisfaction. A crowd which has waited long and worked hard for this day witnesses the laying of the cornerstone of the campus hospital. The stone rests on the platform beside Mayor Short (left) and Major Marriott, Chairman of the Board. The stone contains the usual items. Coins of the realm — including the large copper penny and small silver five-cent piece, lists of officials, copies of the three daily newspapers: Journal, Bulletin and Capital. This photograph is reproduced from the front page of the Capital which proclaimed the stone "well and truly laid." Many years later it would be well and truly mislaid during construction of the Clinical Services Wing, but turn up safe*

Now the date of this ceremony was not chosen at random. It was the final day on which the south-siders could run the show. On the morrow would occur that "rearrangement of the board. . .making the hospital a civic institution" which was a condition of the construction grant. The provincial legislature had amended the Edmonton charter creating a super-board with responsibility for all public hospitals — the Royal Alex, the Strathcona and the isolation.

This board took control the next morning. Seven of the 15 members were appointed by the Edmonton Hospital Association. This body which spear-headed construction of the Royal Alex, had been set up as a civic entity with stature equal to the Exhibition Association. Five members were nominated by the city and three by the university. The university's trio were Dr. Revell, E.C. Pardee the investment man, and O.M. Biggar, the fabled legal counsel of the Grand Trunk Pacific Railway, whose name was already made immortal by that sign on a station in Saskatchewan: *New York is big but this is Biggar.*

The new order seemed to pose a threat at a critical time but what actually happened was another illustration of the maxim that the more things change the more they are the same. Major Marriott was one of the city's nominees on the super-board. The day after the cornerstone ceremony this board set up a five-man committee to supervise things south of the river, and the team of Marriott and Revell carried on as usual.

In the final push to reach the campus the hospital's first medical superintendent came on the scene. He was Dr. James Fyshe, who left the position of General Superintendent at the Montreal General, attracted to Edmonton by an offer of $6,000 a year to run all three hospitals controlled by the Edmonton Hospital Board. One other candidate was put forward. Dr. Revell suggested that his pal Lieutenant-Colonel J. Smyth, Sanitary Commissioner for the state of Mysore, India would make a good superintendent, and doubtless he would have too, but Montreal was closer and Dr. Fyshe arrived in November, amid a flurry of last-minute decisions.

The grounds of the campus were spongy and muddy. There must be a plank walk and driveway — 12 feet wide — from the street to the main doorway of the hospital. There must be a plank walk from the main entrance to the outpatient clinic on the south end. There must be a sterilizing plant — Dr. Revell and Miss Baird recommended a Scanlon Morris costing $1,350 and it was ordered. The laundry was equipped for $4,400 and the kitchen for $4,521.50. The action of the lady superintendent in ordering $4,250 worth of equipment and furniture for the operating rooms was approved.

On January 24 1914 the building was ready for official opening. Patients and staff were packing up to leave the Oddfellows Hall, including the student nurses — who now numbered 12. Miss Baird had doubled the size of the school of nursing to cope with the impressive number of beds. In one year, in three locations, the bed count had risen from 20 to 50 to 96.

As of January 24 1914 the institution, and the locale of this history, were fixed on the campus of the University of Alberta. It was a Saturday.

Major Marriott spoke on behalf of the board. "Our policy has always been the best in the west consistent with funds available."

Mayor McNamara declared the building officially open. "In all my travels through the United States and Canada I have never seen a finer hospital."

Dr. Tory spoke for the university and the new faculty of medicine which would work in conjunction with the hospital. "Teaching hospitals do an immeasurable amount of good."

# Chapter 4

# 1914—1916
*The Ninety-bed Hospital*

D r. Tory had been his busiest self creating the faculty of medicine which would make a teaching hospital of the building opened that day. And his vision of a framework within which the practice and pedagogy of medicine would develop in partnership had the guidance and backing of a classic study on medical education. Funded by the Carnegie Foundation for the Advancement of Teaching it was the famous Flexner Report.

At the request of the Foundation Abraham Flexner visited all 155 medical schools in the United States and Canada and published judgments of startling bluntness on all. He graded their entrance requirements, teaching staff, resources, clinical and laboratory facilities. Of 56 of the institutions he graded Flexner wrote "there is not a shred of justification for their continued existence."

His Canadian travels brought him only as far as Winnipeg and the University of Manitoba, but he predicted that "other institutions will in time be established nearer the Pacific coast as the country grows in population." (Doubtless Dr. Tory said Amen to that.)

"In the matter of medical schools," Flexner wrote, "Canada reproduces the United States on a greatly reduced scale. Western University is as bad as anything to be found on this side of the line (a wretched chemical laboratory, a few hundred books in cases to which the janitor carries the key); Laval and Halifax Medical College are feeble (though at Laval 'obstetrical opportunity is abundant'); Winnipeg and Kingston represent a distinct effort towards higher ideals; McGill and Toronto are excellent."

Flexner emphasized a relationship of medical school to university and where none existed the school soon disappeared. He found relationships of all sorts and sizes — Halifax Medical College had a "peculiar" one with Dalhousie, "staff appointments are made by the government for its own reasons; the medical college is forced to confer professorships on these appointees." Pointing to the future the report concluded that "medical schools will, if rightly conducted, articulate not only with the universities, but articulate with their general system of education."

Abraham Flexner published his landmark report in 1910. By October 3 1912 when the university senate took the first step towards establishing a medical school in Alberta the report had the force of holy writ. The ranks of the senate, which held authority over academic matters, included "Paddy" Nolan, Calgary lawyer, who in youth earned a gold medal for oratory at Trinity College, Dublin.

"Paddy" put his talents to work in the following resolution: "The senate is of the opinion that the time is closely approaching when a medical faculty should be established in this university."

The sentiment was seconded by the godfather of the university, A.C. Rutherford, and went to the board of governors, which held authority over spending and hiring. On March 20 1913 the governors said: "We agree to proceed with the first three years of a five-year medical course." Alberta students would take a pre-medical year, two of medicine, and the final two years of their training at one of the older institutions to the east. And while Henry Marshall Tory could not claim an Irish gold medal for oratory he was to say later that it was "the only medical school between Peking to the west and Winnipeg to the east."

When the hospital moved on campus in January 1914 the faculty of medicine was close to its first meeting, which took place April 3, with Dr. Tory presiding. The only medical doctor in attendance was Dr. Revell as Professor of Anatomy. Dr. F.J. Lewis represented botany, Dr. A.L.F. Lehman — chemistry, Dr. R.W. Boyle — physics and C.E. Race was university secretary.

A course of studies was drawn up from a book Dr. Revell had brought from Chicago — *The Model Medical Curriculum* — prepared by 100 leading educators of the United States and Canada, as a committee of the American Medical Association.

The program got underway in the fall of 1914 with 26 students taught by two full-time professors and six part-timers. However, events beyond the scope of the Senate or the Board of Governors or the Edmonton Hospital Board were beginning to control the destiny of the hospital, and the proposed partnership between hospital and the faculty of medicine. The assembly of the first class coincided with the opening battles of the first World War. The students were to spend two years in the classroom and in the third year have clinical medicine and surgery in the hospital. But the program reached the third year in the fall of 1916 when the hospital was about to be requisitioned by the Army.

This put off till long past the armistice the development of that partnership of hospital and faculty, that partnership so baffling to the layman, in which hospital and faculty exist distinct from each other but in association so tightly interlocked that the outsider seldom knows where one leaves off and the other begins. Events on distant battlefields halted development of that testing partnership but the evolutionary process was working when Strathcona Hospital moved to the campus in January 1914.

At the time of the move Mayor McNamara had apparently forgotten a promise to furnish a room and the secretary was instructed to remind him. Room charges were adjusted to conform with those at the Royal Alex. A bed in a public ward still cost $1.50 a day and a semi-private $2.50 but private rooms were reduced to $4. And there was some angry correspondence from the Canadian Pacific Railway about increased charges for railroad patients. Perhaps the CPR was paying for not contributing to the building fund.

The new hospital required a bigger ice house. It cost $550 and Eben Wilson, the chap who'd cleared the site, agreed to supply 300 tons of ice and pack it in sawdust for $1.25 a ton. Dr. Fyshe, the medical superintendent, wanted to spend $800 to put washbasins on each floor for doctors doing dressings. The board held off on the basins but took immediate action on Dr. Fyshe's concern about the night nurses, whose hours for sleep were disturbed by the din and bustle of the daytime hospital. The contractors no longer needing their construction shack the board bought it for the night nurses for $95.

Mishaps were inevitable in the high-technology environment. Defective safety locks on the freight elevator caused an employee named Frank Partridge to fall to his death.

*The new Strathcona Hospital
as seen by the Edmonton Daily
Capital*

Also inevitable were moves by the university to expand its influence. Dr. Revell resigned from the Edmonton Hospital Board to make way for Henry Marshall Tory. A.C. Rutherford came on to the board and into the committee which oversaw the pressed-brick building at the end of 85th Avenue.

The board decided to establish pathology labs at both the Royal Alex and Strathcona and then accepted an offer by the university to take over the conduct and management of the south side laboratory. The university was given permission to set up a drug storage room in the basement of the hospital and a pharmacy dispenser was hired personally by Dr. Tory.

But Emily Murphy couldn't find the dispenser when she made her inspection. In July 1914 Mrs. Murphy's inspection of the hospital caused a sharp commotion, inside and outside the walls. To student nurses of today's hospital the name connotes a riverbank park, a favoured gathering spot for parties, but the park commemorates a resounding activist of early Edmonton, who shared the honour of being first woman magistrate in the British Empire. Mrs. Murphy had no official position with the hospital board or any branch of government which might have an interest, and no one asked her to inspect the hospital, but such fine points would not deter Mrs. Murphy from duty as she saw it. She inspected the place and declaimed her findings to a well-publicized meeting of the hospital board.

Mrs. Murphy had no compliments for anybody, in or out of the hospital. People had got it into their heads that the place could not be made to pay, but they were wrong. The staff of 50 was too big — at times staff were one-on-one with patients. (Sixty years later the ratio was five-to-one.) Patients were allowed to stay too long — it wasn't a convalescent home — and there was laxity in collecting accounts. Too much was being paid for food. The laundry seemed efficient but she counted 12 barrels of soap chips, too much. Management was inefficient. She couldn't find anyone in charge of the boilers, or track down anyone in charge of any department including the dispensary — (which suggests they may have been in discreet hiding). Fire escapes were blocked by furniture. A man with DTs was shouting at an open window from which he might easily have thrown himself. The maple floors were warping. There were echoes in the operating room which made communication difficult. The nurses' dining room was next to the morgue; the nurses should have their own residence. Water for the south side didn't go through the Edmonton treatment plant so patients had to drink impure water or resort to the bottled kind. The hospital board thanked Mrs. Murphy for her inspection, but in August war broke out and the Murphy report was lost in greater commotions.

Dr. Fyshe was off immediately to join the army, leaving three hospitals minus a medical superintendent. This was the university's opportunity. Dr. Tory said the faculty of medicine would provide a superintendent for the hospital campus.

He was Heber Moshier, the original young man in a hurry, and had to be to cram such achievement into his short life. He grew up in Toronto where his father was superintendent of schools, went through the system in a hurry, and took an MD from the University of Toronto at age 20. He wasted no time getting to Calgary to start practice, found an outlet for his energy in the militia, jumped to Edmonton as Professor of Physiology in the faculty of medicine, and at age 24 became the second Medical Superintendent of what is now the University Hospital.

H.H. Moshier was a relentless stickler for what he perceived to be the right way. He immediately took on doctors who parked patients in hospital beds and let them lie. At his instigation the board required that patients be visited daily. And he took on personally the job of providing an outpatient service, that essential characteristic of the teaching hospital, where students gain experience of real patients under supervision of a qualified doctor. He opened an outpatient clinic in January 1915 and attended three afternoons a week.

In February, a full year after the move, the hospital recorded 2,179 patient days at $1.79 per capita — 1,793 days in public wards, 213 in semi-private wards and 173 in private rooms.

A salary list is reproduced across the page. The student nurses, of whom there were about 18, didn't make the list but the hospital couldn't have functioned without the young ladies serving a three-year apprenticeship for the right to wear the pin and the cap of the graduate nurse.

They lived a regimen which didn't change until they were grandmothers: ward duty from 7 am to 7 pm with two hours off in the middle of the day and a half-day free each week. Theirs was a daily round of trays, dusting, dressings, sponge baths to cool pneumonia and typhoid patients, and hairdressing. Women of the time wore their hair long, and brushing and braiding were part of the students' routine.

They took lectures in the evenings, when a medical practitioner could be pressed into service, and studied their textbooks. Evelyn Smith Shrigley, a member of the only class to graduate before war broke up the school, kept her books till they became historic. *Practical Nursing* (1907) by Anna Caroline Maxwell and Amy Elizabeth Pope of Presbyterian Hospital, New York. *Obstetrics for Nurses* (1913) by Joseph B. De Lee of Northwestern. *Materia Medica for Nurses* (1906) by Lavinia L. Dyck of Bellevue. *A Dictionary of 34,000 Medical Words Pronounced and Defined* by George M. Gould, AM, MD. Mrs. Shrigley used the dictionary through a 40-year career in the profession.

The labours of the student nurses were often compounded by language barriers. The language of the frontier doctors was not a problem. Though often colourful and salty it was invariably in English. Many patients knew no English and a student named Dorothea Engelcke was still learning. Dorothea had grown up in Holland. In her second year she was taking her turn of night duty when a band of workmen arrived with an injured comrade and proposed putting him on the nearest empty bed. Even the victim laughed when she carolled: "Oh no. Oh no. That bed is preserved."

Despite the hard regime and constant moves from one crowded billet to another it was a happy time for the students. Not happy though for their chief, Annie Baird, heroine of the transition days. With the arrival of Dr. Moshier it was made clear to her that she was no longer regarded as chief executive officer.

Friction was inevitable between the experienced nurse who saw the place as a community institution, and the 24-year-old whiz kid impatient to make it a teaching hospital. Her control over hiring — even of nurses — was given to the medical superintendent, and in the obvious disagreements over quality of service Dr. Moshier had the ear of the board.

Whatever the reality of conditions, by September 27 1915 the board had come to view things darkly. "Owing to complaints of a serious nature concerning the internal administration of the Strathcona Hospital, from members of the

Strathcona Hospital

| | | | |
|---|---|---|---|
| Lady Superintendent | 100 ″ | Cook | 50 |
| Asst & Housekeeper | 65 ″ | Kitchen help | 30 |
| Surgical Nurse | 60 | ″ maid | 20 |
| Graduates 3 @ | 45 | Ward maids 5 @ | 20 |
| Book-keeper | 85 | Nurses dining room maid | 20 |
| Telephone Operators 2 @ | 30 | Laundry Engineer | 60 |
| Seamstress | 30 | ′ ″ Women 2 @ 35 | one at 2c |

| | | | |
|---|---|---|---|
| Engineer day | 90, ∞ | cleaner | 25 |
| Fireman day, night | 50 ″ each | Orderlies | 30 |
| Seamstress | 30. ∞ | ″ | 25 |
| Stireman | 30 | ″ | 25 |
| Polisher | 25 | Total $1285 |

---

*1915 — handcrafted minutes of the Edmonton Hospital Board disclose the payroll list of the Strathcona establishment for the month of January. The grand total of $1,285 does not record the $5 honorariums paid the dozen student nurses, a vital component of the work force. The payroll for January 1986, punched from the computer, registers $8,812,575 for 5,800 non-medical staff, with another $825,000 for doctors*

medical profession and from patients, which have been verified by the medical superintendent, it was resolved that a reorganization of the nursing staff be carried out."

The overhaul was entrusted to Dr. Moshier and Mr. Rutherford, whose strategy, while interesting, would not be useful to someone attempting such a task today. To start the process all salaried nurses (including Miss Baird) were notified that they were fired as of November 1. Next, the reformers hired six nurses, on the understanding that when a matron was appointed one of the six would have to go.

*A significant change at the top. In the campus setting the head nurse loses her place as chief executive officer of the hospital. Dr. James T. Fyshe is brought from Montreal as superintendent of all city hospitals 1913-1914 — Dr. Heber H. Moshier, from the faculty of the new medical school, consolidates control of the university and the medical profession — 1914-1916. The change is less than amicable*

This arrangement struck the board as practical and enlightened, but the board was used to conducting business in private and in this matter the public took an unexpected and presumably unwelcome interest. While the ladies aid might have been reluctant to speak at the cornerstone ceremony there was no reluctance whatever about speaking up in support of Miss Baird. And a number of doctors engaged an expensive lawyer, C.C. McCaul, to ask that she be reinstated. There might well have been moves in this direction but then Miss Baird spoke up. She demanded a public inquiry into allegations of mismanagement.

Caught in the spotlight the board moved for an official inquiry — by a judge of the supreme court. Everyone thought well of that idea, everyone, that is, except the judges. To a man they refused to become embroiled in arbitrating differences of opinion over efficiency in a hospital.

The board then had to negotiate a way out. Miss Baird was offered four months salary and a letter of recommendation so glowing it was nothing less than a tribute. The letter described "progress towards a fully modern and excellently-equipped hospital. The whole of this advance has been carried out under your direction and the results obtained have given the liveliest satisfaction. . ."

Annie Baird was able to leave Edmonton with head high, and with an additional reason. She went to England as a nursing sister in the Queen Alexandra Imperial Nursing Reserve, a prestigious group to which only two or three Canadians had been appointed before. "The honour paid Miss Baird will be heard with pleasure by many Edmonton friends," commented the *Bulletin*.

She left in January 1916 and in March Dr. Moshier left too, in command of XI Field Ambulance, bound for the warfront. He took with him 16 medical students, an equal number of divinity students from Robertson College — and Reg Lister. Young Reg was well-known around the campus as a handyman and checker on building sites. Dr. Moshier got him on strength as his batman. Reg Lister survived the war and came home to be a campus legend with a student residence named in his honour, and was luckier than his commanding officer. In relentless pursuit of his difficult ideal Heber Moshier was killed in the front line at the age of 27.

And when he led XI Field Ambulance on the march to the troop train only months remained before the entire hospital would be drafted into the army.

They were months of drift. With no medical superintendent the burdens of the chief executive officer reverted to the lady superintendent, Lucy Sanders. Nursing training in all city hospitals was put under Miss Gilmour, matron at the Royal Alex. When the pharmacist hired by Dr. Tory joined the army the nurses were left in charge of the dispensary, amid fears that they might be deceived by salesmen with faulty ethical values.

Although the hospital was in a state of drift an enduring personality came into it at this time. Lucy McLellan was hired as housekeeper-cook-dietitian. She served through the military phase of the first war and into the second war as well. One of her first assignments in 1916 was to organize a course in dietetics for student nurses — for which she was allowed $20 for expenses.

Despite the drift patients continued to be served — though there was difficulty collecting from some who enjoyed private or semi-private accommodation. In September the hospital recorded 1,899 patient days at $2.09 per capita. Expenses for the month were $3,990.38, in a total of $11,000 for the three board hospitals. The monthly deficit of $6,000 was referred to the city treasurer for payment, and this seemed only fair. The debenture borrowings, raised for hospital purposes, had been put in "the common purse" and spent on other things.

By September the city agreed to lease the establishment to the Military Hospitals Commission, and the university governors agreed to add the ground on which the buildings stood. There were academic implications, of which "Dr. Tory stated that the medical faculty of the university had been consulted, and though they would be somewhat inconvenienced they gave their consent. . ." There were consultations with the student nurses, who had to be relocated to complete the training sorely needed by a nation at war. Seven were moved to the Royal Alex, others went to Regina and Vancouver at a cost to the board of $285. A special committee of Mayor Henry, Alderman Bush, and M.R. Jennings, publisher of the *Journal*, was sent to negotiate with the ladies auxiliary, who agreed that "all furnishings of the hospital provided by the ladies aid should be turned over to the Hospitals Commission with the exception of those in the maternity ward."

The agreement was complete and signed on November 20 1916. The lease was to run "during the war, and thereafter for a period of three months. . ."

Three months? How little they knew.

# Chapter 5

# 1916—1918
*Strathcona Military Hospital*

The official records of the Strathcona Military Hospital are a military secret. That's because the records became lost somewhere in the many shuffles before all documents of the first world war were consigned to the Public Archives of Canada. Not a scrap of paper remains to certify that it ever existed though many records survive on the military service of St. Stephen's College. Then known as Alberta College South, it was leased from the Methodist Church of Canada to be a convalescent home for veterans who had progressed beyond the need for active treatment.

The college was on military service from May 16 1917 to September 1 1920. The lease is preserved in the national archives along with minute details of what the government took over. One hundred and twenty-two cots with iron-coil springs at $7 each, two with wooden springs at $5 each. Forty-two kitchen chairs valued at 40 cents each. Thirty-two pounds of coffee at 30 cents a pound. Ten pounds of lard at nine cents. One egg beater valued at 10 cents.

But of the Strathcona Military Hospital, we have only occasional glimpses, — in the newspapers or minutes of the Edmonton Hospital Board, which retained an owner's interest in the plant. There was the item of the flagpole for example. The board received a request from Captain Pinder, the officer commanding, for a 30-foot pole on top of the building. The board agreed to put up a 40-foot pole, of iron, at a cost of $70. And on March 29 1917 the committee reported that it was "in fine condition with the exception that the pulley at the top was stuck but it was being put right."

Then there was the roothouse. Captain Pinder requested and received permission to build one and the roothouse became important in the depression of the 1930s when patients paid their accounts in vegetables.

Pinder himself was a mystery. It seemed that the commanding officer of a military hospital would be a medical man but no medical association in Canada had him on its rolls. The mystery was explained at long last when he turned out to be a surveyor! Further information then came from his son, Tom Pinder of Cochrane, Alberta, who revealed that George Pinder had some knowledge of doctors, if not of doctoring. George's father and brother were medical practitioners in Manchester, England, where George was known as an outstanding rugby player. Tom supplied an important clipping from the sports page of the *Manchester Evening News*. On September 9 1907, the paper lamented: "The Manchester Club will sustain a loss in the forward division by the retirement of

G.Z. Pinder who has gone to the backwoods of Canada . . ."

Although the editor may have been facetious about the backwoods there wasn't much else north of Edmonton and George Pinder worked on survey crews, learning the skills and passing the exams until, on March 13 1913 he was commissioned an A.L.S. — Alberta Land Surveyor. War broke out the next year. On January 4 1915 the 49th Battalion began recruiting and on the first day George Pinder was sworn in as a lieutenant. In June 1916 he was wounded in action on the Somme and came back to Canada with the Military Cross. Unable to return to combat, in a few months he was fit for administrative work.

*Captain George Z. Pinder, MC, the land surveyor who commanded the Strathcona Military Hospital*

The army converted a resort hotel at Frank to a convalescent hospital for soldiers with TB, and another clipping supplied by his son shows him there as commander. Very shortly after, he took charge of the Strathcona Military Hospital and served until May of 1919. And then, rather than the backwoods, George Pinder spent the rest of his long and active career on irrigation projects in southern Alberta.

Little is known of Lucy Sanders, the matron, who took over from Annie Baird and stayed on under the army. The only information is an army Statement of Service which shows that she was born in 1882 at Gull Lake, Saskatchewan,

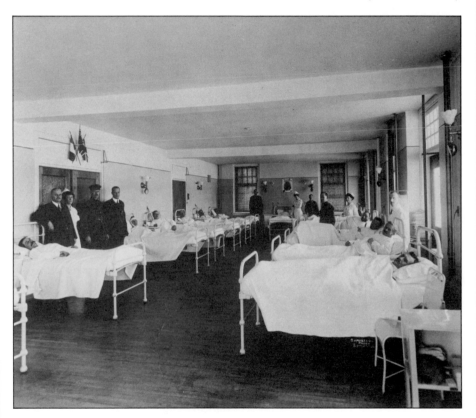

A ward in the Strathcona military hospital, a place of convalescence for men wounded in France. Captain Pinder (in the doorway, the officer commanding) is not a doctor but he too has been wounded in the fighting and has recovered. The nurse at his side is presumably Lucy Sanders, the matron

went overseas in April 1918 and eventually took her discharge in Halifax. Concerning the non-medical support staff, an army spokesman announced on November 23 that "the whole staff would be retained although of course the authorities would have discretionary powers in the matter."

Of the medical staff it's known that Dr. Evan Greene and Dr. W.A. Wilson continued to work in the hospital under the army. On November 30 the army announced two appointments: Dr. C. Carlyle Tatham and Dr. H.L. Collins. Dr. Collins was still in France, with the First Field Ambulance when his appointment was made. He was a specialist in diseases of the heart and circulatory system. When the war ended he performed another service for the returned men, organizing the campaign to build the first Memorial Hall. This was a nice thing to do for the boys. While they were away fighting, the province of Alberta voted in prohibition, and the Hall was a haven to which they could retreat to enjoy a lawful beer.

In December 1916 the soldier patients began moving in, and on January 5 1917 the *Edmonton Bulletin* provided a rare historical glimpse inside the hospital. The paper printed the names of all the lads, and the units in which each had served. There were 62, 20 of whom were on an outpatient basis — 13 were from the 9th Battalion, recruited in Edmonton in the first month of the war. The 49th Battalion, Captain Pinder's group, was second to form and was represented by 11 casualties of the fighting. And more were on the high seas.

The situation threw an extra load on Edmonton's hospital facilities, as everyone knew it would despite assurances to the contrary. On February 14 the *Bulletin* carried a long headline over a long, long, story:

*"No Room" was reply to Edson Lady and her New-born Baby!* Use of Strathcona Hospital for military purposes is causing congestion in other Hospitals of City. Only three vacant beds yesterday and these are at the Misericordia. Royal Alex has waiting list.

But there are steady reports of community help for the veterans. "Fine Concert at Convalescent Home. Vocalists and Amateur Actors Contribute to a Most Enjoyable Program. . . a more perfect memorization of the lines would have contributed greatly to the smoothness of the performance."

On March 12 the papers report a donation of land. T.J. Alexander, a well-known lumberman, contractor and rancher donated five acres at Alberta Beach as a summer resort for the convalescing soldiers.

On May 17 there's a glimpse of a sad parade. Captain Pinder and a party of walking wounded marched to the CPR Station with the coffin of Private C.H. Annand, going home to his native Nova Scotia. Eighteen months before, Annand had been hit by fragments from a German shell. He succumbed finally after a long personal battle in hospitals in England and Alberta.

And the wounded kept coming. By midsummer there were 150 in the hospital and as many in St. Stephen's College.

On January 4 1918 there is a report of good marks for Pinder and Co. under a story headed *Military Board on Inspection Tour.* "A party of military officers from the east, appointed from the Canadian Army Medical Corps, made a complete inspection of the Military Hospital and Convalescent Home Saturday. They expressed the greatest satisfaction with the condition of those institutions as they found them, and complimented the officials in charge in the warmest of terms."

By March 23 1918 the Germans were mounting another big offensive but one section of Alberta was beginning to think of the hospital in post-war terms:

"Rural municipalities surrounding Edmonton are still discussing the question of central hospital accommodation in the city. . . and the suggestion is now advanced that the problem could be solved by an addition to the Strathcona Hospital. Its position is central and in the future, as the medical work of the university develops, it is bound to become one of the big hospitals of the west."

We have very few personal glimpses of life in the Strathcona Military Hospital. Dr. Ross Vant once had a conversation with the late Mrs. Mae Emslie, who recalled that she and four other young women were sent to Toronto for a three-month course in handicrafts. Then they came back and taught the soldiers. As Mrs. Emslie said: "To do a simple thing like weaving, a man had to sit up in bed, maybe put his feet over the side, maybe even move to a chair."

Dudley Menzies, an Edmonton city commissioner for many years, was a schoolboy during the first war with a paper route in Garneau. His route included the hospital where he delivered some 60 papers to the soldiers. The customers were packed in, three to a room, pretty dense it seemed. Many were amputees and Dudley never forgot Paul Rudko. He had lost both legs and had gangrene which made his room overpowering. Private Rudko was a long time dying and had little to look forward to except the daily paper which Dudley brought.

Peace came in November 1918 but it was not the end of the Strathcona Military Hospital. The armistice marked only the beginning of the end — which was four years off.

# Book II
*Dr. J. Ross Vant with Tony Cashman*

## 1919—1962

# Chapter 6

# 1919—1922

*The Army Holds the Fort*

Ifirst saw the hospital in 1920, when Dr. Tory had just obtained a grant of half a million dollars from the Rockefeller Foundation to put up a building for the faculty of medicine and extend the medical program to the full five years. But getting hold of Mr. Rockefeller's money was considerably easier than getting hold of the hospital. The war was over but a tug-of-war was being waged for possession of the hospital and the army was demonstrating how possession makes nine points of the law.

Mind you, I don't recall that the hospital made a very vivid impression on first sight. I was up from Saskatoon to play hockey — the University of Saskatchewan versus Alberta. We played in the South Side Covered Rink, along the tracks near the CPR station. It was a rickety building that got a good shaking-up whenever a train happened by, and this may have been an advantage to the home team. I have to say that we lost the game because Bruce Smith was playing defence for Alberta, and the man who went on to be Chief Justice would be sure to correct me if I tried to say otherwise. So we lost, but that night they had a dance for us on campus.

It didn't take our hosts long to show us the campus. St. Stephen's College, the Arts Building with the powerhouse behind, and across an open spot the three residence halls — Pembina, Assiniboia, and Athabasca where we had the dance. Saskatchewan Drive was no more than a trail but 112th was viable as a street and the hospital faced on the street. It still does, just as it did in 1920 when it stood alone with bush and open fields falling away behind as far as you could see. But it doesn't make a very vivid impression on anyone who passes today. It's lost in a jumble of wings which have sprouted as the institution grew.

It was my good fortune in life to spend many years in that hospital and its outcroppings and to work with many wonderful people including Margaret Malone who became my wife. But my first view was a passing glance, even though at five storeys this was the tallest building south of the river. In addition to having my mind on hockey I was still an arts undergraduate with only hopes for a career in medicine.

When our hockey team returned next season — and enjoyed more success — the tug-of-war over the hospital was still going hot-and-heavy.

According to the lease signed in wartime, it should have reverted to the city three months after the armistice, or on February 11 1919 to be exact. The south side would have its community hospital once again and the university would have it for teaching.

But this plan went agley. Nothing happened on the appointed date, and on the 27th of the month Captain Stewart appeared at the hospital board to say that medical facilities for veterans would be needed for a long time. Twenty-five thousand men would be discharged in Edmonton during the year, and even as he spoke some 30 returned soldiers were on a waiting list for surgery in city hospitals. This news gave Dr. Eardley Allin a thought. Perhaps the veterans who were raising money for a memorial *hall* should put up a memorial *hospital* instead. It was a noble thought, but no doubt there was also a need for a place where

Dr. J. Ross Vant

returned men could drink beer free of the prohibition laws which had been passed while they were away fighting.

A report circulated that the army wanted to keep Strathcona's hospital for five years, and this report stirred such a strong feeling that the hospital board had to call a special meeting for March 10 1919 to hear the views of the south side. The north side had the Royal Alex, the General, the Misericordia, even a small maternity hospital in Rossdale maintained by the Salvation Army. Five doctors from south of the river turned up to argue the rights of the community. Later on it would be my privilege to know them well.

All were general practitioners. Jim Brander had a leaning towards obstetrics, and the growing of peonies for which he and his father were famous. The name is still part of the south side as Brander Gardens. Fred Keillor, as we all know, had a leaning towards horses. His stables were on the riverflat near Whitemud Creek and Keillor Road still runs down there. J.A. McPherson was unique. He'd started out as an engineer but switched to medicine where he was a natural orthopaedic man. He was renowned as a great bonesetter. Stanley Kauffman's daughter was a fine artist — she painted a picture of my daughter. And later on I delivered some grandchildren for Frank Crang.

At the protest meeting, Frank Crang told the board the hospital had been turned over to the military for little or nothing, that many south side people had helped the ladies raise funds for furnishings and were greatly interested in getting their hospital back. J.A. McPherson said a considerable injustice had been done. South side people should at least have some beds available to them in their own hospital.

There wasn't really anything the board could do about the situation. The soldiers remained but there was a hopeful sign. Control of the hospital passed from the army to a civilian agency, the Soldiers Civil Re-establishment. To administer the hospital the SCR installed a man who was to be the dominant personality there for nearly a quarter of a century. He was Roderick T. Washburn, sometimes called Doctor, sometimes Major, sometimes Rod, sometimes "Wash." I was to know him well.

The Soldiers Civil Re-establishment had broad financial powers. It could arrange loans for hospital construction, and through the year 1919 a series of federal cabinet orders provided funds for the city of Edmonton to build a permanent veterans hospital as a wing to the Royal Alex.

This was encouraging to the south side community, as well as to the university, impatient to acquire a teaching facility. The university was able to press its claims through three members it appointed to the Edmonton Hospital Board: Dr. Tory, W.A.R. Kerr the Dean of Arts, and, shortly thereafter, A.C. Rankin the Dean of Medicine. The south side residents wanted more clout on this board — to which the city named five members and the Edmonton Hospital Association appointed seven. The solution was obvious to anyone versed in political action of the time. The south siders had only to gain control of the association, which they did by turning out in force at the next annual meeting. The executive elected that night then appointed some vigorous advocates to the board: Dr. Crang, Jimmy Douglas, and T.P. Malone, my future father-in-law. Thomas Malone had been in business on Whyte Avenue since 1904 and Old Strathcona never had a booster more keen. The Malone Block, at Whyte Avenue and 104th Street, is newly designated a site of historical interest.

At the very first meeting, on February 5 1920, Margaret's father clashed with Mayor Clarke, which wasn't unusual. Almost everybody clashed with Joe Clarke, a lawyer who got his start in the Yukon gold rush. You may think Klondyke Days is something new, but when Joe was in politics it was Klondyke days all the time — loud and colourful. Joe roared into the meeting and

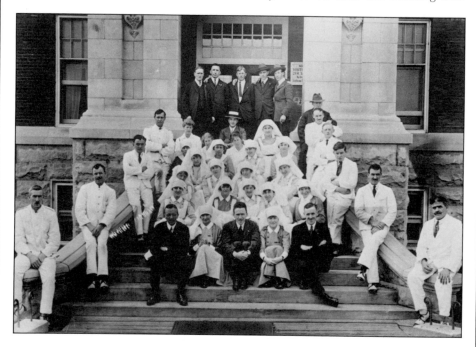

*War is over but it's still a military hospital. About two-thirds of the staff assemble on the front steps. Surrounded by nurses wearing the military veil, Dr. R. T. Washburn, superintendent then and for twenty-odd years to follow, is front and centre. Beside the main doors a sign gives stern notice about the visiting hour. On either side of the steps iron scrapers give notice that boots are to be cleared of mud and scuffed to a high polish on the mat before a visitor ascends the steps*

announced a new policy. The board's only concern was operating hospitals after they were built. Location and design were none of the board's business.

That didn't sit too well with Dr. Tory, who fired off a letter to the Minister of Health: "Certainly all plans should be subject to the hospital board, otherwise it might as well go out of existence." And it didn't sit too well with T.P. Malone, who moved that the soldiers unit be built as a wing to the Strathcona hospital rather than the Alex. T.P. certainly showed the old Strathcona spirit. He not only wanted the hospital back, but an addition which would be a plus for the community.

Joe Clarke accused him of bringing up a "purely sectional" proposition, to which he took vigorous exception of course.

The die was cast, anyway. On May 26 1920 the SCR was given a further two-year lease on the south side hospital and the federal government lent $200,000 for an immediate start on the addition to the Royal Alex. But the joke of it is that the scheme my future father-in-law put forth actually came about. In the politics of those days truth was often more fun than fiction.

A year went by. In April 1921 the city paid the first instalment on the federal loan — and then came the comic opera twist. Gilbert and Sullivan would have loved it. The city wanted out of the deal. Demonstrating again how possession makes nine points of the law the city decided to keep the addition intended for the soldiers. It proposed that a veterans wing be built at the Strathcona, and here's the grandest touch of all — the city would pay for it out of the $160,000 it still owed the federal government.

In the meantime the provincial government had added another comic opera twist — curtailing the powers of the south side people on the hospital board. The Edmonton charter was amended so the city would appoint nine members instead of five, and the Hospital Association was cut from seven nominees down to three.

Malone and Co. had gained their objective, but in the meantime another whole year had gone by, a year in which south siders were forced to travel overtown to reach a hospital, as they'd had to do before they pitched in and built their own. Also in the meantime, Dr. Tory had settled the matter of who controlled plans. The city wanted to put an isolation hospital behind the veterans wing but Dean Rankin found the design not up to acceptable standards and the city was turned down. Cecil Burgess, the university's architect, began designing the soldiers wing and he and Dean Rankin apparently disagreed about the shape of the building.

On July 12 1921 the dean wrote to Dr. Tory: "Burgess should be told to concentrate on the L-shape and that only. Much will be saved by so doing." The dean asserted that the tunnel from the main building would be made 50 feet shorter, plumbing costs would be cut one third and the number of beds increased from 70 to 84.

This letter included a sketch of the first floor plan as Dean Rankin saw it, and it's really a good picture of the place we oldtimers remember — a wooden L-shaped building of three storeys which stood to the north and west of the main hospital until another world war made it inadequate.

When the SCR's two-year lease expired on May 26 1922, many more months of delay were to follow — allowing for construction and negotiation involving the city, the university and the federal government. An agreement was not ready to sign until October 22, and it's fortunate that the university board of governors had the great legal minds of the time to sign the mind-boggling document on their behalf. The chairman was Chief Justice Horace Harvey.

In a nutshell the university paid the city $150,000 and agreed to treat city patients for 37½ cents a day. The terms on which the veterans were cared for were also laid down. For a year the SCR would pay a flat three dollars a day per man. After that compensation for "maintenance of patients" would be based on a complicated formula counting in the actual cost of wages, food, utilities, laundry, medical and lab supplies, upkeep of the grounds, plus interest of $15,000 on capital cost of the SCR wing. Deducted would be revenue from the sale of garbage, meals, laundry and x-rays.

The historic change of command occurred on November 1, nearly four years after the final shots were fired on the western front. But the event made no difference to the soldier patients or the 73 employees. "Wash" Washburn was on duty in the superintendent's office, where he had been since 1919 and would remain until 1942. In the accounting office Tommy Cox was busy with administrative concerns which would keep him employed for 20 years as treasurer and briefly, at the end, as superintendent.

The historic day made no impact on the patients or the staff, nor on the newspapers either. The event made history, but not news. The only word of the university which got into the papers that day concerned George Hardy, the popular Professor of Classics, who spoke to the Gyro Club about his trip to Chicago. The *Journal* was boasting of 400 new houses built in Edmonton during the year. The city's residents had enjoyed a quiet Hallowe'en, with no major pranks, thanks to the cold damp weather. But the coach of the Eskimos, Deacon White, had a complaint about the weather. His team was to play Regina in the western football final on the coming Saturday and only nine players turned up for practice. In Calgary the "Minimum Wage for Women Commission" was conducting public hearings and heard the superintendent of a local hospital explain that student nurses were really getting better than the minimum wage — their free room and board was worth $40 a month. Overseas there were bombings in Ireland, Bonar Law was winning the British general election, and in Italy Mussolini's fascists had dispensed with elections and marched on Rome. Back in Edmonton the Hudson's Bay Company was selling men's winter overcoats for $29.75. The Princess Theatre was showing a movie called *Dream Street*, starring Tyrone Power, Senior. Those who preferred to stay home for entertainment on November 1 could hear the evening radio program on CJCA, featuring a visiting vaudeville performer named Baby Enid.

The people listening to Baby Enid on their crystal sets were little mindful of the historic event of the day. But there'd been a long, long trail a-winding since the founders of the university and the City of Strathcona set out to create a teaching hospital. On that day the end of the trail was reached.

# Chapter 7

# 1922—1926
*Grasping the Future*

Whike the trail was a-winding 150 medical students had begun their program at the University of Alberta and after three years had shuffled off to "finishing schools" in the east. With a training hospital, and Mr. Rockefeller's money in hand, the program could be extended to completion right at home. Still another year would be required but the art of patience had been learned.

The first action in the new order of things occurred on November 24 1922. Members of a new board were called to an inaugural meeting. They gathered in Dr. Tory's office in the Arts Building, at 4:30 in the afternoon, when, in late November, lights would be burning in the few buildings of the campus and thoughts of the 950 students would be turning to supper. The atypical student who needed to create an appetite might be out crunching snow trails through the woods of Windsor Park — which the university could have been buying for a song for future expansion, but didn't.

Dr. Tory informed the gathering that the University Governors had appointed a committee of management to be known as the University Hospital Board, with himself as Chairman, plus the Dean of Medicine (A.C. Rankin), the Dean of Arts and Sciences (W.A.R. Kerr), the University Bursar (Archibald West), and the Deputy Minister of Public Health (Dr. William Laidlaw).

An air of mystery surrounds this body. According to the latest provincial legislation on the subject — the University of Alberta Hospital Act, placed on the statute books only nine months previous — the board of management was to be nine, three appointed by the university, three by the city, and three by the cabinet. Perhaps the government chose to look the other way while the Act was ignored. For whatever good reason, all members were named by the university. Then Dr. Laidlaw informed the first meeting that while he appreciated the honour of the appointment, as an employee of the government it was not appropriate for him to accept. I'm sure Dr. Laidlaw's view will cause some amusement as it was not held by his successors.

Proceeding without the government man the board confirmed the positions and salaries of the non-medical staff inherited from the Soldiers Civil Re-establishment, and discussed creation of a *medical* staff — the people with MD after their names.

On December 5, a medical advisory board was created to make recommendations on who among Edmonton's medical practitioners should be appointed to the medical staff. The names of the advisers were Frank Mewburn, Heber Jamieson and Johnny Ower, names which took on lustre in the new era of the hospital.

Their task was not enviable. Their choices were bound to cause hard feelings and stir up "town-and-gown" controversy, because the chosen few were given dual appointments — to the medical staff of the training hospital and teaching staff of the faculty of medicine. A teaching program needs specialists so the men appointed had to have a specialty. This left out the general practitioner, so that only one of the five men who spoke so eloquently for the south side community back in March of 1919 could be on staff. Through the medical staff the university achieved its aim of a teaching institution but the south side did not realize entirely the old dream of a community hospital.

Since the first round of appointments, people in the community have had trouble understanding the separation of hospital and faculty. And little wonder. In each institution you find a department with the same name — and the same man is head of both. Hospital and faculty are complementary, interlocking, overlapping, but distinct. Their aims are usually non-conflicting, but not always and when that happens the department head who wears two hats has to adjust them carefully.

The separation is a problem for the man on the street, for the head with two hats, and also for the poor fellow who tries to write a history of either. In this case he must keep the focus on the hospital and not let his attention stray over the fence to the faculty side, to something interesting but irrelevant.

There's another fact the writer must keep before him, and this is a good point in the story to make note of it. I must hang somewhere, in clear view, a sign stating that the medical staff is not the hospital. A hospital does not live by MDs alone. I have read a number of hospital histories, very well written too, but entirely from the viewpoint of the medical staff. The writers, MDs all, take little notice of the nurses, the orderlies, the cooks, the housekeepers, the x-ray technicians, the pharmacists, the maintenance engineers, the carpenters, the telephone operators, the clerks and others of the so-called "sub" staff. Medical staff tend to be the dominant personalities in a hospital, and they exert the strongest influence on its destiny, but the so-called "sub" staff would be noticed quickly enough if they all, on the same day, found other employment. I'll do my best to keep this important fact before me. I prefer to think of the "sub" staff as the "working" staff.

The medical staff which emerged in 1922-23 had quality. It also had a distinct flavour of McGill. A McGill man was dean of the faculty and the three clinical professorships — in medicine, surgery and obstetrics — were filled by McGill men. Some thought the connection with Dr. Tory's alma mater was overdone, but later on I did a residency at Royal Victoria in Montreal and that makes me a McGill man too so any comments from me would be out of order.

Dean Rankin was a pathologist. He'd originally joined the faculty in 1914, coming from southeast Asia, where he'd been health officer to the government of Siam, but had left almost immediately to join the army medical corps and served overseas until 1919. From his return until 1945 he guided the medical school through its formative years. Patience and tact were his tools. And although others after him held the title of dean, *the* dean has always been Allan C. Rankin. The dean of medicine has a great influence on the hospital. From the very beginning he has been a member of the board and still is. Dean Rankin chose for himself an office in the basement of the new medical building — not impressive by today's standards or even those of his time, but he felt no need to impress anyone.

The McGill men chosen for the clinical professorships were Frank Hamilton Mewburn, first Professor of Surgery in the Faculty of Medicine and Director of Surgical Services in the hospital; Edgerton Pope, first Professor of Medicine in the faculty and Director of Medical Services in the hospital; and Leighton Carling Conn, first Professor and Director of Gynaecological and Obstetrical Services.

In a few years it would be my privilege to know L.C. Conn extremely well, as his partner in practice. "L.C." led a more hectic life than "Edge" Pope or Frank Mewburn, the arrival of babies being harder to schedule than a meeting or operation. However, "L.C." always carried with him the air of stability. Even though he'd be out all hours of the night he'd be the first to show up for his lectures the next day. As Johnny Macgregor recalls, he was outspoken, direct and not afraid to indulge in self-criticism before his students, a trait which left a lasting impression and example.

I was also privileged to know and enjoy "Edge" Pope, whose unruffled calm in all situations became a legend. "Edge" did his rounds "old country style" — that is, in the afternoon rather than the morning which was an American custom, peering at life through a monocle. He dressed impeccably, and spoke that way from his classical education. He was a good artist, a bit of a poet, a beautiful lecturer and after-dinner speaker. One day Ken Thomson came into his office and found Dr. Pope writing a speech for the Friday meeting of the Alberta Medical Association. Ken blurted out that Dr. Pope wasn't speaking — or wasn't on the program anyway. He smiled, with all the polished personality that enabled him to draw Dean Rankin and the medical men together in projects promoting the cause. "Thomson," he said, "I'm recognized as one of the best extemporaneous speakers in Alberta — and I want to be ready."

"Edge's" serene lifestyle was helped along by the happy fact that he didn't have to engage in practice. The university's grant from the Rockefeller Foundation provided salaries for two fulltime professors but the salaries were small. "Edge" could manage nicely because Mrs. Pope had means, but Colonel Mewburn was not so fortunate. He had to resume the practice of surgery — from an office in the McLeod Building.

I never had the privilege of knowing the Colonel, who died a few months before I came to the hospital in 1929. His professional life was an adventure story, beginning in 1882 when he landed in the west as house surgeon to the brand-new Winnipeg General Hospital. The builders of the Canadian Pacific Railway were just pushing west from Winnipeg. Sir Francis Lister's theories about antisepsis in surgery were new in Canada and a subject of controversy. In the 1920s Frank could amaze medical students by telling them his personal experience with injured railroad construction workers which soon settled the matter of antisepsis as far as he was concerned. His military career, from which came the *"Colonel,"* began in 1885 when he commanded an army hospital during the Riel Rebellion.

With the west firmly in his blood he went to Lethbridge as surgeon to the coal companies which put that city on the map, and during his long service there was a prime mover in founding the Galt Hospital. When the First World War broke out he promptly wired Sir Sam Hughes, Minister of Militia, offering his services. Hughes' reply was warm and appreciative but quite definite that at his age — then 58 — he would have to guard the home front. The Mewburn response is on record: "Go to hell — I'm going anyway." So he did, paying his own way overseas, upon which he was given command of a military hospital in England. After the war he was settled in private practice in Calgary when Dr. Tory persuaded him that 65 was an appropriate stage in life to go pioneering again, so he moved to Edmonton.

I'm told he could swear more impressively than any of the troopers with whom he shared his adventures and regret not having heard a performance, but Mrs. Graham Huckell, who was a nurse in his operating room, assures me the Colonel used only *nice words* when cussing. As he told her: "I swear only in a legitimate way." I'm told that the elevator was sure to produce a demonstration of the Colonel's talent. It was a terrible old thing with an open cage that went slow-slow-clunkety-clunk. The Colonel would push the button and cuss without pause till it arrived.

Ken Thomson became a patient in the hospital in his fourth year, thanks to some ligaments torn in a football game. When the Colonel came into Ken's room it was full of other medical students, one of whom was standing against the window. The Colonel said: "If some goddam fifth year man doesn't get out of the light there's going to be a dead one!"

Johnny Macgregor tells me the Colonel could bore right through a medical student with "those cold steely eyes." And Johnny was in the operating room one day when Mrs. Mewburn phoned to interrupt an operation. The old Colonel stormed to the phone, barked "Go to hell, Eliza!" and hung up.

However, Mrs. Huckell assures me that no one was deceived by the Colonel's ferocity. "Everybody loved the old Colonel," she says, and the sentiment is seconded by Christine MacKay, who ran the operating rooms from 1927 to 1952. Miss MacKay says: "He was a dear old man." She'd grown accustomed to his ways — at the Calgary General — and was unruffled when he threw a scalpel against the wall because he found it dull. She says the Colonel "just sang away" at the operating table. Bea Clough recalls that he was possessed of a high thin voice and his favourite song was "Every little movement has a meaning all its own. . ." He also invented a personal slang with a meaning all its own — as Aileen Revell recalls. If he wanted the alcohol he would call for the "Oh, be joyful!" Once, on a Sunday, he paused outside the soldiers' recreation hall to listen to the sounds of a church sevice. "Ya know," he confided, "I've heard a lot of great music, opera and all that, but I still love those damn old hymns."

The Colonel had a chauffeur he was always firing but who paid no attention and managed to know every day exactly what minute the director of surgical services would leave the hospital. One winter day the Colonel decided to walk to work. He caught a chill and in a few days had died of pneumonia. But he was a presence for many years after.

Although I knew the Colonel only by colourful reputation I came to know very well his successor "Sandy" Munroe, and the rest of the original cast assembled in 1922-23. The hospital the Colonel knew bears little resemblance to today's complex of buildings, and if he could come back and take a tour of current facilities he'd doubtless encounter surprises which would evoke vivid comments, but if he were to drop in on a meeting of the medical staff committee he would understand easily what was going on.

The essential structure of the medical departments has changed not at all in 60 years. Functions have evolved and diversified but all elements can be found in the organization assembled in 1922-23. Let's take an organization chart for the present hospital and pencil in the equivalents of the Colonel's time. This chart identifies only the divisions and the names of the head men. Here they are just names, as they were to me when I first came to the University Hospital, but as time went on all became personalities — or downright characters — I'd like to sketch for you in following chapters. This durable gang carried on almost intact through the depression and the next world war.

---

1922-23


Obstetrics and Gynaecology
*L.C. Conn*


Anaesthesia
*L.F. Jones*


Radiology
*Richard Proctor*

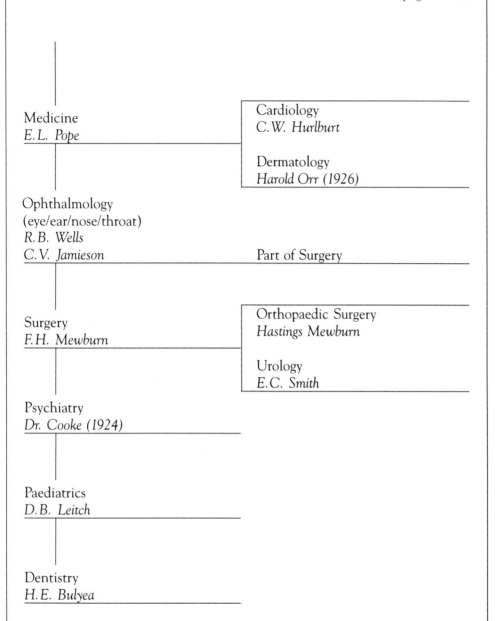

Medicine
E.L. Pope

Cardiology
C.W. Hurlburt

Dermatology
Harold Orr (1926)

Ophthalmology
(eye/ear/nose/throat)
R.B. Wells
C.V. Jamieson

Part of Surgery

Surgery
F.H. Mewburn

Orthopaedic Surgery
Hastings Mewburn

Urology
E.C. Smith

Psychiatry
Dr. Cooke (1924)

Paediatrics
D.B. Leitch

Dentistry
H.E. Bulyea

A comparison with the current chart will reveal four missing departments. However, the services were available all the same. Two missing divisions are Laboratory Medicine and Microbiology. For these services the hospital depended on the Faculty of Medicine — and the Provincial Laboratory which was in the basement of the university's medical building and had as its head one of the faculty's bright lights, Johnny Ower. This convenient dependency persisted for three decades.

Today's hospital has a large, well-equipped Department of Physical Medicine and Rehabilitation. In the 1920s the burden of rehabilitation fell largely on the willing shoulders of Tommy Robson, the physiotherapist from the hospital's army days. Tommy and his few helpers were put to the test following the polio epidemic of 1927 when the government designated the University Hospital the rehabilitation centre for Alberta and built a wooden annex — the Provincial Special Unit — south and west of the main building. Before he retired Tommy Robson saw the formation of the Department of Physical Medicine and Rehabilitation with himself as a member, but to see it he had to stay on the job until his 74th birthday — in 1958.

Ambulatory service was starting, though you wouldn't find it on the

*The splendor falls on castle walls . . . and on the face of the University Hospital, stirring to meet the challenge of a summer day. Partly in shade are the soldiers wing and the kitchen-laundry. A caption of the time states: "This photograph was proudly displayed at the Wembley International Exposition of 1929"*

premises. You had to go looking overtown for the Outpatient Department. It was on the present Churchill Square, in a big brick house with a sweeping veranda where that grand old pioneer Kenny McLeod lived his final years. The clinic was overtown for two reasons: there wasn't room in the hospital and we were pretty remote from the centre of population. In fact, more than 30 years later when the clinic was finally brought into the main hospital the *Edmonton Journal* predicted that patients would not be able to get over to us. The clinic served citizens who were unable to pay. The question has been raised why this service was provided by the University Hospital rather than the Royal Alex which was owned by the city. The simple answer is that every teaching hospital has an outpatient clinic. A broader answer is given by Don Wilson, one of our bright young men who came to prominence after the second war. In the 1920s Don was a teenager, the son of Dr. W.A. Wilson who was a member of the surgical staff of the hospital and a respected teacher, so soft-spoken he was known to his students as "Whispering Willie."

Don says of the clinic: "Students have to learn by doing. You can teach only so much in the classroom. You can't have a Department of Chemistry without a chemistry lab or a Department of Agriculture without a real farm. The Outpatient Clinic is the lab of the Faculty of Medicine."

That was the lineup of medical departments, set up swiftly and surely at the turn of the year 1922 to 1923. Mind you, the organization was drawn up swiftly but there was to be yet another long delay before it could become fully effective. Though the university had the hospital back (after four years' relentless effort) the convalescing soldiers in the hospital had no place to go. Almost another year was to unwind before the SCR wing — the Soldier Civil Re-establishment Wing — would be built and ready to receive them.

And when that happy day came still another crucial addition would be required for the plan to become fully effective — a School of Nursing. A hospital of that time could not exist without young women willing to apprentice as nurses. Nowadays, students supplement nursing care but in the beginning they gave the bulk of it, working 12 hour shifts with a half-day off each week in which to spend their monthly wage of 10 dollars.

The first class of 16 willing hopefuls was assembled during September 1923. Maude Inkin (Hobbs) recalls with a tolerant laugh her introduction to the profession. One day she took the CNR local from her farm home at Irma. On the same day Aileen White arrived by streetcar from her home in Edmonton's west end. The next morning they were taken into the SCR wing and shown 80 brand-new beds and stacks of blankets and sheets. The first skill they learned in the art of nursing was making beds, so the soldiers could be transferred from the main hospital.

Mind you, although the hospital was no longer run by the army it was run on military lines. "Wash" Washburn, the superintendent, was known as Major. Many of the staff nurses had been through the wars and were called Sister. The student nurses wore the military veil instead of a perky cap, and in case you were thinking of the veil as something soft and glamourous the military version was anything but. More of a net, in the form of a bowl, to keep the crowning glory out of sight.

Aged 18, 19 and 20, the students were the largest, and the youngest group in an institution run by people who seemed dreadfully old and of whom they lived in fear mixed with admiration. Colonel Mewburn once inquired with his famous knowing twinkle: "What's the matter with those nurses? They scuttle away like a bunch of goddam rats whenever I come in sight." They loved the old Colonel, but he frightened them all the same, and enjoyed it.

Determination, at every step of the way, was required of a young woman aiming to become a nurse. Josephine Bulyea (Ward) has a story about that. Jo was a member of the first class — her father was our first head of dental services. She and her chum Jean Richards lived right in Garneau and so walked to the hospital to report for training. They arrived on the sidewalk out front, suitcases in hand, and stopped. Dead. Although they had seen the hospital almost daily for much of their young lives they had never seen it look so stern and forbidding. Jo said: "I don't think I'm going in." Jean echoed: "Let's go home." But before they could retreat a sudden rush of courage sent them clambering up the steps and through the heavy doors. And inside they were met by Mrs. Ingalls, the housekeeper, who quickly made them feel at home in their crowded quarters above the soldiers wing.

They were integrated quickly into the work force. On January 18 1924 the superintendent reported to the board: " . . . in one month's time there will be a reduction of two or three nurses on salary, owing to the probationers being put on the wards . . ."

Jean Richards didn't finish the course. She was one of three members of that first class to be stricken by TB, an occupational hazard for all hospital workers of the time. Another girl failed the written work but 12 persevered, to receive diplomas in the first graduation exercises on December 10 1926. In the early afternoon of that day they gathered in Convocation Hall, and one of the exercises was posing for the photographer. They were the advance party of some 4,000 who have graduated through 1986.

The class of '26 left with happy memories of a closely-knit family life in a time that went quickly. For Isobel Secord the recollection that comes to the surface first is the crackle of starch in the early morning. Of being roused before six to climb into uniforms freshly starched overnight by the hospital laundry. Caps, collars, cuffs, bibs, aprons, all so white and crisp they fairly crackled. And then the flurry of activity in the wards, starting promptly at seven, when the students had to clear away the breakfast trays, get the beds made and the patients washed and have the wards in a state of total tidiness by nine o'clock, ready for *rounds*. "Rounds. What a ritual that was," says Isobel, "the superintendent of nurses and the doctors came around to check on the patients — and on us."

As I've pointed out, the medical staff of the hospital had a strong McGill flavour and in assembling the nursing staff Dr. Tory made sure that it too would have the stamp of his alma mater. The first Superintendent of Nurses, Margaret McCammon, came with a certificate from the McGill school for graduate nurses. Her assistant, Ethel Fenwick, who succeeded her after a couple of years, was also McGill-trained. So was the instructress, Miss Sharpe. When the three-year diploma program leading to an RN was instituted in the hospital, the university started a five-year degree program leading to a BSc in nursing, and Mary Black, of McGill, naturally, came as instructor in the degree course.

For economic reasons this program was abandoned after one class graduated, (and Miss Black married a Mister Black), but the same economic stress which shut down the degree program caused the diploma program to be pursued with vigour. Six months after Isobel Secord's group came in, a second class of

Undergraduate Nurses of the
University of Alberta Hospital

**Reception**

to

**Graduating Nurses**

Convocation Hall
Tuesday, October 5th, 1926

December 1926 — graduation for the first class of the University of Alberta school of nursing. In front: Maude Inkin, Eileen Ringwood, Doreen Wood, Nora Glanville, Josephine Bulyea. Behind: Viola Purcell, "Bluebell" Trowbridge, Annie Robertson, Isobel Secord, Aileen White, Carthena Trowbridge. Missing: Hazeleen Manuel

students was recruited, and on and on until there were some 90, too many to live above the soldiers wing. They had to board around at St. Stephen's College, and old Robertson Lodge on Whyte Avenue.

Miss Sharpe instructed in the art of *true* nursing, direct care of patients, and due to a shortage of maids and cleaners they had to practice non-nursing arts, such as wiping down beds with lysol after a patient left, and washing windows. Isobel Secord has vivid memories of the windows, which were high and could only be cleaned by standing on the sills. At mealtimes the students became waitresses. There was a steam kettle on each floor from which the nurse in charge served out the food and sent the students rushing off with the trays.

When one is bedridden by illness or accident the need for medical and nursing care is complemented by the need for a supportive diet. Lucy McLellan, the hospital dietitian, was considered a friend by all the students, even though the concept of dietitian was too advanced for the compilers of Henderson's City Directory, who put down her occupation as *cook*. Lucy was a holdover from the army period. As the hospital made the transition to a civilian institution, with patients brought in by specialists, many of these patients required special menus, and in 1924 Margaret Malone, whose fortune in life was to become Mrs. Ross Vant, was appointed Therapeutic Dietitian. In those days, all the staff were thinking of ways to "put the hospital on the map." Margaret's idea in this regard was to have it approved as a training centre for dietetic interns — by the American Dietetic Association. It took four years to achieve it but the hospital was duly recognized and two interns began a four-month course, later increased to six months.

The students took lectures on dietetics from Lucy and Margaret. They also had classes in massage, bandaging and casts from the famous Tommy Robson, a fine teacher who imparted to many medical people most of what they learned about those arts. In the evenings, some doctors would come to the hospital to lecture but for other lectures the students had to go out during the day. They had to book off their floor duty, rush over to the university Medical Building, and rush back to catch up on their regular work. That had to be finished, regardless of all else.

These wild dashes across campus brought a change in the uniform. Jo Bulyea has that story. The design was brought from the east by Miss McCammon and was modelled on the uniform of the Montreal General, in which the letters MGH were worked into pink-and-white woven stitches. Miss McCammon changed the letters to UAH for University of Alberta Hospital and the design became part of our tradition. But the original outfit had white shoes and stockings. The primitive pedestrian conditions between hospital and Medical Building were impractical for whites, so shoes and stockings were changed to a more practical black, and they too became part of student tradition, though not a very welcome part.

In addition to their other classes the students were required to take two periods a week of physical education. *Upsetting* exercises, Jo Bulyea called them. The sessions consisted mostly of running, which seemed pointless when they were on the run all the time anyway. Student nurses came to a stop only when they met a senior — a nurse, a doctor, even an intern. When they met a senior they were expected to stand, with their hands behind them, regardless of what they were carrying, and in a hospital they might be carrying some awkward things.

Students took on increasing responsibility as they advanced. Towards the end of the second year came an important test of their ability to cope with the stresses of the profession. Each had three months of night duty. From seven in the evening till seven next morning the hospital kept one graduate nurse on duty, checking on things and available for help if needed, but the patients were actually under the eyes of second-year students. Maude Inkin still recalls the first traumatic experience of moving silently through a ward with her flashlight and finding that a man had died. She was so upset that a young intern got up and talked to her for a long time, telling her she would have to get used to death — people died in hospitals. At appointed times during the night the student on the top floor would take her flashlight out on the roof to check the tents where the TB patients lived. And if the wind was blowing she'd take off her cap so it wouldn't be carried away. Then, as dawn lightened the wards, she would set out the breakfast trays and rouse the patients, to have them ready for the start of the day's routine.

In the senior year the apprenticeship included three months in the operating room, where Maude Inkin took a turn as a patient. Colonel Mewburn relieved her of her appendix. This is an operation that is still done, though less is heard of it now than in those days, when every family seemed to have an "appendix" story. Much of the senior year was spent overtown. Three months at the outpatient clinic was a work experience all enjoyed. Less enjoyable was two months in isolation. And they boarded at the Royal Alex for three months because their own hospital did not yet boast a maternity ward. At the Alex they found the atmosphere less military — they were called by first names — but then the food wasn't so good. And they weren't encouraged to make tea and toast for country people visiting patients, as they were at the university.

On top of other responsibilities, members of the first class helped pioneer an outstanding Canadian medical discovery. The University Hospital held a unique position in regard to insulin. Insulin was discovered in 1922 by Drs. Banting and Best of Montreal, with the purification process being developed by Dr. J.B. Collip of the University of Alberta. The Alberta connection so impressed John D. Rockefeller, Junior, that when he was disbursing the Rockefeller Foundation's gift of half a million dollars for the medical school, he sent his personal present of $5,000 to extend the use of insulin. The intentions of the Rockefeller gift were fulfilled through the University Hospital. For nearly half a century insulin doses were made up in the hospital pharmacy and mailed to diabetics around the province. Dr. Johnny Ower, who eventually succeeded A.C. Rankin as Dean of Medicine, was one of the first diabetics to take insulin. And an important role was played by D.J. Whitfield. Whitfield was an orderly in the hospital by day, and at night a patient in the men's ward. He gave insulin and taught students the art. Poor Whitfield died on a hunting trip when his system went suddenly out of balance, but he imparted his knowledge to many nurses and helped the hospital extend the use of Canada's most famous medical discovery.

As Christmas approached the students made time for another activity by getting up an hour early. They would meet in the Red Cross hut, the wooden recreation building out behind the hospital, gather around the well-thumped upright piano and rehearse Christmas carols. And during the season they would parade through the wards, along the halls, up and down the stairs, carolling as

*Life-stile. Student nurse Annie Robertson negotiates the stile over the marshy rivulet which once ran between St. Stephen's College and the hospital*

*Nursing training included a stint at the Outpatient Clinic, overtown on the site of Sir Winston Churchill Square. The clinic occupied the brick mansion of the late Kenny McLeod, a renowned pioneer whose office building was the highest in town. Isobel Secord points out that on Wednesday the ear-nose-and-throat clinic is held at 9 am*

they went, while Harold Vango, a young doctor on the medical staff, played the violin. Patients would hear the sound of approaching music, then the parade would come in sight — in uniforms white and crisp and even as the snow on which the good king looked out on the feast of Stephen. It was a moving demonstration of what nursing meant to the students and the students meant to the hospital.

In 1926 I had an opportunity to see the hospital again. The transition from the military era could be considered an accomplished fact. One ward in the soldiers wing was being used by the general public. In October "Wash" Washburn reported to the board that he had 157 civilian patients and 31 ex-soldiers. The university's Faculty of Medicine, with the use of its own teaching hospital, had graduated the first class of 11 MDs the previous year and the hospital's first class of nurses was close to graduation.

Mind you, I had to learn all this later. Though I caught a glimpse of the hospital it made as little impression as in 1921 when I came to play hockey. By this time I was a medical student at the University of Manitoba but I had my sights on being an intern at the Winnipeg General Hospital, and my immediate concern was still with hockey. And on this visit I carried the burdens of coach, responsible for the girls team from the Manitoba varsity. We played the Alberta girls overtown at the old Gardens and managed a tie. And we were entertained so royally on campus I missed entirely the significance of the University Hospital.

# Chapter 8

# 1926—1929
### *The University's Hospital*

In the 1920s it was truly the *University* Hospital. The University Governors added Professor Norman Pitcher, the mining engineer, to the four-man hospital board and then reached out into the community for Harry Cooper, the wholesale grocer. However, a chronic financial weakness was undermining the delightful independence from government. Money was often a theme in "Wash" Washburn's reports. No matter what the economies, expense ran ahead of income. If costs were cut, revenue declined too. "The replacing of male help has assisted in the reduction of the payroll," he wrote in one annual report. But still the losses mounted. "I am sure members of the public would be gratified if they could inspect the garbage cans and see how little is the waste of food," he wrote. And you can be sure that "Wash" inspected the garbage cans and every other detail of hospital life. Superintendents of that time did not hold with delegating responsibility. Delegation would strike them as close to dereliction. I have to laugh at the story about "Wash" and the clock in the operating room.

He liked to spring surprise inspections and find some deficiency and then give the staff hell. One day word leaked out that there was to be a surprise party in the operating room, so the staff there was ready when "Wash" arrived. Every last item was immaculate and exactly in place. They smirked behind their masks, knowing they had put one over. But he took a chair and looked all around the room until his sharp gaze rested on the clock. "Let's see the inside of that clock." The inside of the clock had not been cleaned to the standard expected by the superintendent. That was much better. Now he could give them hell.

He also gave the board hell, year after year, about the health of the nurses. In 1927 he wrote: "For the year just closing, 1384 days were lost through illness. It seems obvious that . . . overwork, coupled with the complete lack of provision for relaxation and recreation, are seen in the increasing amount of time lost through illness. In this connection I would respectfully draw the attention of the Board of Governors to the absolute necessity of providing a nurses home in the very near future . . ."

Nothing was done about the nurses till after the second world war, but in the late '20s two pavilions appeared on the grounds southwest of the main building, each of which had a brief career as an independent hospital "approved" for government grants. The Provincial Special Hospital for Poliomyelitis came first. In 1926 there were just two cases of polio in the province, but in 1927 an epidemic which began in Edmonton brought 354 cases and 53 deaths. The epidemic subsided with colder weather, but the government recognized that special facilities were required for those suffering the aftereffects, and moved with exemplary speed — as a later government did during a post-war epidemic. On November 15 1927 a foreman from the Department of Public Works arrived with a gang of day labourers and started construction of a wooden pavilion with two wings. The pavilion didn't have a foundation. No time for that. The gang literally hammered away at the project and the Special Hospital received its first patients on the following January 31. It cost $20,000.

"The unit has a capacity of 60 beds, 15 of which are cots." That's how Hank Mewburn described the matter in his report to the Minister of Health on the first year's operation. "Hank" was a son of the famous colonel. He was superintendent of the special hospital while continuing to head the University Hospital's Department of Orthopaedics. Independent though it was, the special hospital relied heavily on the main hospital for support services. The work of physiotherapy fell on the broad and willing shoulders of Tommy Robson, and the skill of Miss Lennox, the masseuse, and her assistants. Meals were supplied to staff and patients at 25 cents each. The extra laundry strained the main hospital's faltering facilities to near breaking. It was too much for the laundry manager. When he resigned the crisis was relieved by hiring his wife and son. The special unit had a staff of four graduate nurses and four ward aides. As "Hank" wrote in his report to the minister: "The ward aide is an innovation in Edmonton hospitals . . ."

The pavilion had wide verandas with awnings and the patients could be moved out into the sun and fresh air on nice days. In fact, as they began to recover they were wandering off in search of excitement. This brought an appeal to the Gyro Club, whose members provided Edmonton with its first playgrounds. The Gyro Club came through with playground equipment for the polio kids. In 1929 the pavilion was put on a concrete foundation. The whole thing was moved 40 feet without disturbance to the patients or interruption to any of the utilities. Then it was stuccoed, yellow. Total cost: $5,000.

Standing alongside, in matching yellow stucco, was the Junior Red Cross Hospital — for crippled children whose parents couldn't afford to pay for orthopaedic treatment. The provincial government began the program, shortly after the University Hospital set up an orthopaedic department. The Minister of Health asked teachers throughout the province to send in the names of crippled kids who needed corrective surgery or therapy. As beds became available the government paid for treatment at the University Hospital, and results were heartwarming. In 1925, 88 kids benefitted from the program. The next year the Red Cross offered to take it over, and raised $13,000 to convert a section of the hospital exclusively for kids whose parents were unable to pay.

At this time the numbers of ex-soldier patients were declining and the SCR wing was not being used to capacity so B Ward was converted to the Junior Red Cross Hospital Section. The Red Cross sent the patients, and from its fund-raising activities, paid 62½ cents a day for their treatment.

There was good financial support in the community and the plan worked well for a couple of years — until the SCR patients began, unexpectedly, to increase again. On a typical day in January 1929, the hospital had 203 patients altogether. 90 were civilian public. 25 were children in the Junior Red Cross section. 74 ex-soldiers were in the SCR wing, plus another 14 who had to be billeted in homes in Garneau. The director of the SCR in Ottawa wanted B Ward back, and the board recognized that since the government had built the wing "the request was almost in the nature of a command." There was a difficulty — the contract with the Red Cross — but the way out was another

*View from the air in early spring — 1928. Rural roads mark 87th Avenue and 114th Street. Open country separates a huddle of hospital buildings from those of the University of Alberta. But when summer comes there is not enough space between hospital and the live-stock barns of the university's experimental farm at lower left. Hospital buildings, clockwise from the main block, are the Red Cross hut, the provincial special unit for polio rehabilitation, the roothouse, and the soldiers wing. They are grouped around the laundry-kitchen*

pavilion. Cecil Burgess, the university architect, provided an instant design, and the Red Cross invested $35,000 in a building for 30 beds alongside the Provincial Special Unit. Although administered by the university the Junior Red Cross Hospital was a legal entity, recognized by the government for grants.

There is no keener observer than the proverbial small boy and to describe the hospital and its setting I'm indebted to Steve McEachern. At time of writing Steve was an investment dealer on the board of the hospital *foundation*, an important body which raises and distributes funds for research and equipment, but in 1927 Steve entered grade one at Garneau School and was an early patient

*The "out" patient sector of the TB ward. Out of doors in the fresh Alberta air. That's the ticket — to recovery. The patient's tent is pitched on the roof at the base of the $70 flagpole set up by the city in wartime. Patient, nurses and visitors have a view across the river valley to the grounds of the legislature. One summer they will have the fun of watching the white apartment block being sawed in half and rolled a block north on 109th Street to be reassembled as the Kensington Apartments*

in our children's annex, the result of a broken leg from an impromptu classroom wrestling match.

Steve's father was William McEachern, a free-enterprising teamster and sometime farmer who drove his own Clydesdale horses. In winter he delivered coal from the Rabbit Hill colliery and one of the big customers was the University Power Plant, which supplied steam heat to campus buildings including the hospital. In summer his father's big horses worked on the University Farm, which filled the entire prospect west of the hospital. From the site of the Jubilee Auditorium on the north to the Aberhart on the south was the farm, scene of agricultural experiments by professors and provincial researchers. The farm was on that particular site for a purpose. It had been chosen by the boosters in the Rutherford government to be unmistakably part of the university complex. The experimental farm bore the same relationship to the Faculty of Agriculture as the prized teaching hospital to the Faculty of Medicine.

Patients on the west side of the hospital, or on the sunporches which faced the south, could look out and see the big show barn — on the site of today's hostel. Across what is now 114th Street were frame houses for officials of the farm, an echo of the brick mansions on Saskatchewan Drive which housed the president and deans of the university, and barns for cattle, horses, hogs and sheep. The dairy barn was towards the south and on the site of the Aberhart was the field crops barn, with a technological marvel — a built-in electric threshing machine to clean the experimental crops grown in neat patches on the farm, as well as the prize-winning samples which Alberta farmers sent to international grain competitions. Beyond 116th Street were woods, although there were some natural clearings in which Steve's father cut hay for the horses.

The hospital was an immense presence in the lives of Steve and his young pals. "It was more than a building," he says. "It was a genuine edifice, with wide halls and elevators, everything a kid would be in awe of." Steve could see it from his home, which was along 85th Avenue at 107th Street, in a neighbourhood of small houses created by John Walter, the grand old coal and lumber merchant. At the end of a season, if he had unsold lumber left over, Mr. Walter would add a few more houses. Steve could look west through that archway of trees over 85th Avenue, right to the main entrance of the hospital. It was impressive from that distance, just as the founders of Strathcona had intended it should be.

Wooden sidewalks lay under the avenue of trees leading to the hospital. They gave off a marvelous crunch on frosty mornings and on warm afternoons provided hiding places for Steve and his friends to experiment with Turret cigarettes, obtainable in packs of five-for-a-nickel at a neighbourhood confectionery. There were dips under the sidewalks into which they could crawl, forgetting that telltale smoke would find its way upwards through the cracks.

In the holidays of summer the farm was an idyllic retreat for Steve and his pals. After school in spring or fall they'd take the long way home, going out to the farm to catch a ride home atop one of McEachern's patient Clydesdales. The view of gentle rural activity from the sunporches of the hospital was appreciated by the patients too — mind you, there was a serpent in this Eden.

As Dr. Tory reported to the University's board of governors in 1928: "A complaint had been received from hospital authorities regarding the odour from the hog barns."

The governors' annual report for 1928-29 went into clinical detail: "The expansion of the University Hospital, particularly the children's units which extend westwards from the main building, has raised very definitely the question of moving the animal barns from their present location. During the summer months the fly nuisance at the hospital was undoubtedly accentuated by the fact that the livestock barns and manure piles provide a breeding ground, very

*Winter Nocturne — Dr. Bulyea, head of dentistry, mountaineer, photographer, achieves a poetic impression of hospital and soldiers wing in a setting of snow. With time exposure the windows take on a symbolic glow, assurance that within the walls all is well, and with nurses of the old school in charge, all is as it should be*

undesirable from the public health standpoint."

So in 1930 the farm buildings were moved off to the south and Steve McEachern's idyll ended. But the keen observations of the small boy give us a vivid picture of the hospital as a towering presence in a rural setting.

Of course, the kids who found the edifice so massive and impressive had no idea the university was facing a sea of troubles trying to maintain the hospital by itself. In 1928 Henry Marshall Tory wearied of this and other struggles and went off to Ottawa where he founded yet another institution of higher learning, Carleton University. By the time Dr. Tory left, the hospital had accumulated a

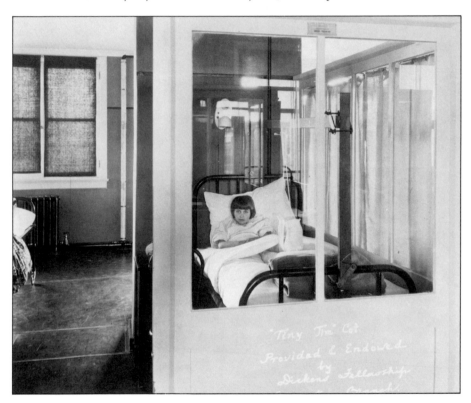

An appealing literary touch. In the provincial special unit for polio victims. The Dickens Fellowship of Edmonton has raised funds for an orthopaedic bed. They've named it for Tiny Tim, a Charles Dickens favourite who overcame a physical handicap

deficit nearing $260,000. And this was in good times with bad times just around the corner. In spite of watchful economies. In spite of the men replaced on the payroll by women. In spite of the graduate nurses replaced by students. In spite of generous support from the community — the Robert Tegler Estate paid $2,000 a year to maintain two beds for charity cases. In spite of all, the deficit was mounting. And the hospital that was costing so dearly was not big enough. Not big enough by half, as the saying goes. From the viewpoint of the medical-teaching staff, and from the viewpoint of potential patients who were being refused admission at the rate of 200 per month in winter, it was not big enough by half.

So the government stepped in. An understanding was reached. The province would undertake to double the size of the plant. Concerning the debt it would back a note at the bank for $200,000, with the remaining $60,000 considered an overdraft with which the hospital must live. And there would be restructuring of the board. Here, I suppose, the old rule of the optimist and the pessimist would apply. The pessimist would say that half the board members were appointed by the government, while the optimist would maintain cheerfully that half were named by the university.

The new order was spelled out in the University of Alberta Hospital Act 1929. And the optimist would point to Section 8, which concerned the simultaneous appointment of doctors to the clinical staff of the hospital and teaching staff of the university.

The act was given royal assent on March 20 and on April 15 an order-in-council appointed the new board. Government nominees were Dr. Malcolm Bow, Deputy Minister of Public Health, W.B. Milnes, Supervisor of Hospital Affairs, and John Gillespie, founder of the grain company of that name. The university's men were Dean Rankin, Harry Cooper and Dr. R.C. Wallace who had succeeded Dr. Tory as president. The board met for the first time the next day.

The new board took over the operation of what I call a small general store — compared with the large department store which occupies the site today. In the summers "Wash" Washburn could afford to leave the superintendent's office and go around the province with the provincial travelling clinic. Each summer the Department of Health organized a team of doctors, dentists and nurses to visit outlying areas with a medical tent show, vaccinating and inoculating one day, taking out tonsils and adenoids the next, filling teeth another. "Wash" could go on tour with this Medical Chautauqua and the hospital could carry on with someone "looking in" on his office. This general store is the hospital to which I came to work — and to live too — in the summer of 1929.

# Chapter 9

# 1929—1930

*Twice As Much of a Good Thing*

Mind you, Fanny Hooson, the famous night cook, came to work at the same time as I did, and I'm sure Fanny would have been missed much more than I. Over the years the hospital has had interns by the hundreds, but only one night cook like Fanny. She served everybody not only as cook but as confidante, for nearly half a century, which shows the true importance of the so-called "sub" staff.

The hospital had little tradition about the intern service when I came. It dated only from April 1924 when the first resident medical officer and three interns were appointed. A doctor in the house is like a bird in hand. In the original Strathcona community hospital, as in small ones in the country today, the nurses were on their own when a medical emergency arose. They had to cope as best they could until a doctor could be brought.

In 1924 the board appointed Dr. H.A. Crawford first resident medical officer, and three interns whose reward was to be experience, room, board, and ten dollars a month, same as a student nurse. One of the interns spent his whole year in pathology; the others rotated medicine and surgery.

They were men from eastern universities, but in 1925 the hospital was able to engage two members of the first graduating class of the University of Alberta. John Glenn and Bill Eadie got the call. At that time you got the degree and then went into residence to prepare for exams to be allowed to practice. There was one set for Alberta, and then the Dominion Council exams, which gave the right to practice in any province in Canada which would accept you. But then the order changed. You took the qualifying exams and then your degree after that. The U of A's five-year medical program was extended to six and the final year was spent in hospital.

Even with a degree from McGill a resident was owned body and soul by the hospital — just like the nurses. I have to laugh when I read the board minutes for July 30 1925, concerning my friend Graham Huckell:

"Dr. Washburn reported that Dr. Huckell had married a nurse on the staff without the knowledge of the Superintendent or the Superintendent of Nurses and he (Dr. Washburn) had been directed by the President (Dr. Tory) to discharge Dr. Huckell at once."

Graham and Jean were married out of town on a Saturday but the news travelled fast and Jean was bounced from her job in the operating room on Monday. It was a major crime to get married all right. Of course the joke of it is that when the coast was clear — after Dr. Tory left — Graham was welcomed back because of his skill in orthopaedics, and later on he ran the Department of Orthopaedics which his son John now heads.

In 1926 the board built a house for the resident medical staff, although the term "house" was used rather freely. It was attached to the tunnel which joined the main building to the SCR wing. The interns rented a piano for their entertainment at $6 a month, and asked the board to pay the rent, but the board "couldn't see its way clear" to subsidizing pianos.

Down in Winnipeg, meanwhile, I was blissfully unaware of all this. I'd got my MD from the University of Manitoba and had realized the ambition of interning at the Winnipeg General, but one day the superintendent called me in and said a senior intern was wanted at the Hospital of the University of Alberta. Would I be interested? The salary was $150. I was interested. He said he'd phone about it, or rather he'd send a telegram, people didn't just pick up telephones then. A few days later he told me "They've reneged a bit. They only want to pay $100." What should I do? He said to hold out for the original contract.

Not knowing any better, I held out, and strangely, "they" went along with the original salary. I came as senior to five undergraduates, all in their sixth year. We lived cheek by jowl in the "house" off the tunnel, and also had another resident, Nesbit Alexander. We were a very close group, literally and figuratively. Two of my group figured prominently in the later history of the hospital. Johnny Macgregor and Jimmy Calder were inseparable companions. Short men and always together, they were known as *Little by Little*.

We were on call 24 hours. If one of us went out he'd ask someone else to take his calls. We didn't go out too often. There wasn't much money for it, but we did have a radio for entertainment. Although the board had declined to assume the rent of the piano we took up a collection among the staff to buy ourselves a radio. Network broadcasting was sweeping the United States and we were able to pick up NBC from KOA Denver and CBS from KSL Salt Lake City and the university had its own radio station. Service clubs would put on concerts for the patients in the Red Cross hut and CKUA would broadcast them.

My group did a rotating internship — quite parallel to the program followed by student nurses. In the intern year a man would spend three months each in surgery, medicine, obstetrics, and eye-ear-nose-and-throat with orthopaedics. Every hospital had its own intern program, designed primarily to meet the needs of the institution. It's significant that in 1929 the Royal College of Physicians and Surgeons of Canada was founded. One of the goals was uniform national standards for postgraduate training, but that program was a long time coming.

We interns had a good rapport with the nurses and I think we gave the patients a very kindly care. There wasn't so much medication then, and instead of giving them a pill about all we could do was make them comfortable. It was really a laying-on of hands.

Interns seemed to be on call for any duty, medical or otherwise. Frank Elliott, who came along a little later, recalls long night hours tending the

87

1929—1930

switchboard. That switchboard was unforgettable, a big oak chest in a sort of cubicle — at the top of the stairs in the main entrance. When I came, the admitting desk was alongside, and it was truly a desk only, with no office in connection. Jo Bulyea, a graduate of the first nursing class, was in charge of the desk, but being closest to the switchboard she often doubled as telephone girl. That was when Bill Beck, the afternoon operator, was unable to answer the call to duty. Bill was a colourful chap who had lost a leg in the war. "Wash" figured the hospital owed him a job he could handle, where he could sell his Irish Sweepstake tickets so Bill ran the switchboard and relayed messages. But poor Bill had a problem with the bottle. As his hour for starting work drew near there were anxious long looks down 85th Avenue to see if he was coming. And if he was seen to be approaching more unsteadily than normal Jo knew she would have to cover the switchboard.

Plugging in cords for an outside call was easy enough, but the board was also the hospital's paging system. In spite of "Wash's" urgings the board had not seen its way clear to buying a modern call system. If a member of the staff was needed somewhere the operator could theoretically ring 40 locations in search of him. And if Mrs. Porritt, the charge nurse on the second floor, wanted somebody in a hurry she would pour a rapid fire of impatient words into Jo's earphones while the hunt went on.

Jo worked the admitting desk six days a week. On the seventh *day* she rested but on the seventh *night* she relieved the night nurse. The job was demanding, but Jo was glad to have it. Two of three graduate nurses in Alberta were unable to find employment as nurses, and the hospitals which couldn't afford to hire them were training more and more students.

Shortly after Fanny Hooson and I took our places in this scene the government began construction of the big addition, the wing that would cure the hospital's condition of not being big enough by half. And I have to think it was a good thing that work was well advanced on October 24 1929 — the "Black Thursday" of the stock market crash on Wall Street. If there'd been any turning back the government might have been tempted by second thoughts.

The new wing extended the facade to resemble the handsome coloured sketch which Meyer Sturm, the Chicago architect, had provided in 1914, and was always hung in some prominent place as a promise of bigger things to come. The extension had the welcome effect of putting the main entrance in the centre rather than at one end. And although the facade was Mr. Sturm's — and we were bound by his plan of central corridors and ceiling heights for this and all extensions — the interior layout was improved. Every major addition is an opportunity to incorporate new technology and accommodate modern points of view. It was true most recently of the Walter C. Mackenzie Health Sciences Centre.

The 1929-30 redesign by Professor Burgess tried to do something for a certain class of patient. One day "Wash" talked to a reporter about the attempt to give a break to the middle class. Mind you, this was in the days before medicare and hospital insurance plans. "Wash" said it had been admitted generally for a long time that two classes received the best medical care — those who had money to pay for it and paupers who received charitable care at the hands of medical professors and great specialists who gave their services generously. But the high cost of sickness was a mighty terror to the great middle class on moderate incomes who found doctor and hospital bills a heavy burden. As a gesture to the middle class the redesign introduced four-bed semi-private rooms, at $3.50 per day, all decorated as attractively as private rooms which cost $5.00.

Psychology was also incorporated into the design, colour psychology included. We were getting away from the cold white associated with hospitals.

*The art and civic spirit of the photographer combine to raise the 1929-30 wing to the high heavens, an improvement bound to please those who believe in the hospital and its destiny. A thin crescent of parking lot adjoins the main entrance. Every car in sight probably belongs to a doctor*

The walls were being repainted buff, alternating with a shade called dairy cream. The furniture would be brown rather than white, and on the floors brown rugs would be placed where possible. Battleship linoleum in the halls was being replaced with brown terrazzo tile, which could be scrubbed down with soap and water, sparing patients the smell of wax, and sparing the board $600 a year which the wax was costing. And something was being done about the admitting desk. Patients would no longer have to give personal details of family and financial affairs in the public main entrance. The board room would be used for admitting, except for the two occasions a month when the board was actually

*Margaret Malone, the hospital's therapeutic dietician, appears on the parapet of the soldiers wing. The SCR wing will be known later as the Wells Pavilion. Margaret Malone will be known later as Mrs. J. Ross Vant*

meeting. These things may seem small and obvious now but in their time they were important advances.

I don't believe anyone — patient or staff — was discommoded by the construction process. Although the staff was pleased because we needed the space I don't recall any air of excitement. However, there was plenty of that on the night of the official opening. It came on October 17 1930. Only 300 invited guests could crowd into the Red Cross hut but there was good news for radio fans. CKUA was broadcasting the event. The local airwaves were clear because CJCA did not sign on till later in the evening but the inaugural speeches were up against tough competition from the American networks — the Cities Service Orchestra on NBC and the Nitwit Hour on CBS.

The speeches were roundly applauded, by the crowd in the Red Cross hut, and doubtless by the radio audience. They came from Dr. Wallace, President of the University and Chairman of the Hospital Board. From George Hoadley, the Minister of Health. And from the Lieutenant Governor, who proclaimed the new wing officially open. Dr. W.G. Egbert could speak with great feeling. He was a pioneer medical man who practiced in Calgary before the foundation of the province.

Some pretty strong visions emerged from the speeches. The hospital was seen as a health centre for all Alberta, which, in the field of clinical research and medical service to the people of the province would one day be comparable to the clinic of the Mayo Brothers. I'm reminded of the lines of the old poem: "Bold words, brave youth!" The speakers may not have been young but the province was.

Following the oratory, the guests went on conducted tours, as they have done at all openings since. They were told about the general plan for each floor. Medical cases on the first floor. Surgical cases on the second. Third floor for eye-ear-nose-and-throat, diseases of women and urology. Fourth floor, tuberculosis. And on the fifth the nurses lived. During the speeches Dr. Egbert had said the Minister of Health should build a residence for the nurses, but even the Journal reporter recognized this as a joke. He observed that it was put forth "as a playful idea."

"Wash" enjoyed showing off the new technological wonders, such as the noiseless automatic electric elevator. "Does everything but talk" he said. And he was proud of the silent paging system which ended the bell-ringing manhunts conducted by the telephone operator. Spaced through the hospital were 20 callboxes which lighted up with a staff member's code number when the switchboard had a message for him. There was a lecture room for 75 people, where demonstrations could be given using a magic lantern. And there was the technology which most impressed the Journal reporter on the tour:

"One operating room is equipped with x-ray appliances and has a developing room attached. Surgeons may take a picture of the patient's disorder, develop it and operate, without the possible dislocating jar attendant upon moving the patient to the x-ray room and back to the operating table. Such is the efficiency of a modern hospital. . ." and such it was, in 1930.

But mind you, keeping a hospital modern is a never-ending fight. It's constantly going out of date.

# Chapter 10

# 1930—1935
*Hard Times*

Obviously the enlarged hospital was going to require more staff. The board agreed to hire a runner (at $40 a month) so the admitting officer would not have to leave her desk unattended while she escorted patients to their rooms. The board also recognized the need for clerical help in the business office and authorized engaging a clerk, "this is to be a man or a very efficient girl." This was certainly "state of the art" male chauvinism. A very efficient girl might be as smart as a not-too-bright man, and in the event that such a girl was actually found, the board would not be inconvenienced by equal pay for equal work.

Money was an inescapable concern, for board and staff. The provincial auditor agreed that the board had power to write off bad debts although he could not confer any power to collect them. In 1930 the board wrote off $219,000 in patient accounts — and mind you, these had gone unpaid in prosperous times.

The Imperial Bank gave the board a break. Interest on the $200,000 note was reduced from 5½ percent to 5¼ percent and on the overdraft from 6 percent to 5½ percent. The reductions were wangled from the head office by G.R.F. Kirkpatrick, manager of the Edmonton branch. Mr. Kirkpatrick also held the overdraft of the City of Edmonton, and with assets such as the city and our hospital it's little wonder he was so willing to serve on the hospital board, even after retirement.

To strengthen the administration Tommy Cox was appointed to a newly-created post of Secretary Treasurer, and Reg Adshead's struggles with the accounts were rewarded with a salary increase to $100 a month. Reg was a keen gymnast, a member of the Y, and he certainly got a workout wrestling with the accounts. Reg had a routine for bills. He wrote out the cheques promptly — then put them in a drawer until there was money in the bank to cover them. The average stay in Reg's drawer was six months.

While money was a concern for the hospital it was even greater for the sick because it affected their health. People were reluctant to come to a hospital unless they had money or were very, very sick. Patients were supposed to pay their way. If a doctor admitted a patient he had to be accepted, but the admitting staff were supposed to get the name of someone responsible for the bill. According to law municipalities were responsible for indigents, but often the municipalities were indigent too.

At night the interns handled admitting. Ken Thomson recalls greeting people from places like Violet Grove where the whole countryside was on relief. Ken would say: "All right, you must come in. How are you going to pay your bill?" It might be January, and the man might say that come fall he would have a pig or a bag of beets or a bag of turnips. Chickens and potatoes were taken in at the back door and bills credited at the market rate — say half a cent a pound for potatoes. The kitchen staff made resourceful use of everything. Produce was stored in the roothouse, out back next to the carpenter shop, and to make sure the bartered beets wouldn't spoil, Bob Sherriff, the gardener, turned them every day.

It was back to the barter system, but barter was not always in the shape of beets. Mr. Nette, the piano tuner, became a familiar visitor. Mr. Nette was from Vienna, where he'd been a railway guard and piano tuner. He'd tried to farm in Alberta, but his wife contracted an illness that required a long hospital stay. He worked out the bill by tuning the pianos in the nurses' quarters and the Red Cross hut. The one in the hut certainly required a lot of service. It took a hammering from amateurs, but was needed in good tune for the weekly variety concerts which were broadcast over CKUA. One of the sensations occurred when a patient being discharged wanted to pay in cash. He had a roll of bills all right, but couldn't sign his name to our account. He signed with an X — so much for literacy!

In the early '30s the hospital grew by building the new wing. It also grew by acquisition of the pavilions on the grounds. The Provincial Special Unit came first. The government felt the acute need for polio treatment was past. The PSU was integrated on April 1 1930, and the staff marked the occasion by having their salaries reduced to the standard of the main hospital.

The Red Cross Junior Hospital was a casualty of the depression. By the spring of 1930 the sponsoring organization was falling behind in its payments. It was able to pay only $1,000 on a bill of $3,261. Fund-raising efforts which had been successful in good times failed to provide any more. In May 1931 the Red Cross unit was absorbed into the main hospital and the board had a chance to decide how best to use the extra units.

The PSU was made a children's ward and the remaining Red Cross youngsters transferred there. It did not develop then as a full paediatric unit. It was considered an overflow for the Royal Alex with most activity in the summer holidays when kids came in to be parted from their tonsils and adenoids. However, it continued to be the centre for polio rehabilitation and all concerned deserve great credit for the exceptional care they gave the children in that small, cramped, ill-equipped space. Tommy Hancocks is an orderly remembered for his kindness to the kids. Another orderly was Jerry Dreger, who became a prominent south side businessman. Jerry had been in the PSU as a patient after the first polio epidemic and was thought to have some immunity although no one knew for sure.

The kids also enjoyed the support of a volunteer organization which typified the "helping spirit" of the depression. In the dark year of 1932, 20 young women formed the Junior Hospital League of Edmonton "to assist with the care of crippled children in the orthopaedic ward of the University Hospital."

I'm indebted to Marion Shipley for details of the early struggles. The girls hired a teacher three days a week, put on parties for the kids, organized a brownie pack, and when the kids went home provided them with orthopaedic shoes. They were so enthused by the work they applied for membership in the Junior League of America and a superior lady came out from New York to see what it was all about. She was courted and dined — a banquet at the Macdonald included — but sent back word that Edmonton was not grand enough for admission to the Junior League of America.

*Here is the vista the boosters of old Strathcona fought for and won. If the University Board of Governors had had their way the trees flanking 85th Avenue would have ended at infinity, as on all grid streets. But the boosters prevailed, the University Hospital was moved slightly south and the trees focused on the central facade of a cherished institution. A view for all seasons, captured in winter by Dr. Bulyea of Dentistry*

The girls were hurt and annoyed, but wouldn't let the kids suffer. They decided to give them the first therapeutic pool in western Canada, which opened in 1934 at a cost of $1,400 — almost twice what they'd been led to expect. They tried every manner of fund-raising. Tag days. A home decorating course at Eaton's. A cabaret at the Rose Room, a posh café in the King Edward Hotel, which made or lost $6.00 — no one was quite sure which. A review at the Tivoli Ballroom in which a chorus line wore "sad" green dresses and sang Boulevard of Broken Dreams. And there was the dog show. The first annual was

*The roof of the hospital is not counted in the total area available for patient care, but it's useful all the same. TB patients sleep there. On this occasion some children come up for air and sunshine. The small boy on the right clutches "The Tale of Peter Rabbit", doubtless the gift of some volunteer group. Off on the skyline rises the Macdonald Hotel*

held in 1934 when the Hudson's Bay Company let them fix up the fifth floor of the old store with cages and runways. The girls worked hard on construction, but on the eve of the event the city health inspectors got wind of it and said there couldn't be a dog show next to the Empire Dining Room. The show went on, after a lot of arguing and pleading. It was always a moneymaker, a hard way to make a dollar, but there were no easy ones. The Junior Hospital League maintained its support of the kids right up to 1959.

The Red Cross Pavilion was made over into a fully satisfactory maternity ward. There was some cost entailed — $700 for equipment, $800 for material, plus day labour, and it was an expense that couldn't be taken lightly — but at last we had an obstetrical ward and teaching unit, right on the premises.

This was the little yellow house "outback" where there was no privacy, where patients lined up for a chance at the toilet or washbowl, where a bath was a luxury, but the kind and efficient attention of nurses and house staff compensated for the shortcomings. I've had many chuckles in recent years as women have recalled nostalgically standing in line for a shower.

Mabel Trowbridge, a graduate of the hospital's first nursing class, was charge nurse on opening day 1933 and for many years after. She had the nickname "Bluebell," but to me she seemed more the Miss Trowbridge type and I always called her that.

Mary Williamson (Rose) joined the house staff on opening day. She recalls that the nurses, maids and mothers were like a small family off by themselves. Their wing was connected to the main hospital by a covered walkway known always as "the tunnel" even though it was above ground. The tunnel also connected the children's ward and the laundry. The maids trundled wagons through the tunnel to the main kitchen to pick up the patients' meals, but had a small kitchen of their own where they made tea for themselves and the mothers. And each morning student nurses came in to make the babies' formulas. It was a u-shape building with a case room and labour room in the middle. It had a "public" side with 12 beds initially and a "private" side with seven cubicles. And the mothers stayed 12 to 14 days.

Margaret Munro (who married Dr. Don Bell) came later as a nurse. She remembers it as a warm, cosy place, in spite of the inconvenience of detachment from the main hospital. If Margaret had to call for an intern at night it would take him seven minutes to get there. One night she was working on a delivery with Dr. Bob Johnston. He had to go to the main building to match a blood sample and when he got back Margaret had delivered the baby.

Rules were strict — no children as visitors — but rules weren't always enforced. I have to laugh at Mrs. Graham Huckell's story. "One day I saw the side door open and in came our children — and the dog too. They said the dog was missing me. Miss Trowbridge just gave a look and shut my door." It was a simple structure, but it served for nearly 20 years until money from oil allowed renewed construction of permanent buildings.

While the Department of Obstetrics made substantial gains in the early '30s, psychiatry suffered a severe setback. The expanded hospital opened with a

97

1930—1935

modern psychiatric ward of 14 to 16 beds, one of the first such units in western Canada in a regular hospital. It treated acute cases of mental illness, including attempted suicides, with the support of all hospital services, just as the hospital does today. The ward was the baby of Dr. C.A. Baragar, a very wonderful man who had come from Brandon to be Provincial Commissioner for Mental Health. His duties included the psychiatric unit, of which he was very proud, and teaching students, at which he was very good. Nowadays mental illness is regarded as an illness — like a broken leg. But some ancient attitudes still prevailed then. Ken Thomson has a funny story about that.

*A summer's day in the 1930s — 87th Avenue and 114th Street intersect in the foreground. Fields planted with experimental crops stretch away to the buildings of the University Hospital and on to Corbett Hall*

The psychiatric ward was in the basement. One night he was having trouble subduing a patient when a nurse pointed out someone peering through the window. Ken simply pulled down the blind, but a minute later there was a furious pounding on the door. Ken found a very determined lady on the other side. She demanded to know: "Why did you pull that blind down? I'm Magistrate Emily Murphy. It's my business to check on these matters!" Back in 1914, as you'll recall, Mrs. Murphy had stirred up an historic commotion by inspecting the hospital and going to the board with her comments. But Ken wasn't having any repeat of history. He said: "Well as far as I'm concerned it's none of your business," and locked the famous lady out.

Sadly the ward closed after three years. It was showing an annual loss of $5,000. Our budgets had to be approved by the provincial government, and the cost was considered too high.

Mind you, despite the straitened times it was considered necessary for the hospital to have beautiful grounds — to give the patients a lift and give prestige to the institution. That accounted for Bob Sherriff, the Scottish gardener. At noon the pool table in the Red Cross Hut belonged to Bob and Tommy Cox, our Secretary Treasurer. Tommy often passed up lunch to rest his ulcers, but I think he lost the benefit because he got so mad when Bob sank one of his spectacular fluke shots.

Bob was a deep-chested chap known by his pipe, his navy blue pullover sweater, his dour humour, and deep growls if someone dropped a piece of paper on *his* grounds. He certainly made them beautiful and did it with little money, one of the arts he'd learned while working for a top landscape designer in Edinburgh. Bob was a typical Scot in every respect, right to a discerning interest in Scotch whiskey. He was in Jasper, visiting a brother who managed the government liquor store there, when "Wash" Washburn advertised for a landscape gardener. Bob started his work in 1931 and went 27 years. During the winter he was by himself in the root cellar, turning the bartered vegetables, studying seed catalogues and sketching his summer campaign of improvements. Bob lived nearby. If there was a heavy snowfall on a weekend he'd come over to the hospital and shovel the walks. Nobody thought this was part of his job except Bob. He supplied the flowers for hospital occasions, and for brightening the grounds he had a special fondness for marigolds. I have to chuckle at how disgusted he was during the royal visit in 1939. The soldiers were brought out on the lawns to meet the King and Queen and the reporters trampled Bob's marigolds trying to get pictures. Bob believed the soldiers should have something to look out on and probably spent more time outside their wing than any other part of the hospital. Unless it was the children's hut where he had a field of poppies. Bob is gone now, and so are the grounds on which he laboured. They've been paved over and built on. There's a lot of greenery *inside* the new Walter C. Mackenzie Health Sciences Centre, but there's no room for it *outside*.

Mind you, Bob was not the only native of Scotland to serve the cause in the '30s. If you were to go out behind the hospital and shout: "Are ya there, Scotty?" you'd raise a chorus of "Ayes."

One of the Scots says the sub-staff was mostly Old Country — either Scots or English — and this helped resolve the annual debates over who should have Christmas off and who New Year's with the Scots opting for Hogmanay. However, the division led to other disputes. The same Scot says of Percy Stone, the famous orderly in urology: "He was a typical Englishman. He wouldn't listen to anybody!"

Out behind the hospital was a concentration of non-medical staff. The roothouse, carpenter shop and paint workshop were in detached huts, and in a sort of stub wing extending from the main hospital there was a lot of activity. The boiler room was in the basement, supplying steam for the laundry on the floor above and the kitchen on the floor above the laundry. The stores were also included, and in close proximity was the linen room. You couldn't see the building with the kitchen and laundry from the front of the hospital. Nowadays of course you can't see it from any point in the hospital. The kitchen and laundry are in a remote building on the way to Mill Woods, and the meals come in heated tanks.

In 1931 the kitchens turned out 528,000 meals at a cost of 12.07 cents each, plus three cents for labour. One hundred and ninety-six thousand meals were for the staff and were considered part of the remuneration. That figure, of course, doesn't include the late-night snacks which Fanny Hooson provided for the interns, doctors who came in for emergencies, and members of the maintenance staff who were called out of their homes to fix something which was going "bump in the night." Some of the best meals I ever had were at night when I came in for a delivery or a lecture. The kitchen was short on high technology, but it did boast a Hobart potato peeler and an apple peeler. I'm indebted for this information to Gladys Scoffield, who worked in the kitchen in the '30s and married Bob Sherriff. Gladys became a specialist in pastry, the way doctors became specialists. She pursued an interest. Gladys got so she could bake 75 pies at a time. They were baked in a three-tier oven and had to be raised twice during baking.

Below the kitchen, Dan Schneider had an all-girl crew of a dozen. Doris Blachford (who married Joe Kibbler the storesman) was one. Doris dropped out of Percy Page's Commercial High School in 1931, feeling the lure of money. It was $50 a month, which was a lot when you'd never had any. And the hours were shorter than some. Doris and her pals started at eight a.m. six days a week and left at five if the work was done. Sometimes, especially in winter, the steam would go off and they'd have to hunt up Fred Shaw, the engineer. The steam came from the university's central plant through underground pipes and was relayed through the boiler room. The mangle ran on steam and so did the two driers. The driers were vitally important. They were like closets. The nurses' uniforms and surgical gowns were hung on racks and rolled in, to emerge crisp and white, the sign of a well-run hospital. No one went home until the uniforms were sparkling white for the next day.

The linen room was just across from the laundry. Williamina Nicoll, another of the Hogmanay crowd, was in charge of a ceaseless salvage operation.

Mending was unending. Sheets, pillowcases and tablecloths were mended till they could be mended no more and then were cut up for slings and binders which went through the laundry till they collapsed in shreds and tatters.

No one got inside the walls of this institution without a valid reason. They wouldn't get past Hill, the commissionaire at the front door. It was not the open house of today with people coming and going at all hours. If you didn't satisfy Hill you stayed outside and he was especially vigilant in the matter of insurance salesmen, who liked to infiltrate hospitals. His manner was well-described by the kids, who called him "Jimmy Durante," but Hill was doing his duty as he saw it, which was a sentry in a place still run in a style established when the army was in charge.

The regimental style was evident in the dining rooms, where people sat according to degree at tables with white cloths to be served by waiters. Staff nurses, administrators and office staff ate in the equivalent of the officers mess, and when the senior officer — the Superintendent of Nurses — entered, all stood until she was seated at a place she reserved for herself. The students had the equivalent of a cadet mess. To the "other ranks" mess the so-called sub-staff came from the linen room, the laundry, the kitchens and the maintenance shops and dined at two tables set for 12, with three sittings for the hearty noon meal which was part of their pay. It came at the midpoint of what was essentially a 12-hour day and those who can remember those days do so with real affection. They led a close-knit family life and enjoyed a lot of laughs. Mary Williamson (who married Ellis Rose the storesman) puts it this way: "We had to have fun at work. We worked such long hours we were too tired to go out for fun in the evenings."

Mary recalls some typical high jinks with Tommy Mathieson who used to tease the girls by threatening to put them on ice. Tommy was one of the Hogmanay crowd. He'd been head storesman when the army ran the hospital and stayed in that position for 20 years after. Out behind the hospital was an icehouse, which the Arctic Ice Company kept supplied with blocks cut from the river, just upstream from the city. One winter the river froze so thick the blocks weighed 700-800 pounds. There was only one refrigerator in the entire hospital — in the maternity wing to keep the babies' formulas, so the ice was cut into smaller pieces to fit the iceboxes on the floors. Tommy was often slowed down by asthma, but if he was in top form the girls had to be wary of the icehouse. Tommy would appear chortling: "I'm going to put you on ice." And if a girl wasn't quick enough he'd swing her off her feet and set her down on a frozen block of Saskatchewan River. Mary describes one occasion when she averted this fate. "I threw an egg at Tommy and ran like heck." I hate to think what the human rights commission of today would say about Tommy Mathieson putting girls on ice, but at the time it was just having fun on the job, and Tommy had a serious job.

Stores did all the purchasing, including food, and had the task of preserving the milk and vegetables without refrigeration. Joe Kibbler had to combine food preservation with courtship. Joe was a delightfully profane Yorkshire man who worked in stores from 1926 to '61 and took over as head when Tommy's asthma finally drove him to a better climate. When Joe was courting Doris Blachford of the laundry, they'd go for walks in the evening and would have to go past the roothouse so Joe could adjust the vents and keep the temperature right for the vegetables. A storesman was also involved in the Sunday night suppers, which were simplified to give the kitchen staff a few hours freedom. Ellis Rose used to prepare the desserts. Dessert was always Neapolitan ice cream, layers of strawberry, chocolate and vanilla. Ellis would cut pint bricks into seven servings. Ellis recalls: "The meals cost an average of 12 cents, but they used to say the Sunday dinners cost only 5½ cents." Ice may have been the only disposable item in stores. Nowadays surgical and hypodermic needles come cased in plastic and are thrown away after one use, but in the '30s Ellis and Joe and Tommy had to sharpen them till they wore out.

Every economy was seized on and promoted, and I have to chuckle at the report of J.M. Sisson, head of our Pharmacy Department, in the hospital's annual report for the year ending March 31 1932. He writes: "The amount of liquors purchased decreases annually, due to our rigid triple check system and the cooperation of the medical staff." This is an in-joke that takes a word of explanation. The interns, those ingenious rascals, had discovered that pure alcohol from the pharmacy would mix with fruit juice to make as nice a drink as they would otherwise have to buy from the government store.

Mr. Sisson also notes the increasing pressure of the Outpatient Department on the pharmacy. The number of outpatients treated increased by nearly half to 13,426, and fewer than two percent of them could pay for their prescriptions.

A statistic like that can be worth a thousand words in painting a picture of a period in history. Reading further in the annual report for the year ended March 31 1932 I find others. The hospital cost $507,000 to operate and posted a deficit of $43,000, double the previous year. The hospital ran at 75 percent capacity. It had 3,558 patients who stayed an average of 28.2 days. Two thousand and eighty-six were in for operations, a quarter of which were classed as major. And 45 percent of the patient accounts had to be written off as uncollectable. There lay the deficit.

The community helped to the extent it was able and no contribution was too small to be acknowledged in the annual report. The Robert Tegler estate continued to place $2,000 a year on the sunny side of the ledger and added $750 for the care of indigent crippled children. The Fort Augustus Chapter IODE raised $134. The Maguire estate of Calgary offered $70. The Braemar Community Club of Nanton sent $5. "Hank" Mewburn gave the hospital some cystoscopes. Most contributions were for comforts for the patients. The Junior Hospital League made several important contributions to the entertainment and welfare of the children. Typical private gifts were a giant tinker toy from Mrs. C.E. Morris, a tricycle from Mrs. S.A. York and two Boys' Own Annuals from Mrs. A.H. Elliott. The soldiers were not forgotten. Twenty-five dollars from the "Lest We Forget" Club of Lacombe, $13.50 from the Canadian Legion at Wainwright, "smokes" from the COTC boys at the university. Everything was welcome. The ukelele from Mrs. McVittie of Riley. The magazines from George Steer the lawyer. The Christmas trees from Dr. Johnny Ower's boy scout troop. The plants from Mrs. McCoppen, the undertaker's wife. The deck chairs from the Order of the Eastern Star. And the yoyos.

Yoyos were enjoying their first wave of popularity in the year ending March 31 1932. They were contributed for amusement and therapy by the *Edmonton Journal*, by Mr. Peck of the CNR and by John Michaels of Mike's News Stand. It's easy to scoff at the yoyo, but against the ancient principle that what goes up must come down the yoyo offered hope that what goes down must come back up. As the people in the hospital contended day after day with the depression, they strove in the hope that the economy would rise again.

# Chapter 11

# 1935

*The Medical Departments*

This chapter is about the medical staff, the people who wrote MD and other code symbols after their names. With one notable exception the original cast of characters assembled in the early '20s were carrying on at the peaks of their careers in the '30s. The exception was the late Colonel Mewburn, whose role of Professor of Surgery in the university and Director of Surgical Services in the hospital was taken by "Sandy" Munroe, likewise a member of the original cast.

This dynamic and durable crowd — if two dozen can be called a crowd — dominated the medical philosophy of the hospital through the '30s and beyond. As a group, they had led adventurous lives, were widely-read, widely-travelled, and active in the cultural life of the city of 80,000.

Each man was a specialist. "Wash" made a big point of that at the ceremonies opening the new wing and he was correct, as the term was understood then. Each had a specialty, but it was based on personal interest rather than formal training in a universally-recognized program, which is the case today. Specialization was non-restrictive. The original cast did general medicine with an emphasis somewhere. But a trend to specialization as we now know it was setting in. I would say that a trend in medicine is like a pregnancy. It begins with a very small seed, gets bigger over a period of time and eventually matures and you have a birth. Specialization wasn't delivered till after the second world war but the trend was there in the '30s.

I have before me the hospital's annual report for the year ending March 31 1935. Reports of those years followed an unvarying format. Inside a grey cover (certainly appropriate to the economic outlook) three opening pages list the entire medical staff. The name J. Ross Vant is among the names for 1935 and as I have the honour to be one of the few survivors of this lively crew, I'd like to reproduce the pages of the report and tell you something about each man.

Except for "Edge" Pope, all were part-timers, making their living looking after patients. They attended at the hospital in the morning, went to their offices in the afternoon, and taught as well. It was considered an honour to teach. My stipend for the year 1932-33 was $200 and I'd like to think my instruction was worth it.

Just as the term *specialty* means something else today so does the term *department*. Nowadays each department has full-time medical staff and office staff too. In 1935 a department could be one man working part-time with the

*The Medical Staff —
University of Alberta Hospital*

*This picture was taken in 1931, though one almost identical might have been had in any year from the mid-20s to early '40s. The founding generation of doctors was a group with staying power — literally and figuratively*

*In the front row: R.B. Wells, Harold Orr, L.C. Conn, Edgerton Pope, Dean A.C. Rankin, Superintendent R.T. Washburn, John Darley Harrison (dean of the city's medical community who came to Edmonton in 1889 to die of*

*TB and confound medicial experts), A.R. "Sandy" Munroe, W.A. Wilson, H.H. Hepburn and Claude Jamieson*

*In the second row: Heber Jamieson, I.W.T. McEachern (whose wife Cora McWhirter was first nursing student in the Strathcona cottage hospital), J.O. Baker, Doug Leitch, R.F. Nicholls, George Malcolmson, L.C. Harris, John Scott, Richard Procter, Walter Scott, G.G. Stewart, Hastings "Hank" Mewburn and G.C. Gray*

*In the third row: C.W. Hurlburt, F.S. McPherson, J.E. Carmichael, J.L. Petticlerc, John Ower, J.A. Blezard, Harold Vango, George Hunter, W.S. Armstrong and C.T. Fitzpatrick*

*In the top row: J.A. Macpherson, N.L. Terwillegar, Irving Bell, Ken Hamilton, Evan Greene (who practiced in the Strathcona cottage hospital), Jack Fife, Mark Marshall, Graham Huckell and E.C. Smith*

"office" mostly carried in his head. The term *division* has also entered the language. Service identified as a *department* in 1935 might now be known as a *division* of the *department* of medicine.

Let's start with medicine.

---

## MEDICINE

### Director of Medical Services

Egerton Llewellyn Pope, B.A. (Queen's), M.D., C.M. (McGill), F.R.C.P. (London), F.R.C.P. (Canada).

### Senior Physician

Heber Carss Jamieson, M.B. (Toronto), F.R.C.P. (Canada), Associate Physician in charge of Division A, and Metabolic Department.

### Associate Physicians

Irving Russell Bell, B.A., M.B. (Toronto), F.R.C.P. (Canada), Associate Physician.

Walter Hepburn Scott, M.C., M.D., C.M. (McGill), F.R.C.P. (Canada), Associate Physician in charge of Division B, and Chest Ward.

Charles Watson Hurlburt, M.B. (Toronto), F.R.C.P. (Canada), Associate Physician in charge of Cardiological Department.

Douglas Burrow Leitch, M.C., B.A., M.B. (Toronto), F.R.C.P. (Canada), Associate Physician in charge of Pediatrics.

Harold Orr, O.B.E., M.D., D.P.H. (Toronto), F.R.C.P. (Canada), Associate Physician in charge of Dermatological Department.

Charles Arthur Baragar, B.A., M.D., C.M. (Manitoba), Associate Physician in charge of Psychiatric Department.

John William Scott, M.D., C.M. (McGill), F.R.C.P. (Canada), Assistant Physician, Division A, in charge of Biochemistry Department.

Kenneth Hamilton, B.A. (Toronto), B.A. (Oxford), M.B.B.Ch. (Oxford), M.R.C.P. (London), Assistant Physician, Division B.

---

I've written about Dr. Pope, the director. He carried on, a true scholar and gentleman, unruffled by the depression. I don't suppose an earthquake or a hurricane would cause "Edge" to alter his style.

Heber Jamieson (1922-46) was on the laboratory side of medicine, a lifelong student. He was interested in everything. On almost any subject a member of the medical staff could bring up Heber would be the most widely-read on that subject. He wrote too. A classic reference work is *Early Medicine in Alberta*. His interest made him an interesting lecturer, and if you were to name an overriding interest it would be *metabolism*, which covers most of internal medicine. Diabetes was a consuming study. Heber was one of the first to work with the insulin purified on campus by Dr. Collip. He was into endocrine problems — thyroid and pituitary diseases — and worked with L.C. Conn, helping ferret out some of the diseases of women related to endocrine glands. Harold Orr, the dermatologist, saw many skin problems related to thyroid and Heber worked on allergies with Harold. Heber took the laboratory approach to everything he found of interest. He got curious about the physical effects of a long canoe trip and set off by himself, paddling down the river all the way to

North Battleford. At age 60, he set about learning to fly, studying the problem in a Moth biplane with his pal Captain Burbidge of the Edmonton Flying Club. People stopped being surprised at what Heber did. Once he began to wonder about the effects of hard work on kidney function — and when the football team came in after practice one day, Heber was waiting with a case of specimen bottles.

Irving Bell (1925-55) was in charge of therapeutics. And you might say that Irving spent the '30s waiting for penicillin. His specialty of therapeutics meant treatment of disease by drugs, and medical science hadn't provided any new ones for a long time. He had the old-fashioned remedies — Aspirin. Digitalis. Codeine. Morphine. We were just on the brink of "wonder drugs", but Irving had to get through the '30s without them. He had a habit we used to joke about — of shaking his head at meetings. But it was a good lesson. He doubted things until he could prove them. In the meantime Irving was bringing up three doctor sons who had parts to play in the later life of the hospital.

Walter Scott (1923-50) worked in all medicine, but his special interest was chest problems. During the '30s he attended the hospital's TB ward, where he handled pneumothorax, the treatment of collapsing the lung. Walter had been through the first war and had come home with the Military Medal. I have to laugh when I remember how gruff he could be. The interns called him "Woof Woof." Walter's father was a Justice of the Supreme Court from Calgary. One night in the Edmonton Club someone commented to Judge Scott that Walter was a pretty good billiard player. "He should be," the judge laughed. "He cost me a whole year of university while he was learning."

Chuck Hurlburt (1922-44), another veteran, was easily recognized from a distance by his tall straight figure. He was also recognized as the first cardiologist in Alberta. In the hospital, Chuck had reasonably modern equipment for electrocardiograms, but in the Faculty of Medicine there was an ancient contraption for obtaining electronic news of the heart. The *victim* had electrodes attached to his arms and chest with wires — but to produce the necessary electric pulses he had to put his bare feet into two Medalta pottery jars containing a weak battery solution. I suppose this helped medical students understand the principle on which the hospital equipment worked — and appreciate the equipment too.

Doug Leitch was in charge of paediatrics for a full 30 years, from 1923 to '53, and like most of the older staff, he'd been through the first war. Although Jimmy Calder's name does not show on this list he had returned from very advanced training in the east to join Doug in private practice and at the hospital and eventually succeeded him as head of paediatrics. Jimmy Calder did his intern year with me in 1929-30. From there he went to Sick Children's Hospital in Toronto where the famous Dr. Allan Brown was creating a new cereal for infants, and had the pleasure of eating lots of yummy experiments. While it's widely known that insulin is a product of Canadian invention, few know that the same claim can be made for Pablum. From Pablum Jimmy went on to more work in New York and Chicago before joining Doug Leitch back in Edmonton. Doug and Jimmy had a wonderful way with children. It was touching to watch them allay the fears of children in pain. They were very busy in the polio scare of 1935 which closed the schools for a month, and little wonder they were busy. Dr. Swallow was the only other paediatrician in town.

Harold Orr (1926-52) was a travelling man. Many doctors worked in two hospitals, but Harold is the only one I ever knew of who worked in two cities. Edmonton didn't provide enough dermatology patients to absorb all his interest in the subject so he used to go down to Calgary and make an office of his hotel room. Harold also found time to run our venereal disease clinic and struggled along with the ineffective creams and lotions that were available before penicillin.

C.A. Baragar is still shown in charge of psychiatry. However, our mental ward had been shut down by the depression, and in November '35 Dr. Baragar went to Ponoka as Superintendent. Sadly, he soon died of pneumonia, and in our hospital we hadn't even the shadow of a Department of Psychiatry until the '50s.

Ken Hamilton (1928-58) specialized in internal medicine, though not in a restrictive way. Ken was a very astute and knowledgeable physician, with an unusual education. In 1922 he'd gone to Oxford as Rhodes Scholar from Saskatchewan with a BA. He took his medical training in England where he obtained a very broad knowledge of medicine. Ken was a fine teacher and kept meticulous records, and for relaxation he followed the ponies. He used to go to all the races, though mind you, in those days we had only one week of races during the Exhibition and a spring or fall meet of another two weeks.

Internal medicine was also the special interest of John Scott (1932-55). Frank Elliott, who worked closely with him, points out that John Scott unlike many of the original cast, was not a character. He was a calm, kind gentleman who never got tired.

Like many a man born in Ireland, John sailed to Boston in steerage. Before the first war he had his medical degree from McGill, and after the war came to Alberta to a country practice near Provost. Then in 1923 he came to the university as assistant to Dr. Collip in biochemistry.

He had strong personal convictions about his role in a teaching hospital and his convictions forced him into an encounter he described in his quiet humorous way as "wrestling with the devil." One day in 1931 a big cheerful farmer from the country district where he had practiced arrived at his desk and announced: "My daughter is pregnant. I want you to look after her." John tried to explain how this would be in conflict with his responsibilities to a teaching hospital. His friend listened with attention and good humour and when John finished he produced a roll of $10 bills and began dropping them on the desk. One. Two. Three. Four. All cash on the barrel and John with a young family to support. John Scott said that sticking to principle, in the face of his friend's concern for his daughter and the $10 bills on the desk, was the hardest thing he ever had to do.

Frank Elliott remembers Dr. Scott's tenacity and meticulousness in the early attempts to conduct metabolism tests. Nowadays a simple blood sample analyzed by a computer gives an instant reading on the speed of metabolism. But in the '30s the process was awkward and cumbersome. The patients breathed into a big sack called a Douglas bag. A lot of heavy breathing was required to fill the bag, which was then sealed. John Scott would collect the bags and carry them on his back to the Faculty of Medicine where the air inside was analyzed for oxygen and carbon dioxide.

In addition to Douglas bags on his back, John carried a great load of things in his head. He could lecture brilliantly without notes, on breezy subjects like "the analysis of spinal fluids." He had photographic recall for prescriptions and phone numbers, and if a question came up about a prescription for a patient he could dial the correct pharmacist and discuss the problem without having any paper in front of him. John Scott capped his association with the hospital by becoming the third Dean of Medicine, and in retirement he wrote a 50-year history of the Faculty of Medicine, a brief, but rich reference work.

---

### SURGERY

**Director of Surgical Division and Surgeon-in-Chief**
Alexander Russell Munroe, M.D., C.M. (McGill), F.R.C.S. (Canada).

**Senior Surgeon**
Wilfred Alfred Wilson, M.D., C.M. (McGill), F.R.C.S. (Canada).

**Associate Surgeons**
Howard Havelock Hepburn, M.C., M.D., C.M. (McGill), F.R.C.S. (Edinburgh),
    F.R.C.S. (Canada), in charge of Neuro-Surgery.
William Fulton Gillespie, M.A. (Alberta), M.B., M.S. (Toronto), F.R.C.S.
    (Canada).
John Alexander McPherson, M.D. (Toronto).
John Keith Fife, M.D., C.M. (McGill).

---

"Sandy" Munroe (1922-42) became head of the department on the death of Frank Mewburn and he was certainly a worthy successor. Like the Colonel "Sandy" was a McGill man and had served at the Colonel's military hospital in England. Unlike the Colonel he was a quiet man. Ken Thomson remembers "Sandy" as quiet, direct, very upright in his bearing, a kind man who kept his warmth under control, one who inspired his patients with confidence and perhaps a little fear, a quick decisive man who didn't want students to give him 47 reasons for a course of action, but only the vital ones. Time was not for wasting. Once when Ken was assisting at an operation and wasn't moving fast enough to suit the surgeon he said quietly: "Come, Thomson, you should be on that like a tiger. *Like a tiger.*"

Bob Macbeth was a student in the '30s and eventually the sixth man to head the Department of Surgery. Bob wrote an article for the *Canadian Journal of*

*Surgery* in which he recognized "Sandy" Munroe as the man who had the time and the enthusiasm to develop the educational requirements of the undergraduate surgical program. Bob cited the "ward rounds" which were established with the support of Heber Jamieson on the medical side. These occurred each Wednesday morning. Medical staff, senior students, and doctors from country towns would spend the morning going from bed to bed, with Dr. Munroe the central and dominant figure of the stimulating exercise.

I expect W.A. Wilson's title of Senior Surgeon was "Wash" Washburn's idea. It recognized his seniority over everyone else connected with the hospital. It began in 1914, carried on through the military phase, and persisted through the university phase, right to 1943. I have to laugh remembering W.A. The rest of the city was on Mountain Standard Time but he had his own time. We reckoned his appearances not by the minute or the hour, but by the day.

When W.A. Wilson reached Edmonton in 1904 he'd already had an adventurous career. In his native Carleton Place, Ontario, he completed a three-year apprenticeship in pharmacy before going on to a medical degree at McGill. He made two voyages around the world as ship's surgeon with the Elder Dempster line. He did advanced work in Edinburgh where his grandfather and great-grandfather had graduated in medicine. Back in Canada he went where most young men were going. In 1904 he set up an office in the old Johnstone Walker store on Jasper Avenue, and walking to work from the west end he could pot ducks on the slough at 112th Street. His early hospital affiliation was with the Royal Alex, where he met Edith Tait, one of the nurses from the Royal Vic of Montreal who had come out to establish a school of nursing there. They were married and hired a contractor to build them a house, but old Jim Hay was so slow and methodical that they lived a winter in a tent. At this time he made the acquaintance of a young school teacher whom he urged to pursue a career in medicine. This the teacher did with immense success — his name was Howard Havelock Hepburn.

W.A.'s specialty (in the hospital and in university lecture rooms) was bone fractures. He spoke so softly that he was known to his students as "Whispering Willie" but he was worth listening to. Four times he was President of the College of Physicians and Surgeons of Alberta — in 1928, then again in 1933, '37 and '38. In 1935 W.A. was accepting congratulations for his son Don, who was Alberta Rhodes Scholar that year and eventually became head of our Department of Medicine.

Fulton Gillespie (1930-49) was a likeable chap and one of the broadly-educated people who made Edmonton a much richer place than the population indicated it ought to be. His field was bowel surgery, although it wasn't a restrictive specialty, in keeping with the views of the time. As a boy, Fulton suffered a collapsed lung, which kept him out of the army in the first war, but he found adventure going to teach in the Yukon. Afterwards he came to Edmonton and taught in the Department of Classics at the university. He took his medical degree from the University of Toronto and returned to Edmonton in 1925. His father, Dr. A.S. Gillespie, had suffered a stroke, but wanted very much to continue in practice to the extent he was able, so they went into partnership from the father's home. Later Fulton and I had our offices on the fourth floor of the Birks Building and built our houses across the street from each other on Edinboro Road. Fulton had a good command of English which helped make him a fine teacher and he played the piano well and loved playing the organ at First Presbyterian Church when the regular organist was away. When "Sandy" Munroe resigned to go into private practice in 1939 Fulton became head of surgery.

I had a lot of respect for J.A. McPherson (1925-47), a very nice chap. He

*When cameras see only black and white, a fall of clinging snow is a heaven-sent opportunity. Here, snow makes a photographer's dream of half-grown spruce trees and the trellised archway, fashioned of discarded pipe by Bob Sherriff the Scots gardener. In years ahead parking lots will trample Bob's gardens, but the arch will be moved to greet visitors to his own home. It's there yet —*
*11115 University Avenue*

was a bonesetter, and he had the best possible training for the specialty — he was an engineer. In 1906 he earned a degree in mechanical engineering from the University of Toronto and then went on to another degree in medicine. There was no intervention in fractures then. You just brought the bones together, put on a splint and then a cast. Dr. McPherson was as good as an orthopaedic man. Some said they were mechanics, but he was an engineer.

Jack Fife (1927-47) was the first graduate of our university appointed to the staff of the hospital. Jack was a very skillful surgeon and his special interest was thyroids. I have to laugh when I read the board minutes concerning Jack's first appointment. Dean Rankin informs the board that Jack has been interning successfully at the Royal Vic in Montreal and wonders if he might receive an appointment if he were to return to Edmonton. The board agrees it is certainly their policy to encourage young men who stand high in their profession. It will be in order to assure Jack that if he returns he will be granted an appointment at the outdoor clinic, though at present no remuneration can be offered.

Apparently that was enough encouragement. Jack came back. A little later he did a residency at the Crile Clinic in Cleveland, quite a famous clinic specializing in thyroids. Jack was the first staff surgeon to carry specialization to the point of restriction, which caused some concern for "Sandy" Munroe. Jim Metcalfe was a student in the '30s. He recalls: "Jack was really hot on thyroids. He could take one out beautifully in just minutes, but often couldn't get up the nerve to schedule the operation — it was so risky."

Frank Elliott was a student and intern then. Frank recalls: "We saw a lot of things we don't see much now. Goitre was one. Many were among people from central Europe who had developed theirs before coming to Canada. Thyroid was the problem. Only two things could be done — take out the thyroid or control it with iodine. Sometimes the patients would come in with their basal metabolisms so high that surgery had to wait until it could be slowed down."

As many recall, Jack was a fun-loving chap who was sometimes hard to find. Ironically, Jack's specialty has declined in the trend towards increasing specialization. Iodized salt has caused goitre to almost disappear.

The career of Howard Hepburn (1922-51) is a case study of the trend to specialization. In his hospital years "Hep" made himself the pioneer brain surgeon of western Canada. And before the hospital his life was an adventure worth a book on its own. "Hep" was the most travelled man in the hospital, perhaps in the entire city. Starting from McGill (where else?) he had gone to Siam to work in the government health service, and performed 2,000 cataract operations among others. He visited Japan, China, Malaya, Ceylon, Egypt, and other countries which, in those times, seemed more fable than fact. When the first world war broke out he was in Germany studying the brain and the nervous system. He was interned in Berlin, but escaped to England through Holland and in three weeks was back in France with a British medical unit. He was in France a full five years and in the worst fight of all, at Paaschendaele. There he was wounded and won the Military Cross. "Hep" was in the University Hospital working with veterans when the university got it back from the army.

Views are in a state of constant evolution in the medical world. It's unwise ever to say flatly that something *is*. Better to say *is thought of as*. When I was in medical school neurology was thought of as part of medicine. When I came to Edmonton neurology was coming to be thought of as part of surgery as well. But "Hep" was already thinking of it as a specialist branch of surgery.

There was no one he could turn to for help, no one he could consult. He even had to invent the tools. One useful instrument was fashioned in the basement workroom of the hospital from scraps of steel and strips of rubber innertube. The resulting device resembled a set of ice tongs. He'd developed the idea originally during the war for treatment of wounds to the knee, and adapted it to neurosurgery. As early as 1933 the tongs attracted attention in Britain. An article in the journal called *Surgery* described "the Edmonton tongs." Also described was a British invention with the same purpose, using a metal locking block instead of cut-up innertube. The original "Hepburn tongs," as they were called here, are proudly preserved today in the hospital's Department of Neurosurgery.

I'm indebted to Guy Morton for personal insights into the Hepburn style. Guy's association began in the 1930s when he was a student and resident. Dr. Hepburn inspired Guy to pursue a career in neurosurgery which he did so well that he eventually succeeded his mentor as head of neurosurgery.

Guy recalls: "I could set my watch by the time he'd arrive at the hospital, seven days a week. He'd be right at the bedside at eight o'clock every morning. About two or three in the afternoon, after his duties at the hospital and the university he'd go to his office in the old Bank of Montreal Building at Jasper and 101st Street. The office had cold running water, but no hot. There he would find a waiting room full of people.

"Although his specialty was neurosurgery it was never restrictive. Before a plastic surgeon came to Edmonton there was no one to help poor children born with cleft palates and harelips. Dr. Hepburn did that work because there was no one else who could. He was subject to migraine headaches in the operating room. When that happened he'd go out and vomit and come right back. With all his duties, once a year he did an appendectomy — just for the fun of it." Guy concludes: "There were some truly big men in those days. Dr. Hepburn was one."

There's a classic Hepburn story. It's been told a number of ways but this is how Bob Macbeth heard it. "Hep" was using a brace-and-bit to hand-drill two holes in a patient's skull — an operation that's now done electrically. The patient was not too well. "Hep" dropped the bit on the floor and told a nurse to go sterilize it. She was gone about 20 minutes and as she came back there was a clatter outside the door — she'd dropped it again. The nurse wanted to take it away for a further 20 minutes, but "Hep" said: "Hand it here. I can treat sepsis but I can't treat rigor mortis."

In 1938 there was an addendum to the list of surgeons. Roy Anderson was one of our graduates. He grew up at Lamont, where the influence of Dr. Archer's Methodist mission hospital was strong, and began his career as a country doctor at Smoky Lake. He was able to go to the University of Toronto for postgraduate work and a fellowship in the Royal College of Surgeons of Canada. Thus qualified to teach he received a joint appointment in the faculty and teaching hospital of the University of Alberta. Like most men of the time recognized as surgical specialists he considered himself a medical man first, and had a general practice in medicine with the addition of work in obstetrics. This rose from two convictions — that it was the right thing to do, and there was better chance of eating on a regular basis. In 30 years on our staff Roy was to see many changes in the delivery of health care. Along the way he was first chairman of MSI — Medical Services Incorporated — a plan of health insurance provided by Alberta doctors which was to prove irresistible to governments.

---

## OBSTETRICS AND GYNAECOLOGY

### Senior Surgeon

Leighton Carling Conn, M.D., C.M. (McGill), F.R.C.S. (Canada), F.C.O.G., Director of Obstetrics and Gynaecology.

### Associate Surgeons

Jermyn Oscar Baker, M.D., C.M. (Queen's), F.R.C.S. (Canada), M.C.O.G.
Allan Day, M.B. (Toronto).
John Ross Vant, B.A. (Saskatchewan), M.D. (Manitoba), M.C.O.G.

---

L.C. Conn (1923-42) received his appointment when the only patients were soldiers recovering from the war, so the hospital was obviously looking to the future. He was one of those men whose standing as a specialist was acknowledged by his peers. At the formation of the Royal College of Physicians and Surgeons of Canada in 1929 "L.C." was made a foundation fellow.

On graduating from McGill before the first war he'd spent two years residence at the Royal Vic, which was considered great. The trend to specialization was noticeable in 1930 when I went to the Royal Vic for two years residence. "L.C." had done general work, but my program was totally obstetrics and gynaecology.

Allan Day (1925-50) was a specialist whose knowledge came from experience rather than formal training. Allan liked the work and was good at it, which attracted the notice of Dr. Conn and led to his appointment to the university hospital staff. Allan also worked at the Royal Alex. The custom of restricting practice to one hospital came later.

J.O. Baker (1925-59) was a gregarious, likeable fellow. "J.O." we always called him. J.O. was Edmonton's first medical entrepreneur. In the '30s he was founding the clinic which still carries his name and now has almost as many MDs as the entire hospital did in 1935. J.O. graduated from Queen's in 1910. If a graduate of that time spent a year interning it was good, if he spent two years it was great, and J.O. spent two. He was a kind man who knew a lot of people. He was a good doctor, but knew his limitations in surgery and always had good young surgeons with him, which was the start of the Baker Clinic. Before the first war he'd come west as medical officer with the Grand Trunk Pacific Railway and it was interesting to ride the train to Jasper with J.O. and hear him reminisce about the construction days and the people he'd known.

---

### ORTHOPAEDIC SURGERY

#### Senior Surgeon
Frank Hastings Hamilton Mewburn, V.D., B.Sc., M.D., C.M. (McGill), F.R.C.S. (Canada).

#### Associate Surgeon
Robert Graham Huckell, M.D., C.M. (McGill).

### UROLOGY

#### Senior Surgeon
Emerson Charles Smith, M.D., C.M. (McGill), F.R.C.S. (Canada).

#### Associate Surgeon
Gordon Nichols Ellis, B.A. (Queen's), M.D., C.M. (Queen's).

### EYE, EAR, NOSE AND THROAT SURGERY

#### Senior Surgeons
Ophthalmologist—Robert Bruce Wells, M.B. (Toronto), F.R.C.S. (Canada).
Oto-Laryngologist—Claude Vernon Jamieson, M.B. (Toronto), F.R.C.S. (Canada).

#### Associate Surgeons
Mark Robert Levey, M.D., C.M. (McGill), D.L.O. (England).
William Sloane Seale Armstrong, M.D., C.M. (McGill).
James Gould Young, M.D., C.M. (Queen's).

---

"Hank" Mewburn was head of orthopaedic surgery from 1922 to '48. You wouldn't expect a son of our famous Colonel to be a shrinking introvert and "Hank" certainly wasn't. Like his father he was a McGill man and a military man. In the first war he served in both the artillery and the medical corps and was an enthusiastic member of VOMO — the Volunteer Overseas Medical Officers. He loved parties and was crazy about trains. He had an electric train system in his basement and liked to entertain by putting on an engineer's hat and going through the motions and sound effects of a steam train. He advised interns to read up on model trains because he liked to discuss them during operations and such was his personality that they surely did. On New Year's morning he'd make rounds still in his evening clothes, then call at each nursing station to apologize for all the cussing he intended to do in the year to come. However, I'm told that "Hank" didn't inherit the Colonel's consummate skill in this art, and he was hampered by asthma, which would sometimes strike during a colourful passage.

To illustrate how new was the principle of specialization, "Hank" was only the second man in Alberta to be registered as an orthopaedic specialist. Graham Huckell, who went through the war with the First Canadian Mounted Rifles, and served the department from 1927 to '58, was the third. There were no set programs for becoming a specialist. You had to identify an institution where advanced work was being done in your field of interest and be accepted to work there. In 1920 "Hank" went for 18 months work in Boston. On graduating from McGill in 1924, Graham found two months advanced work in New York and two months in St. Louis. From then on they became specialists by experience.

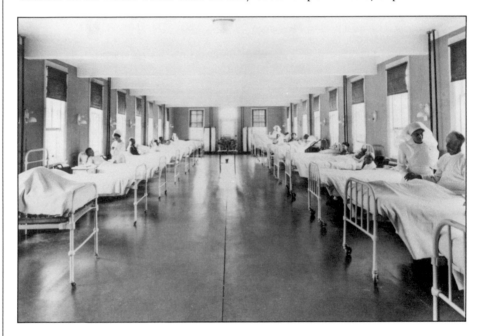

*The twenty-bed ward is the standard of hospital care in the 1930s. The charge of $2.50 a day is the responsibility of the patient. Washing the windows is a responsibility of student nurses. Orderly "Slim" Waters is responsible for the high gloss on the floor. It's "battleship" linoleum, appropriate to the management style of certain head nurses*

Certification was done locally in each province. In Alberta the senate of the university was the authority. This body granted registration to the entire orthopaedic department of the University Hospital, which consisted of "Hank" and Graham.

Mrs. Huckell recalls that Graham chose orthopaedics because it was the biggest specialty in surgery — everything except soft tissue. He would laugh about it as he did so easily and say: "But if you make a mistake everybody sees it."

The Mewburn-Huckell duo were busy all through the '30s helping victims of the polio epidemics, which came in 1927, 1930 and '35. And Christmas was a special day for Graham. On that day he'd pick up Tommy Robson and tour the children's wards acting as Santa's assistant to Tommy's very convincing Saint Nicholas. But playing Santa Claus was thirsty work. Afterwards their Christmas tradition was relaxation back at Graham's with a few bowls of cheer.

Orthopaedics had 10 beds in the hospital, the same as Urology. Emerson Smith, a member of the original cast who founded the Department of Urology, was a McGill man. In 1937 he was succeeded by Gordon Ellis, the youngest-ever graduate of Queen's, who was chief for 20 years. But the third head of the department was to be an Alberta man. Jim Metcalfe entered our medical school in the late '30s.

Jim notes that in those days urology patients were very, very, very sick. A lot of them were country people referred by their GP. They came in suffering terrible back and kidney damage and a lot of kidney failure. The prostate operation was open surgery and was so distressing that patients and their doctors procrastinated about taking action.

Patients trusted completely in the orderly in the urology ward, the famous Percy Stone. Percy was not a member of the medical staff, of course, but it used to be said that patients would take advice: first from the orderly, second from the nurse, third from the intern, and fourth from the doctor on the medical staff. Percy would countermand orders of the doctor if his intuition told him something else. This used to make Gordon Ellis really mad but if Percy said a man wasn't up to surgery at the scheduled time the operation would usually be put off. Percy used to travel around the wards in the morning with a wagon of catheters which were supposed to be sterile, although there were some doubts. He had an art about putting in a catheter and junior interns went around with him to learn his art. Sometimes the patient was sent home to the country with a catheter. Jim Metcalfe knew one country man who wore it wrapped around his hat. In the '30s, Jim notes, the morbidity rate from prostate operations was 20 percent. Nowadays, with modern techniques and early treatment the operation is performed on men in their nineties and the rate is down to a half of one percent.

In the realm of Eye, Ear, Nose and Throat, ophthalmology focuses on the eyes and oto-laryngology the other areas. Both R.B. Wells and Claude Jamieson were members of the original cast and graduates of Toronto. Claude was a nice chap like his brother Heber, quieter, very precise, and knew a lot of people. In the age before penicillin mastoids were an acute concern for Claude. Without antibiotics a minor ear infection could travel to the mastoid process and become very dangerous, leaving surgery the only recourse.

Though R.B. Wells was chief of ophthalmology we seldom saw him at the hospital because his practice related to office work. However, his rare visits were impressive. Dr. Wells was driven by a chauffeur, and made a grand entrance wearing a cape rather than a topcoat.

We saw a lot more of Bill Armstrong (1929-60), a McGill man certified as an EENT specialist in Ontario before coming here. Bill capped his long service as chief of oto-laryngology. Bill's work schedule made a lasting impression on John Gibson, a carpenter who joined the hospital staff a little later. John remembers Bill coming to work at seven in the morning, ready for the operating room to open at eight. He'd have the whole corridor lined with stretchers. He was going to be pulling tonsils that day.

We saw a lot of Mark Levey (1928-61), known later as Mark Marshall. When Drs. Wells and Jamieson left the scene at the end of the '30s Mark took over both their positions at the hospital. Mark had a unique career. Before the first war he came from Austria to Montreal. He was befriended there by a family named Marshall, whose name he adopted later as a sign of gratitude, but only after he made good under his own name of Levey. Mark was at McGill when war broke out. He went overseas with the artillery and devised routines for targeting heavy guns which were taken up by the army. He's said to have been the youngest brigade major in the Canadian army. Back at McGill again, he got his MD, and on the way showed his powers of persuasion by being elected president of the Students' Union. He planned a postgraduate program for himself, and arrived in Edmonton with clinical experience in England and Europe. Our nurses found Mark impatient and exacting in the operating room, and perhaps he wasn't always gracious to those who disagreed with what he said, but he was a kind man, and a fine surgeon. Cataract surgery wasn't being performed in the '30s, but when it came in later on, Mark did mine. Because of his own self-made career Mark had a feel for the trend to specialization. When postgraduate programs leading to specialist recognition were introduced after the second war Mark was recognized as the man to take charge.

**DENTISTRY**

**Director of Dental Services**

Harry Ernest Bulyea, D.M.D. (Harvard).

**Dental Surgeon to the Hospital**

William Scott Hamilton, L.D.S., D.D.S. (Toronto).

**ANAESTHESIA**

**Chief of Anaesthestic Service**

John Albert Blezard, M.B., M.D., C.M. (Queen's).

**Assistants**

James Ernest Carmichael, B.Sc., M.D., C.M. (Queen's).
John McDonald Oswald, M.D., C.M. (Trinity).
Ernest H. Watts, B.A., M.D. (Alberta).

**RADIOLOGY**

Richard Procter, M.D. (Manitoba).

We had lots of McGill men on staff, but H.E. Bulyea (1922-42) was the only Harvard man. He lived for 103 years and his interests and talents kept him busy the whole time. In 1930, at age 57, he succeeded after several failures in climbing Mount Geikie, a difficult 11,000-foot peak in Jasper. He built boats. He was a pioneer in colour photography. He produced instruments and sketches and models of teeth for dental training, and this was useful in the '30s when the school was hard-pressed for funds.

Dr. Bulyea's successor Scott Hamilton (1925-58) could tell of being a patient in the hospital's military phase after service with the artillery and flying corps. Scott was a likeable chap, a keen Rotarian and an even keener member of the Burns Club. A dental internship was established in the hospital in 1929. Hec MacLean, a U of A grad who eventually succeeded Scott, points to Scott Hamilton as the man who really built up the hospital side of the dental program.

Like many of the original cast Dr. Blezard (1922-36) served overseas with the army medical corps. Before that he'd been medical officer on construction of the Edmonton Dunvegan and British Columbia Railway. A biographical sketch published in 1922 said: ". . .in the practice of his profession he has specialized in anaesthesia and obstetrics." Anaesthesia was certainly a very sketchy department in 1935. Many surgeons preferred to do their own in their own way, using the means available. That meant nitrous oxide and oxygen, combined with drops of chloroform and sometimes of ether. They used to say of one respected practitioner — who worked at another hospital — that he got so close to the ether he took in more than the patient. A few people were beginning to think of anaesthesia as a specialized branch of medicine. Not many, mind you, but a few. Ernie Watts was one. Ernie graduated from the University of Alberta with the class of '31 and went to Wisconsin to pursue his interest with postgraduate training under the celebrated Dr. Waters. When Dr. Blezard went back east in '36 Ernie was named Chief of Anaesthetic Services, the first Alberta grad to head a department.

Dick Procter (1922-52) was already on x-ray staff when the university regained possession from the army. Dick had been around. After graduating from Manitoba he was a medical officer with the gangs building the railroad from Edmonton to Edson. He went overseas with the RCAMC and learned radiology with the army. Dick likely spent more time at the hospital than any other department head. At his home in Garneau he was always on call, and often showed up late at night when the interns had trouble taking x-ray pictures or developing them in the wet tanks. By day Dick had the help of the faithful George McMillan, who came into the hospital as an orderly in 1924 and became an x-ray technician by showing a knack for it. Dick was a kind fellow, very helpful in difficult cases. Radiology was just coming into its own and with the state of development of the hospital he was never able to establish a major diagnostic centre. But there was a lot of work done, so much that storing the plates was a problem. Plates had to be kept five years to satisfy the statute of limitations. There was no room inside the hospital so they were stored on the roof, over the heads of the interns.

We used to enjoy Dick and his dogs. One time Johnny Gibson the carpenter was to do some work in the Procter home. Dick said: "Come over now. I'll show you what I want done and I'll introduce you to the dogs and tell them you're coming." Well, Johnny thought Dick must be joking but as they approached the house three dogs were watching from the front window. Dick called each in turn. Johnny shook their paws and when he came to do the job the dogs let him pass as a friend.

Dick was a close friend of Walter Scott, as Hec Duggan, his eventual successor recalls. Hec was a student in the '30s and was destined to learn radiology in the army in the second world war, as Dick Procter had in the first. Dick and Walter were on a committee to study chest diseases. The committee would watch a film, make a diagnosis of the case being shown, and discuss it. The discussions always got to be arguments, with Dick and Walter shouting and swearing and calling each other stupid. The words got so heated that other people had to walk out of the room. And then, in the afternoon, Dick and Walter would go play golf together.

---

### PATHOLOGY AND BACTERIOLOGY

**Director of Pathology**
John James Ower, B.A., M.D., C.M. (McGill), F.R.C.P. (Canada).

**Assistants**
Robert McLeod Shaw, B.A. (Dalhousie), M.D., C.M., D.P.H. (McGill), F.R.C.P. (Canada)
John Watt MacGregor, B.A., M.D. (Alberta).

---

I have to laugh at the sly suggestion that the hospital had a Department of Pathology and Bacteriology. All we had was a common-law marriage with the lab in the Faculty of Medicine. It was in the basement of the Medical Building and was in with the Provincial Lab as well, a real mixed-up business. Surgical tissue from the hospital was examined there.

Johnny Ower (rhymed with Orr as in Harold) was on the hospital's Medical Advisory Committee and Committee on Laboratory Practice, but we didn't see anything of Bob Shaw. On the other hand we saw a lot of Johnny Macgregor, a U of A graduate and one of my interns in 1929. He was with the lab for 43 years, from 1931 to '74 and took over as head of the department when Johnny Ower became Dean of Medicine. Through the '30s Johnny was a busy figure around the hospital.

To explain his contribution in layman's terms we can say that *histology* is the study of human tissue, *pathology* is the study of *change* in tissue. Many agents can cause change — infection, inflammation, a bruise from a blunt instrument, cancer. Pathology provides a diagnosis or confirms it — and may refute it too, in which case the surgeon hears about that.

As Johnny says, it was some lab — one room, one technician — in the basement of the Medical Building. But it served our hospital and the Misericordia and General too.

Johnny had a Ford coupe. In the mornings he would drive around collecting specimens for analysis — while the mailman brought in samples from hospitals all over northern Alberta.

Under Alberta law, all surgical tissues had to be examined in a pathological laboratory so this "one room — one technician" operation eventually processed 30,000 specimens a year, one of the busiest centres in North America.

Most pathological examinations were done after the fact but Johnny spent many mornings in University Hospital operating rooms, analyzing "frozen sections" while the operation was in progress. Tissue removed by the surgeon was frozen with carbon dioxide, mounted on a metal block, then a razor, mounted horizontally, took off thin slices from which the pathologist could make a quick diagnosis and advise the surgeons how to proceed. The principle is the same today — but, oh! the equipment. When Johnny attended the opening of the Walter C. Mackenzie Health Sciences Centre in 1983 he proclaimed himself "floored."

Brave words are part and parcel of official openings. It's fun to check back on the brave words which inaugurated the hospital addition on October 17 1930. Talk about the specialist qualifications of the doctors. Predictions that the expanded facility would soon be a health centre for all Alberta, comparable in the field of clinical research to the clinic of the Mayo Brothers.

In the '30s little progress was made in that direction. The medical staff had three responsibilities: patient care, teaching, and research. We did well to cover the first two. We were too rushed to be research-minded and the expectations of the patients certainly kept everyone on the rush. Ken Thomson has a story which tells a lot about that.

Most of the medical staff attended the Outpatient Department as part of the teaching commitment. One night when Ken was a resident he received an urgent call to drop other duties and proceed at once to a house in Norwood where a lady from the Outpatient Clinic was in dire straits. Ken got there as quickly as he could — and met Dr. Hepburn coming out. He was greeted by a

121

1935

friendly laugh and some interesting though not really surprising news: "Dr. Munroe has been here too."

Busy as they were, the original cast found time to be warm human beings, exerting a strong personal influence on their patients, on the hospital, on the state of the art in their profession, and on the city of less than 100,000 in which they lived. As I write, only three of us whose names appear in the 1935 annual report are here to remember them. Johnny Macgregor, Mark Marshall and myself.

A hospital may be the most complex of all human institutions, the sum

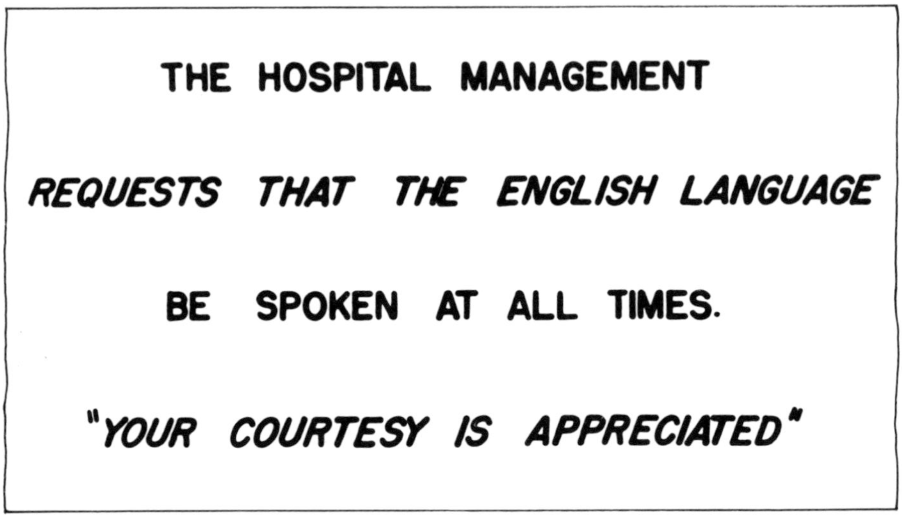

---

**THE HOSPITAL MANAGEMENT**

*REQUESTS THAT THE ENGLISH LANGUAGE*

**BE SPOKEN AT ALL TIMES.**

*"YOUR COURTESY IS APPRECIATED"*

*A sign of the times*

total of many personalities working in different spheres. The medical staff is one set of personalities. The original cast of doctors, who established the medical departments in the early '20s and carried on into the second world war, were a gallant crew. It was my privilege to know and work with them, and to salute their memory here.

# Chapter 12

# 1935—1939
*Up from Depression*

In the history of Alberta, 1935 is identified with Social Credit. Mr. Aberhart and his friends, few of whom had ever been inside the legislature, swept to power with new economic theories, one of which was scrip, the famous "funny money," which wasn't quite so funny when the medical staff of the hospital had to take 20 percent of our salaries in it. However, it was accepted at face value by the government's new Treasury Branches so we all had accounts there.

"Funny money" lasted only a year or so but the Minister of Health in the new Social Credit regime lasted 22 years, and there was certainly nothing funny about Dr. W.W. Cross or his association with the University Hospital. The government of the United Farmers had put Deputy Health Minister Malcolm Bow on the board. Dr. Cross put himself on.

He was a small-town general practitioner, from Hanna, rather dour, a very practical man who believed strongly in "pay-as-you-go" and urged the principle on fellow board members with lectures on the perils of deficit finance. It's fair to state that his vision did not encompass the ideal of the teaching hospital. As Ken Thomson has written, and Ken had some encounters with Dr. Cross later on: "His almost total preoccupation with municipal ownership of hospitals so coloured his attitudes that he saw hospitalization in no other terms than the district model."

In no sense was he a scientist, but by the same token he must have had some vision of the trend in medicine because he very soon began to concentrate cancer treatment in one provincial institution. When he came on our board in 1936 we had 210 deaths for the year and 80 percent were cancer-related. Each hospital had its own treatment. We had our supply of radium which was carefully guarded and so did the Royal Alex. In the 1940s he began in a small way the Provincial Cancer Clinic. The W.W. Cross Cancer Institute is his legacy.

When Dr. Cross came on the board there was another important change — in which the university lost a little more control. The President of the University had, as a matter of right, been Chairman of the Hospital Board, but when R.C. Wallace left Alberta in 1936 to be Principal at Queens, there was a change. Since that time the president has been a member but the chairman has come from the community. Harry Cooper, the wholesale grocer, was chairman for two years, and knew the routine, having been on the board earlier. Then G.R.F. Kirkpatrick, Edmonton's first bank manager, served from 1938 to '43.

Although he had retired, the Imperial Bank still held the overdraft which Mr. Kirkpatrick had arranged while manager.

When Social Credit was coming to power we were assessing early results of the first group hospital insurance plan. This plan was an ancestor of Blue Cross. The University Hospital endorsed it on March 24 1934, joining the three other hospitals in the city. The scheme was devised by Dr. A.F. Anderson, medical superintendent at the Royal Alex where he was "number-one-man, number-two-man and number-three-man," in personal charge of everything. "A.F." was a crusty old fellow (MD from Manitoba in 1903) and a great organizer of curling competitions as well, so much so that he was made a life member of the Dominion Curling Association.

The Anderson plan was not open to individuals, as Blue Cross is, covering employees only, in groups of 5 to 24. Plan members paid $7.20 a year — $6 for dependents — and got up to 30 days free hospitalization in a public ward with half-price on extra services such as x-rays. A lot of selling was required — the agents taking a commission of 25 percent.

The plan did less for the University Hospital than the others because it was open only to residents of Edmonton and 40 percent of our patients came from the country. We also had the Outpatient Department and half the city folk referred to the hospital were indigent. It's doubtful that the benefit to us offset the cost of granting staff nurses a 52-hour week, but it was a start — and Blue Cross had to start somewhere. It was certainly a small start. The administrator of the plan, insurance agent J.O. Pilon, was voted an honorarium of $50 a year.

The average length of a stay in hospital was growing shorter — from 28.1 days in 1931 to 19.9 days in '39, on the way to 9.7 days in 1986. When a patient of the late '30s arrived he or she was handed an information booklet listing the possible charges. I have the booklet before me, and incidentally it belongs to Frank Elliott, a souvenir of his intern days, so I'd best remember to return it.

The cover says: *Welcome! Your room number is* _____ .

If the room was private the charge was $5 a day, but we had mostly public wards, shared by 10 to 20 patients, for which the charge was $2.50 a day. Children were $2.00. Babies 75 cents. Babies admitted with mother, for keep only, 25 cents. A public bed in the maternity unit was a flat $25, covering all costs for a period of *12 days*. If the patient faced a major operation the fee for the operating theatre was $10. Anaesthesia — ether $1.00, gas $2.00. A minor operation, such as tonsils and adenoids, was $6. X-rays if needed were $10. Electrocardiograph $10. Basal metabolism $5. Urinalysis $1. Pneumonia jackets $1.25. Plaster bandages 50 cents each.

There are some nice homey touches which show how long ago and far away all this was, and how impossible to duplicate it today. "Meals to Friends: Friends of patients in private rooms may be furnished meals, if so desired, at a cost of 75¢ per meal, excepting afternoon tea when the charge is 25¢."

A message from "Wash" Washburn assures the patient that he or she is getting good value for the money. He has written: "It is our desire to give you a high standard of service and to be of such assistance to your attending physician that you will make a rapid recovery and . . . will have pleasantest memories of your stay with us. Each member of our staff of 250 is specially trained for his or her work."

The reader might have felt less optimistic if he had known that some 90 of the specially-trained staff were student nurses, learning the art under the apprentice system. Students still lived under para-military discipline. Each morning before breakfast they lined up for inspection of uniforms by the matron, and then recited the Lord's Prayer — not a bad idea considering the financial state of the hospital.

The students were used to being yelled at. Slim Waters the janitor would yell at them if they trod the corridor where he was mopping, and Slim would add his frightening talent for popping his eyes into a mad stare. Students were yelled at by Mrs. Porritt. Jim Metcalfe saw a girl so terrified of the second-floor charge nurse she dropped a jug of water on the floor — and breakages were deducted from the student's honorarium.

Jeanie Clark, who entered as a student in 1936 and became Superintendent of Nursing some 20 years later, says her class "learned assertion" from Mrs. Porritt. I have to laugh. Certainly if they wanted to learn assertion there wasn't a better teacher. She treated students as though they were older children — and interns too if they happened to be women. She'd tell them off if she thought they were in need.

By the same token, the Mrs. Porritts of the world really cared about the girls. Sadie Duggan likes to make this point. Sadie was a student in the '30s. She and Hec were courting, between 7 pm when she got off work (if the work was done to the charge nurse's satisfaction) and 10 pm when she had to be back in. It was a typical University Hospital romance of the time. They went skating at the Garneau Community League, or walked to the *Rite Spot* by the High Level Bridge where that marvellous coffee sold for a nickel and wonderful cream pies for a dime. Once when Sadie was on psychiatric training at Ponoka, Hec and Sam Hanson thought they'd like to go to the nurses dance there, but had no transportation. Almost as a joke Hec asked Mrs. Porritt if they could borrow her car. She agreed instantly — as long as there was no liquor in the car and they took Miss Crosweller, a staff nurse. Sadie was surprised to say the least, but the loan became less surprising later as she and her fellow students realized the value of what had been drilled into them and understood the burden of responsibility which fell on charge nurses of the time.

Years later Jeanie Clark came to understand what Helen Peters had to put up with. Helen was an important person in the history of the hospital — from 1927 until her death in 1954. She came out with a McGill certificate as assistant to Ethel Fenwick, the Superintendent of Nurses, and moved to the top job in 1935 when Ethel resigned to marry Harry Cooper. (Incidentally the interns were happy for Ethel, but sorry to lose the rumcake which she received each Christmas from a relative. It was so heavy on the rum that Ethel redirected it to the interns.) Helen was entirely different from the spritely Ethel. A shy sort of person, rather abrupt, rather rigid in outlook. But I suppose she had to be to make sure her nurses got the respectful credit they deserved. Among some doctors there was considerable putting down of nurses, whose duties ranged from "true" nursing to menial tasks. Helen demanded a high standard of efficiency in both and was always ready to take on a doctor in defense of her nurses.

As a student in the '30s Jeanie was aware of Miss Peters as an austere person, making rounds of the whole institution twice a day, apparently in touch with everything that went on. She didn't comprehend Miss Peters' true position until she returned as her assistant and successor in the '50s. The floor of her

*The Red Cross Hut. Pool hall, concert hall, social hall, lecture hall, dance hall, Christmas party hall, a veritable hall of fame due to become a mess hall in world war two, a cafeteria to accommodate the growing staff*

office was terrazzo tile, softened by only one small rug in front of her desk, and the rug was threadbare from all the people who had stood on it when called in to see the matron. Supplies had been tightly controlled. Helen had obtained an eraser or paper clips only after demonstrating a valid reason. For carbon copies of her letters she'd had to use the backs of condition sheets.

A poignant letter survives, dated October 21 1937, from Helen to "Wash" Washburn: "May I submit for your consideration a request for added stenographic assistance in the School of Nursing. All (letters) must be written in pencil and taken to the (hospital) stenographer. With the pressure of work in that office it is frequently two days or longer before these letters are returned to me. . . after careful consideration of the work to be done I think that uninterrupted services of a stenographer for three hours every morning would be sufficient. . ."

As Hec Duggan said of Dick Procter: "It's pretty hard to be a genius when nobody is giving you any money. Nowadays it's a lot easier to look smart." Looking back on that time I recognize a lot of people like Helen Peters who deserved a lot of credit they didn't get. They worked under the difficulty of just making do, with tools they could gather, with no prospect of any leeway to try out innovations they might have had in mind.

Another faithful servant whose burden of responsibility came to be appreciated through later experience was Christina MacKay. Miss MacKay ran the operating rooms for a full 25 years, from 1927 to '52. We had three operating rooms — on the third floor at the north end, two big ones and a small one we called *the tonsil room*. Until the very late '30s we had no antibiotics to combat infection, so it had to be headed off by asepsis in the operating room. To prevent the introduction of infecting organisms into wound areas we used boiling water, washing hands, and rubber gloves courtesy of Harvey Firestone. (Incidentally, I once worked with an English surgeon who didn't believe in rubber gloves. He dipped his hands in acid, hard on germs no doubt but hard on his skin as well.) The responsibility for asepsis in our operating rooms fell on Miss MacKay, an Alberta pioneer born in Scotland.

Miss MacKay had a means of physically moving a nurse or intern who was in the wrong position. As Jim Metcalfe recalls, in each room she kept a Kocher Forcep in a glass of disinfectant. Kocher's contribution to medicine was a clamp with two great claws. She could grasp a gown with the sterile claws and move the delinquent to the correct place.

Miss MacKay was tall and regal. Students found her stern and demanding and fond of rhetorical questions such as: "Miss Markstad, how can you be so stupid?" and "Miss Jones, don't you know anything?" However, when she went to lunch and they peeked in her record book they'd find she had written nice things about them.

In addition to guarding against sepsis, Miss MacKay had to prepare the saline solutions for intravenous injections for all the wards. There were small sterilizers in each ward, but the one autoclave was in the operating room and dressings had to be sterilized in the OR. Tina, as she was known, certainly earned the little relaxation her schedule allowed, and I have to laugh at her story of her favourite recreation. She was a good friend of another Scot who happened to be the pro at the Mayfair Golf Club. The pro would know which members were out of town and when Tina had an afternoon free for golf he'd send her out on the course on the card of an absentee member.

While the newspapers of 1935 were full of stories about Social Credit I don't recall a single mention of an event that took place in Germany that year. The event had the greatest impact on our hospital (and hospitals everywhere) and eventually removed much of the lonely responsibility from the Miss Mac-Kays of this world. A German bacteriologist named Gerhard Domagk published a research paper — on the antibiotic properties of a drug called *prontosil*. Prontosil was the commercial name of a sulfonamide developed early in the century as a red dye for German woollen mills. News travels quickly in the medical world and by the end of the '30s we in Edmonton were finding out the uses of the first of the "wonder drugs." Mind you, the newspapers invented the term "wonder drugs" but in this case there was no exaggeration. Sulfas inhibited the growth of bacteria present in septic wounds, puerperal fever (it was known as childbed fever), mastoiditis, erysipelas and non-viral pneumonia. Sulfas weren't effective against tuberculosis (still a threat to our hospital workers) but another antibiotic was on the way which would do just that. Sulfas are based on chemicals. Penicillins, based on molds, were just over the horizon. In the operating room, antibiotics formed a second line of defense if asepsis failed.

Sulfas were introduced to our hospital sometime in the period from July 1936 to June '37. Frank Elliott was an intern then and recalls their debut. He recalls that Prontosil soon had the nickname "Pro-Tonsil," and that the drug retained the properties which made it a successful dye in the woollen mills. Given intravenously it turned everything red, including the urine.

In Frank's time interns could observe at close hand a year's inner-workings of an entire hospital. They were called "house" staff though, mind you, "house-bound" staff would be more to the point. In effect they were on duty 24 hours a day, and were on standby service for any duty, medical or otherwise — otherwise including admitting and answering the telephone. The institution was smaller then, easier to keep under surveillance, and all residents followed the same program, unlike today when graduates specialize.

In days before the blood bank, interns got closely involved in cases by having to make the arrangements for transfusions. They had to contact relatives, do the cross-matching and the lab work. And if a relative could not supply the needed type, they'd institute a call for an outside donor, who had to be paid, $25. On the streets of Edmonton then, there was a celebrated character named Stonewall Jackson, who wore a Hudson's Bay coat and a deerstalker hat and made a living selling blood.

The house staff were a group unto themselves. Being about 24 years of age the group they were closest to were the nurses, although I think the girls were jealous of the special attention the young doctors got from Fanny Hooson. Our famous night cook used to bawl them out for not being the men their predecessors were, but she saved the best for them. And she cooked special orders of the ducks they shot, and corn, which, unknown to Fanny, was acquired by dead of night from the university's experimental farm. Fanny appreciated their low financial state, a condition that caused the failure of an innovation by Tommy Cox. Our treasurer set up a petty cash account, and a box with $20 was kept in the admitting office so the medical staff could meet small unscheduled expenses or buy off a tradesman who refused to leave an item without being paid. One day "Wash" Washburn went to the box and found no cash, petty or otherwise, just IOU's signed by the interns. That was the end of the petty cash account.

*In the diet kitchen. Although this picture is from the 1920s nothing has changed*

In Frank Elliott's resident year he had daily contact with afflictions no intern is likely to see now. Today's resident won't see a case of typhoid, and few of tuberculosis, although in the '30s we had a full ward of TB patients on the top floor. Nor will he likely see anyone die of bacterial pneumonia or peritonitis. It seems to Frank that at times half the pneumonia patients died and that a case of generalized peritonitis meant an almost automatic call to the undertaker. The only method of treatment was the naso-gastric tube. With luck the hospital staff could get it through the victim's nose and into the lower bowel and draw off some of the infection. And today a graduate will certainly get no experience of *actinomycosis*, known in the vernacular as *lumpjaw*. It's a fungus associated with cattle. Frank and his friends were forever draining the lower jaws of country folk who contracted lumpjaw from the pleasant rural custom of chatting with your neighbour while pulling haygrass through your teeth.

Every case of lumpjaw and other long gone diseases had to be faithfully recorded and kept available for future reference. That burden fell on Jessie Nairn, a faithful servant of the hospital from 1923 till 1967. Jessie got into it when "Wash" Washburn's stenographer resigned and she took over the departed girl's duties — typing the superintendent's letters, doctors' reports, x-ray reports, and operating room notes. Jessie started out doing all the recording for a hospital of 150 beds. When she retired a staff of 26 were recording histories of the occupants of 1200 beds.

Medical library science was not taught in Canada — though it is now, of course, in many schools. The only available instruction was a correspondence course provided in the United States by the Association of Record Librarians of North America. Jessie passed the mail-order program and was awarded a certificate dated January 14 1937. Hers may have been the first in Alberta.

By this time four stenographers were gathering, typing and filing case histories. And there was more of this work at the University Hospital than others because many patients came on referral, and extra reports had to be sent to their doctors or the compensation board. The librarians were kept busy transcribing the handwritten notes of doctors, interns, nurses and lab technicians. While the nurses' writing was always legible that of many doctors was at best decipherable.

So modern technology was introduced to save the time wasted in deciphering mysterious scratches. It was another example of what can happen when technology intended to save work creates more. A handwritten report might run two inches, but when a doctor could dictate his comments the report could run to a page.

Storing records was a real problem before microfilm. X-rays were kept on the roof. Jessie Nairn's medical records were stored in the carpenter's shop out behind the hospital. There was no heat in the shop, and that made for some shivery fact finding expeditions in winter.

Some new faces appeared in the staff dining rooms. Roy Anderson was an important addition to the Department of Surgery. Among the so-called "sub" staff a significant newcomer was Gabe Lefebvre, the orderly, known better as

Slim. He was certainly a tall skinny young fellow, but I had lunch with him several times and could hardly believe how much he could eat. I was afraid Slim would starve if the kitchen ever ran out of food for a couple of hours, but obviously that never happened because he worked 40 years to the day. When Slim started on June 1 1935 the orderly had no status and no definite qualifications. Slim Waters, who mopped the floors, was an orderly. Slim Lefebvre, who worked in the wards and had been taught by Dr. Blais how to remove stitches, which he did like an artist, was also called an orderly. Some reported to the charge nurses, others to the housekeeper, Mrs. Strang, an English lady who was

*June 1939 — With another world war imminent Queen Elizabeth visits soldiers of the first war still in University Hospital. King George VI, R.T. Washburn (in uniform again) and Helen Peters, Superintendent of Nurses, witness a personal triumph that will be re-enacted 46 years later*

so terribly upset when Edward VIII abdicated the throne. In Slim's 40 years at the hospital the orderly advanced to become a full member of the patient-care team and Slim was a leader in bringing it about, as we'll see in a later chapter.

On the business side two newcomers were George Sherwood, who became Business Administrator, and Johnny Beaton.

Johnny was a short fellow. He remembers having lunch with me in the basement dining room and my telling him: "Johnny, if your mother had given you an ounce of orange juice a day you'd be bigger." The story of Johnny's hiring tells a lot about the time. Tommy Cox had been given permission to hire an accounting clerk, so he phoned Percy Page, principal of McDougall Commercial High School, and asked for someone he could recommend. In those days principals could know all the kids in a school and follow their progress after graduation. Percy Page, of course, coached some of his graduates to be the best girls' basketball team in the world. In 1936 Johnny was attending Commercial in the morning and delivering *Journals* in the afternoon. The principal called him out of class and said: "I want you to write a letter of application to Mr. Cox." Johnny was made to write it over and over again until Mr. Page was satisfied. The next Monday he went to work and stayed 40 years, with time out for war service in India, and became head of purchasing.

The individual stood out then. Edmonton was inching up past a population of 80,000. The student body of the university was verging on 1,800. The hospital was a family, as many have observed. John Huckell recalls making Sunday rounds with his father and being introduced to Graham's patients and meeting kids of other doctors on the same family outing. Louise Davis (in 1986 an Assistant Director of Nursing) remembers being taken to the Christmas parties by her father Slim Lefebvre the orderly and asking him why Santa Claus had a limp. Slim explained quickly that the old gent had fallen off his sleigh but when Santa (played by Tommy Robson) had the same limp next Christmas Louise experienced her first doubts.

Individuals did not blend into the mass. In the minutes of the Hospital Board you find worried references to Bill Beck, the night telephone operator. Bill has called in to say his artificial leg is hurting too much for him to come to work but he has been seen that very day in the Memorial Hall, presumably drinking beer. What is to be done? There are vague hints that Bill might be fired, but Bill, in effect, continues to come to work when he feels like it and eventually collapses and dies on the job, at the little switchboard by the main entrance.

The lawns of the University Hospital looked their best on June 2 1939. Bob Sherriff had seen to that. It was the day of the royal visit to Edmonton, and the hospital was to be a major stop of the motorcade. The old soldiers from the SCR Wing were to be brought out on the lawns to meet the King and Queen. It had been 20 years since the war. On that beautiful day it was hard to believe that another war was coming fast, but it was only three months away. The hospital had passed through a testing time of depression, but another test was almost on us.

# Chapter 13

# 1939—1945
*The Battle of Edmonton*

I called it "the Battle of Edmonton." The war reached us quickly. The army called our superintendent back to active duty and in November, at age 60, "Wash" went overseas as Colonel Commanding Number Four Casualty Clearing Station. He also took four of the younger men with him. And that was to be part of "the Battle of Edmonton." The young men left for more interesting theatres of combat as soon as they could. I wished to go too, but the army didn't want me — didn't think they needed obstetricians. Eventually 35 percent of our medical staff was on military service and our graduate nursing staff was 30 percent below strength. Many of the nurses who had spent the depression cooped up seven days and nights a week took the opportunity to see the world too, and no one could blame them for that. Looking back now it's hard to believe that when war was declared we had the feeling it would all be over within a year. To keep the home fires burning we had half the number of hands doing twice as much work, and our medical staff included most of the "original cast" who had begun the show and were nearing retirement.

That should have been enough trouble, but there was more. Due to unforeseen and difficult circumstances the hospital had to go through half the war without a full-time Medical Superintendent. As I mentioned, when "Wash" went overseas the board expected "the duration" to be brief, and sought an interim replacement. The search led to J. Ross Vant, which was certainly a surprise to me, so much that I forgot to inquire about salary. I don't believe it was ever discussed but $150 a month was added to my remuneration, the same amount I'd held out for when I came to the hospital as an intern.

My term began January 1 1940 and lasted six months. I acted as Superintendent in the time between eight o'clock lectures at the university and office practice in the afternoon, and relied heavily on Tommy Cox, as everybody did. He and Reg Adshead and George Sherwood ran the hospital as a business and at the start of the war they did a smart piece of business concerning surgical dressings. In 1939 a box of a thousand dressings cost seven dollars. From the history of the first war they figured the price would rise so they bought three rooms full of dressings. And when they had to reorder three years later the price was $42 a box. By the same token, some hedges against inflation didn't work out so well. Mrs. Bob Sherriff was a pastry cook in the kitchen, and she recalls: "At the start of the war they thought the price of flour would go up so they bought a bunch and stored it under the floor of the Red Cross Hut. Well, the flour got damp, so the last thing at night we'd have to sift it and put it out on the stoves to dry." The hospital was not the complicated institution it is now. It was smaller in size of course. Activity was not so varied and "cross-indexed" and that was a blessing. The war was a time when we all worked like beavers just to keep the place going. If there'd been a lot of extras it wouldn't have been possible.

Tommy and I made what we thought was a major addition to the efficiency of the hospital. We persuaded the board to buy a high-speed electric washer for the laundry room, the very latest mechanical marvel for a large institution. However, we failed to convince the board that we should build a nurses' residence.

We felt it would greatly improve the morale and efficiency of the nursing staff. The charge nurses were "living above the store," on the sixth floor, and were never free of hospital atmosphere. That didn't seem right. And the student nurses were scattered, some in St. Stephen's College, others in Robertson's Lodge on Whyte Avenue about 110th Street. We drew up plans for a residence, nothing very fancy or imaginative, and got a price of $180,000. We had no particular location in mind except that it would be on hospital property of which there was certainly an abundance at that time. It was a gala day when our nurses moved into their own residence but that day didn't come until after the war.

Mind you, even if the nurses' home was put off, I had the satisfaction of designing our new outpatient clinic. On January 8 1940 we moved from the McLeod house to the third floor of Eaton's old department store — at 10048 - 101A Avenue. Eaton's put up their new store and moved out and the government bought the building. Laying out rooms on what had been an open sales floor I wasn't bound by rooms already there, which had been a problem in Kenny McLeod's old home. The clinic was still just an examination place. We weren't doing anything we hadn't done before, just more of it, and the new location gave us space.

By May of 1940 France was falling and we began to realize·we were in for a long long war. And there was other news from overseas. "Wash" was being released from active duty and coming back to recruit a reserve component of the outfit he had taken overseas. I have to laugh at the story of how this happened.

It seems "Wash" told the army authorities he had to get back to Edmonton because: "there's a young fellah there running my hospital into the ground." Of course he would think of it as *his* hospital. So he resumed the office of superintendent on July 1 but his friends soon noted a sad deterioration in his powers, a premature decline that affected the memory. The decline advanced swiftly and early in 1941 he went on sick leave and never returned. Uncertainty about R.T. Washburn's condition dragged on for a full year with the board unable to decide what should be done. He was still superintendent in name so the burden fell on Tommy Cox, certainly no benefit to Tommy's fragile health.

Not until March of '42 was "Wash" officially retired, and after a year of covering the office Tommy Cox was rewarded with the title of Superintendent while a search was conducted for a permanent successor. It was a nice tribute as

Tommy's whole life had been centered on the institution, since he'd arrived as a convalescent soldier in the first war. He enjoyed the title until the permanent replacement took office on July 1 but poor Tommy lived only a few months after that and was genuinely missed. The new man, however, was made of very durable stuff, and was also the stuff of which enduring stories are told. Angus McGugan stood in awe of no one, and was in charge for 18 years.

Angus was a shrewd Scot who always let you know what he thought and was a good friend of mine. He came to the University Hospital with a feel for the institution. He'd been a student in the place, class of '27, and knew most of the

*Two superintendents —*
*Tommy Cox 1941-1942 and*
*Angus McGugan 1942-1960*

medical staff personally. I'd met him in 1929 when he was in the provincial Department of Health as Director of Communicable Diseases. In 1931 he went away to study public health administration on a grant from the Rockefeller Foundation, and was gone for several years — on working studies at hospitals in Ontario, Michigan and Minnesota. He returned in 1935 as medical officer at the Ponoka Mental Hospital. In 1938 he was named Assistant Deputy Minister of Health and in 1940 took on the extra responsibility of Medical Inspector of Hospitals for Alberta. He was in this double-position when he "received a call" from our board.

Angus is a storied character, one of the most storied in the history of our hospital. George Sherwood says that if he had to write one of those "My Most Unforgettable Character" articles for the Reader's Digest it couldn't be anyone but Angus. George says: "He overwhelmed people. I disliked him on many occasions but in retrospect I think kindly of him."

That's the kind of man Angus was. Don Wilson has a story which couldn't be about anyone else: "I darn near fainted one time when "Swede" Gourlay and I invited Angus to go shooting prairie chickens. We arrived dressed in old clothes for tramping around the bush. But Angus came out of his house wearing a suit and a double-breasted overcoat. 'I'm going to hunt properly,' he said. 'You fellows are going to be the beaters.' So we chased chickens out of the bush and Angus sat by the car hunting properly."

Garnet Hollingshead, who came to work as an accountant in 1943, says: "I got along just swell with Angus McGugan. Of course he was very dogmatic about certain things, the English language for one. Expressions like OK and *pretty soon* drove him up the wall. And he despised signs. People were always putting up signs like *Close This Door* and *Switch Off Light*. Angus would around tearing 'em down."

John Gibson, the carpenter, recalls: "He was a very strict kind of but I always got along very well with him. One time he called me in office and reached in his desk and pulled out a little glass. It said *Strath ospital*. He'd spotted it in the window of a junk shop. He figured the opening of the hospital in 1914 they'd served whiskey in souvenir like that."

Angus arrived in a discouraging stretch of war. We had been grinding away for nearly three years and seemed to with the raid on ople on the home front the cause and Roy Anderson ep" put up a petition in the medical staff room — *Close the Mayfair Golf Links as a War Effort*. Roy laughs that he was the only one to sign and is glad now he was the only one. Anyway, we of the medical staff were advised in 1942 on how we were going to make an extra effort for the war. The university's medical education program was being accelerated to meet the country's urgent need for doctors. We were already teaching (for small honorariums) on top of clinical and office practice, but had breaks from lecturing in summer and midwinter. The breaks were to end for the duration. We became like rabbits, scuttling from burrow to burrow along a narrow path with seldom a glance left or right. Roy points out that medical men who weren't in uniform were making a big contribution too, and has a story by way of illustration. On one memorable day he performed three operations for ruptured ulcers — all on doctors.

By mid-1942, with enlistments and retirements, Roy was one of only six general surgeons on the staff of the hospital. Gillespie, Hepburn, McPherson, Fife, Alexander and Anderson — that was the entire list. With attrition in the Department of Surgery and acceleration in the Faculty of Medicine an extra clinical and teaching load was thrown on the survivors. Roy points out that he had some room to maneuver which a surgeon wouldn't enjoy now. Surgeons still did family practice and Roy manufactured some time by getting out of obstetrics. Each of us, in our own way, contrived time for acceleration.

Mind you, I have to laugh when I think about "Edge" Pope as we were scrambling to accelerate. I'm sure "Edge" didn't accelerate in any manner. Bob Johnston says: "I'll never forget being on intern duty on Sundays and seeing Dr. Pope arrive in his chauffeur-driven limousine with the two poodles. He only lived five blocks away but he always came in the limousine." Taro Yoneda, who later joined my own department, was an intern at the same time. He recalls that "Edge" made Sunday rounds in formal clothes. "Edge" reached retirement precisely at the end of the war, just as his impeccable grasp of "the right thing" would have planned it.

It was the worst of times and the best of times, to borrow a description from Dickens. The worst times bring out the true character of an institution and the University Hospital passed every test. There weren't enough hours in the regular working day to maintain the routines and then came emergencies which were veritable exercises in pulling together. A memorable test came late in 1942. On a Sunday afternoon, November 15, an unpredicted blizzard appeared from the north, dropping 19 inches of snow, driving it into tightly-packed drifts, and establishing a claim to the title "the big storm" which has never been challenged. The big storm hardened our *esprit de corps*. Fanny Hooson made it to work all the way from the Highlands — on foot as ever. George McMillan, the faithful x-ray technician, lived out by the exhibition grounds. He walked, and when he found the traffic deck of the High Level Bridge blocked by drifts, he went up top and crossed on the open train deck. Bob Roberts, the maintenance engineer, mushed in from King Edward Park. Charlie Moore, the official snow shoveller, also mushed in and camped in a corridor till the emergency was past. Charlie was a butcher by trade, but after five years without regular employment in the depression, had taken the snow job for $75 a month and two meals a day. The downtown snow was piled in a mesa 10 feet high across the present site of Churchill Square and the City Hall. We were grateful for the help of the U.S. army in this test of character. Maternity cases arrived in tracked vehicles and jeeps with four-wheel drive. The city at large was grateful for the Americans' heavy mechanized equipment which adapted to moving snow. Charlie Moore laughs that the only snow-moving equipment he had was a shovel.

Another test came when a troop train hit a rockslide at Blue River, west of

138

———

*1939—1945*

Jasper. A lot of boys were badly injured, and then another slide closed the line behind. In a few hours the army made up a hospital train in Edmonton, and many of our doctors and interns — Ollie Rostrup was one — went out to the scene. Forty men on stretchers had to be carried out over the slide. They began arriving in the hospital early the next morning, and some of our staff stayed on duty 48 hours, including Betty Greig, the night nurse, and Slim Waters, the sometimes cantankerous orderly, who was around everywhere, putting up beds or screens, anything to help. The intern dietitians played their part, walking among the crowded beds and joking with the injured men about what they'd like to eat.

A point must be made about these exhibitions of true grit. They were carried out amidst a dizzying turnover of staff. From April '42 to March '43 Helen Peters hired 49 graduate nurses while 54 resigned. It was said that we had to hire everyone who came in the front door to replace those going out the back. But there were some notable exceptions. One was Peggy Price, who started in the admitting office in 1939 and stayed there 32 years. The war kept Peggy in Canada. She'd taken a course in dress design and wanted to go to New York for further study but the government wouldn't let her take the necessary money out of the country. If the sombre bureaucrats of that time considered dress designing an occupation, which is unlikely, they didn't see it as essential. Throughout the war Peggy was in a good position to observe the comings of our patients. Alternating with Joan Hunt she worked 13 straight days and then enjoyed a Sunday off.

Peggy observed at first hand the hospital's growing involvement with the military. Army and Air Force bases in the area had infirmaries but cases requiring serious treatment were sent in to us. The Lovat Scouts sent many patients. The famous British commando unit took ski instruction at Jasper, and in war and peace skiing is hard on limbs. The Royal Air Force had a base at Penhold which made unnecessary extra work for Peggy. The RAF was casual about informing us when patients were *en route*, and the admitting office would have to get histories from groggy young airmen as they came in on stretchers.

With the Japanese attack on Pearl Harbor the United States was in the war and by early 1942 Edmonton was a major centre for construction of the Alaska Highway, the Fort Norman-to-Whitehorse oil pipeline, and a refueling stop for military planes being ferried to Russia. Edmonton, which had always been off the beaten path, was suddenly a crosswords of the world. We would hear a sudden roar and look up to see two dozen fighter planes circling the city and peeling off one by one to land at the municipal airport. A hospital staff gets used to death but Peggy remembers the distress when an American bomber crashed in south Edmonton. Everyone knew the boys had been killed, but the routines of admission had to be followed until a doctor could make an examination and issue death certificates.

Through "the battle of Edmonton" the population was growing from 90,419 to 111,745. And on top of that the city was bulging at the seams with a transient population in uniform — almost every uniform on the allied side. It was certainly an interesting time for our student nurses, who were still responsible for half the actual patient care. In their quarters at St. Stephen's College they were under house rules designed for their protection, as were the young airmen around the corner at "the Joe Hall" — St. Joseph's College, for those who may be out of touch with campus slang of the 1940s. Although airmen and nurses were under protective rules these were obviously not insurmountable obstacles to meeting at the Tuck Shop, or going overtown to a famous dance hall called The Barn on 103rd Street, or even the ultimate in nights out — the Saturday supper dance at the Macdonald Hotel. This function was the social highlight of Edmonton in wartime — requiring reservations three weeks in advance.

Our nurses had Canadian airmen for company, along with young fellows from New Zealand, Australia and the British Isles, come to learn to fly in the British Commonwealth Air Training Plan, and Americans, here in connection with the highway, the Canol pipeline or the airlift to Russia. Edmonton became a much more cosmopolitan place than we ever expected to see. The American officers who were based here brought their wives whom we treated, and this practice had some fringe benefits. I was given a membership in the American mess at the municipal airport. There were no dues to pay and we could attend the parties and buy fresh vegetables in winter and whiskey anytime. The liquor was a real treat. It was rationed during the war — right down to 13 ounces a month. I have to laugh when I think of the hardship this worked on some of our leading citizens, even though it must have improved their health.

The "American Connection" helped us with the introduction of penicillin. The arrival of penicillin was certainly the most spectacular advent of the age and I remember ordering the first batch for our department early in 1942, but there was a problem. Ottawa decided to control distribution, with results not hard to predict. To get some we had to send a case history and that meant the patient was either dead or better when we got it.

Ottawa's penicillin policy was on par with another wartime scheme hatched in that quarter. To alleviate crowding in maternity hospitals mothers were offered a $10 bonus to have their babies at home — a policy unsurpassed in the annals of uselessness.

Once I had to deliver a lawyer's wife by Caesarean and the second day the mother developed an infection and ran a high fever. So I went out to the American air base at the airport and asked the Colonel in charge of the medical section for the loan of 50,000 units of penicillin. That amount is like a drop of water in a bucket compared to the millions we give now, but the bacteria hadn't begun to fight back developing immunity to penicillin, so 50,000 units was a lethal dose — for the bugs that is. I swore I'd replace it when Ottawa reacted to my official request. The mother threw off the infection promptly and two months later the stuff arrived from Ottawa. So I went out to return it but the Colonel just laughed and said: "Oh hell, I wrote that off as soon as I gave it to you."

Under pressure of war the medical scientists got penicillin into mass production in astonishing time. In 1941, 26½ gallons of culture liquid would yield one gram of penicillin salt, 25 percent pure. In two years the same amount yielded 10 grams, 98 percent pure.

"Hank" Mewburn had a story which seemed to be the last word on penicillin. It was a joke but not far off the truth. He went down to Boston for a meeting and when he came back some of the boys were discussing a treatment and "Hank" said: "They've got a new idea now. They use this stuff and if there isn't a cure after three days they do an examination."

Penicillin was good news, but there was the other kind too. During the war we got the unwelcome news about the Rh factor. There were two causes. Blood transfusions became much more common and servicemen's wives were moving about the country and seemed to be getting the wrong type. The trick was that the Rh factor didn't show up with the first pregnancy but with the second or third. Although blood seems so basic we came to our knowledge of its qualities rather late. I was still in medical school when the four types were identified. It wasn't until 1941 that the Rh factor was identified in England. Incidentally the term Rh honoured the Rhesus monkeys used in research. In pregnancy a conflict causes a condition that can leave the baby jaundiced and anaemic, or even retarded. We had no way to test the Rh factor here and relied on Dr. Bruce Chowne, a fine paediatrician in Winnipeg. We'd send Bruce our samples and he'd advise us whether they showed positive or negative. We hoped for testing facilities of our own but realized they would have to come in the post-war.

War accelerated progress in many fields of medicine, and one was certainly the system for handling blood. The hospital board took important action in February-March 1942, appointing a committee to "explore ways and means of establishing a blood *depot*." Space for the *depot* was found in the biochemistry department at the university. Then, in June 1942, came a letter from Bob Muir, secretary of the Red Cross, using the term blood *bank*. The Red Cross asked permission to use our Outpatient Clinic — in the evenings — as a central place to register donors and collect blood. The board was glad to oblige, provided that Bob and his pals cleaned up the clinic afterwards. A year later the board asked Angus McGugan to explore the possibility of a blood and *plasma* bank in the hospital. These were small moves, to be sure. We didn't see the full development till after the war but once the trend started there was no going back to "the good old days" of interns trying to match the blood of relatives and sending messages out to "Stonewall" Jackson for $25 worth of his.

Even in the scramble there were permanent changes in the medical staff, in addition to temporary losses to the armed forces. In December 1941 my friend and partner L.C. Conn died after a long battle with cancer and I was invited to succeed him as Professor and Director of Obstetrical and Gynaecological Services. It was for a five-year term. You weren't appointed for life. Like Franklin Delano Roosevelt I was eventually given four terms, but was luckier than FDR in being able to retire during the fourth.

Mark Marshall became very prominent on the medical staff during the war, becoming head of two departments. In 1940 Ophthalmology and Otolaryngology were merged with Mark in charge, and he was instrumental in renaming the old soldiers' wing for his predecessor and partner, R.B. Wells. It's been said that Mark had a sign painted saying *Wells Pavilion* and put it up himself. What the truth of the story is I've no way of knowing but it's certain that the addition was known as the Wells Pavilion even though there's no record of the board ever approving the name.

Dr. Bulyea retired in 1942 and Scott Hamilton took over Dentistry and made it a full department.

Chuck Hurlburt died in 1944 but a successor in Cardiology wasn't named for awhile and the rest soldiered on.

During the war, women came forward to handle many jobs, and a first-class example was in our Department of Anaesthesia. When Ernie Watts went into the Navy in 1943, Effie Dunn became the first woman to head a clinical department in the University Hospital. Effie had trained under Ernie and recalls that he had to be very diplomatic because anaesthesia was a young specialty and the surgeons thought they were boss. A woman had to be even more diplomatic especially when her MD from Alberta was dated 1940 and her only assistant, Ethel Lieberman, was still an intern. But they were accepted, and did an outstanding job, and even were able to add a woman's touch to the procedures. They thought it was nicer for children to have the anaesthetic in their rooms and be spared the extra trauma of being wheeled through the corridors to the operating rooms. Effie and Ethel and two other girls lived together on the top floor, in a little enclave of their own, as it would never have done to have them mixed in with the men. There was only one phone but each girl had her own ring and they developed the art of sleeping through calls that weren't for them.

I used to tell my students that the scope and extent of all surgery depends on anaesthesia, and at this time "Hep" Hepburn's advances in brain surgery made special demands. Effie recalls that neurosurgery was the longest operation they had. The anaesthesia was very, very long but not deep, which meant a lot of monitoring. As a specialty anaesthesia was coming on fast. When Effie was in her first year of medicine she'd had her appendix out and was terribly sick afterwards because the anaesthetist, a GP, had given her too much ether.

Ether, the oldest agent, was still given. So was cyclopropane, which was also inhaled. Spinal came in during the war. I remember in 1942 doing the first Caesarean under spinal, which saved the bother of the hot and cold tubs. Caesarean babies used to come into the world pretty limp and the tubbing was to pep them up. With spinals for the mothers they made their entrance hollering in the approved fashion. Towards the end of the war the Dunn-and-Lieberman team were also using curare-type drugs, the muscle relaxants, known to primitive tribesmen who tipped arrowheads with them. And Pentathol was being used, given intravenously. Fans of Dick Tracy the comic strip detective knew about pentathol as "the truth serum."

After the war, when Ethel lived in New York, she found that the University Hospital was way ahead of institutions in "the Big Apple" in one important respect. Anaesthetics were still being given by nurses. Ethel's move to New York was a result of one of the "hearts-across-the-border" romances of the war. In our admitting office one day she met Captain Charlie Fried of the U.S. army medical corps. They went to the United States but eventually returned to Edmonton. Jess Wilson, who drove the jeep for Captain Fried, stayed here and worked as an orderly at the University Hospital.

Throughout "the Battle of Edmonton" we enjoyed the support of a sympathetic board. It was still the seven-man board — and at this time the term *man* was understood to mean precisely that with no exceptions. Three came from the provincial government, three from the campus, and the chairman (or moderator) represented the community.

The government people were Malcolm Bow, Deputy Minister of Health, H.J. Woodman of the Treasury Department and W.D. Stacey of Public Works. The campus contingent were the President of the University (Robert Newton replacing W.A.R. Kerr in 1941), the Dean of Medicine (still A.C. Rankin) and the Superintendent of the hospital (Angus McGugan from July 1942). Midway in the war the board suffered a damaging loss, as did the entire city. On Friday March 26 1943, G.R.F. Kirkpatrick chaired the regular meeting, as he had done for five years. Two days later he died unexpectedly at home — 52 years after coming to Edmonton as the youngest bank manager in Canada.

But in only a few days we had a capable successor. Ray Staples was an insurance man and he had some knowledge of the hospital — he'd married Gladys Smiley, who had once been our Assistant Superintendent of Nurses. Ray found time to chair the Hospital Board even though he was busy from morning to night organizing Victory Bond campaigns, for which he was eventually awarded the Order of the British Empire.

The board suffered many vexations but there was a bright spot through "the Battle of Edmonton," a spot which grew brighter each year. Finances were improving. In the fiscal year which ended March 31 1945 the hospital cost $528,000 to run and we were short $15,000. In the year ending March 31 1945 the expense was $687,000 — but we showed a surplus of $86,000. We'd paid off the deficit of the depression and placed $155,000 in a building reserve. Even so, I had a concern. Looking ahead I could see costs rising faster than revenues and wrote to Angus McGugan with my fears about where these costs were leading us. Angus wrote back that he could not foresee any circumstances in which the cost of ward care would rise above four dollars a day. I was reminded, as on other occasions, of that quotation from the *Lady of the Lake*: "Brave words, bold youth." Angus' letter was around the house for years. I do hope it will turn up again some day.

Improving economic prospects were reflected in a development of significance to all employees. The hospital had never enjoyed a pension plan but at the request of the board, the legislature amended the Superannuation Act (Statutes of Alberta 1943 Chapter 16 Section 6) to include specifically employees of the University Hospital. And on April 1 1943 our bookkeepers began deducting four percent of wages, which was matched by the board. It's said that the pension plan was put in expressly for Angus McGugan. The story is that Angus had been with the Department of Health for many years and had a large contribution in the plan. When he was offered the superintendent's job at the hospital he was told "You can't take it with you," so he refused to go until he was assured that he could. Whether it happened exactly this way I can't say but it certainly sounds like Angus, and it's certain that the pension plan coincided with his coming and all employees got in on it. Well, not quite all. The board decided it would not cover student nurses, interns or part-timers. Then on top of that there came a cold letter from the Civil Service Commissioner pointing out that under the Superannuation Act it could not include married women whose husbands were gainfully employed!

However, the war witnessed a permanent change in the status of married women. It happened when Helen Peters asked the board for permission to retain Grace Vickers, a nurse in the operating room who had walked down the proverbial aisle. On June 12 1942 the board ruled gingerly that "married women might be engaged if necessary, but certainly no longer than to the end of hostilities." There was much unintended humour in that. Not long after the end of hostilities we had to accept student nurses marrying. It's ironic that the second war saw the demise of the military tradition we'd inherited from the first war. In the '20s and '30s "the strict disciplinarian" was hailed as the ideal hospital administrator and in the period when employees seemed to be going out the back door as fast as they came in the front, some longed for peace so we could go back to the good old days, but I have to laugh at this notion. A strict disciplinarian would very shortly have been talking to himself.

A significant loss of military style occurred in dining arrangements. The Red Cross hut, scene of entertainments formal and improvised since the 1920s, was converted to a staff cafeteria — for staff of whatever degree.

Consigned to history were the dining rooms, based on the military caste system, with white table cloths and waiters and monogrammed napkin rings, and places senior people claimed for their exclusive use at which no others dared sit. The dining rooms were charming but expensive, and above all not big enough to handle the numbers of staff we were expecting in the near future.

Mind you, behind the scenes there was an interesting little war effort going on in the kitchen. Dan Schneider, the laundry man, couldn't get enough soap for the laundry, and asked Charlie Moore to save him the fat. Charlie, by now, had been restored to his original vocation, putting aside the snow shovel and taking up the butcher's cleaver again. Charlie carefully trimmed away the excess fat from beef and pork which passed through the store room. His job also included making the broth from which he skimmed away the fat rising to the top. He rendered about 600 pounds of hard tallow a month which Dan boiled up in a kettle with caustic soda and secret ingredients of his own to make a better product than he could buy. Little did the employees engaged in this war effort realize that soap itself was soon to be a victim of technological upheaval and be replaced by detergents.

At this time Angus McGugan introduced an important innovation on behalf of the employees. He persuaded the board to set up a staff health service. It was the first in Alberta and to run it Angus picked Edythe Markstad, who was just graduating with a BSc in nursing, and after five years around the hospital knew the people and the problems. Angus found Edythe a room in the basement, next to the psychiatric holding room which was all bars and double doors, not the best to make people feel at ease and discuss their ailments. Especially infections. Edythe found staff people were afraid to report an infection — that meant carelessness. She made house calls to staffers who were sick at home, and these visits were considered so important that Angus allowed her to take the hospital car. I have to laugh when I think of that car. We had exactly one, and it was booked out only for grave and sufficient reason. Sometimes Slim Lefebvre, the head orderly, would come with her on visits to rough parts of town, and sometimes an intern. The service brought a satisfying reduction in "days lost through illness."

Towards the end of the war we had labour unrest in the operating rooms. Three nurses requested a raise of $25 a month, and when the board declined to take them seriously, they quit. The army sent some lieutenant nursing sisters to help out, but more were needed. That was how Nellie Lees, a recent Saskatchewan graduate, happened to read in the Regina Leader-Post that Christina Mackay was advertising for OR nurses at the University Hospital. Nellie (now Mrs. Beatty) says that if she had been older and/or wiser she would have known there was something peculiar going on and wouldn't have answered the ad. And wouldn't have had the experience of working in five decades in our operating rooms. And in all three suites — the original, the 1960 version and the space-age model in the Mackenzie Centre.

The OR Nellie came to in 1945 was an "oasis" — in the sense that it was very wet. Scrub sinks were right in the theatres to begin with. Surgical instruments were boiled — small trays 10 minutes, large trays 20 minutes — and brought dripping into the room. Some surgeons liked water and sponges so hot nurses would burn their hands through the rubber gloves. There were many trips to the "solution room" for hot water. At the conclusion of one such sortie Nellie slipped on a wet patch and landed in a sitting position under the operating table on which the patient lay anaesthetized. All those gathered about the table saw the humour of the situation. Even Nellie did after awhile, as long as she didn't think about the consequences if she hadn't held the pitcher upright so it didn't spill a drop.

Operations filled the morning. In the afternoon the nurses did chores, with the aid of Ford, the faithful orderly, who also looked after Tina MacKay's car. Hypodermic and suture needles had to be sharpened and sterilized, rubber intravenous sets cleaned and sterilized, rubber gloves washed by hand, tested for holes and mended. These items now come pre-packaged and used but once.

The nurses also made our unique scrub soap. Lesser institutions bought "green" soap from commercial suppliers but we blended our own. It started with Ivory Soap, which was cut into cubes. Water was added and the ingredients boiled to the consistency of a seven-minute icing. Hydrogen peroxide was added next and the mixture beaten by hand with an egg beater. It was lovely stuff.

The recipe for our soap was not jealously guarded, but supplies certainly were. Nellie recalls: "Miss MacKay kept the supplies in a locked cupboard. Whenever she went away and had to leave the key with somebody we really raided that cupboard."

By midway of 1943 we were planning for the end of the war. Active discussions on a joyful prospect were underway with the Department of National Defense, but they were depressing talks — planning an addition to the hospital to care for hundreds of young men enjoying top health and vigour who were sure to be maimed or disabled in the invasion of Europe. Perhaps this was the harshest reality of the period but war is hell, as General Sherman put it, and he certainly knew his subject. It was decided we must have an addition to handle 240 bed patients and a heavy outpatient load. Contracts were drawn — the federal authority to build it and the University Hospital to run it. Ground was broken in December 1943 with D-Day still six months off. Three storeys high, it was to stand for 40 years and carry an appropriate and celebrated name — that of Colonel Frank Mewburn.

When D-Day was three months off a member of our medical staff received an urgent call from overseas. At Hairmyres, a hospital near Glasgow, a specialist treatment centre was being set up for men who would come out of the impending battle needing orthopaedic help. Graham Huckell was asked to recruit a Canadian orthopaedic team to serve at Hairmyres. In March 1944 Graham's team started for Scotland on a converted bomber which lost an engine and made a forced landing in Labrador.

In June the battle started. In February 1945 the Mewburn Pavilion was ready to receive its wounded. On May 8 news came of victory in Europe.

Edythe Markstad was stuck on duty on VE-Day, in the staff health office. So was "Cappy" Kidd, still an intern. The day began in a mood of quiet thanksgiving, but then word reached the hospital of great celebrations building up overtown. Duty called but the party called louder. Edythe "invented" a patient overtown. She and "Cappy" booked the hospital's only car and joined the parade. Mind you, this course of action was not covered by regulations, but on a day which signalled the end of "the Battle of Edmonton" it was the sensible thing.

# Chapter 14

# 1945—1951
*The DVA Years*

VE-Day celebrations signalled the start of the post-war era. In a particular way, for us, the revels signalled as well the beginning of the DVA years. The Mewburn Pavilion, brand new and highly visible, became the centre of public awareness of the University Hospital. In 1946 and '47 40 percent of patients admitted to the hospital were sponsored by the Department of Veterans Affairs. While no records were kept of visitors it's conceivable that 80 percent were attracted to the Mewburn to visit the veterans. Mind you, it was hard for us to think of all those young men in their twenties as "veterans" when fiftyish survivors of the first war were still around in strength. A third of our revenue was coming from DVA, which had first call on 240 beds in the Mewburn and another 80 in the wooden annex built for the first war. The Mewburn was owned by the DVA and operated on contract by the hospital. We supplied all the services: food, nursing, interns, clinical laboratory, x-ray, operating and physical medicine. On VE-Day we were providing them for $3.65 a day but on April 1 1946 the rate went up to $5.00, as Angus McGugan's prediction that ward care would never exceed $4.00 died an unlingering death.

Timmie Inch was head nurse at the Mewburn, from opening day in February 1945 through the most hectic period of the post-war. She recalls: "The boys were a happy lot. There were some sad sad cases among them but they seemed to rise above that."

Pierre Gariepy was one patient who certainly rose above his injuries. Pierre moved into the Mewburn on opening day, paralyzed from the waist down from the crash of his Lancaster bomber in England. From 1960 to 1977 he was Alberta Director of the Canadian Paraplegic Association.

Recalling the routine at the Mewburn Pierre says: "It was a heck of a way to run a hospital but just what we needed. We were encouraged to try things. We could sneak into the kitchen after hours and fry an egg. If we decided in the middle of the night to go out and get something to eat the staff would help us dress and call a cab and be waiting for us when we got back. At three in the morning we could be sitting up playing cards with a bottle on the table and Betty Greig the night supervisor would come in and ask: 'How are the boys?' She had a nice Scottish accent and never said: 'And who brought that booze up here?' Miss Greig was a real jewel and everyone who knew her tells stories to prove it. Jessie Morrison was another kind soul. So was Muriel Moar. We had all-around nurses, and if something had to be done they dug in and did it. We had a big guy named

John who'd lost a leg in the army and used to get down, and argue, and throw trays, but when he was sick he got the best care they could give. We had a really good staff and we appreciated the tie-in with the University Hospital. We had access to their staff and the communication was good."

Pierre's observation about ties with hospital staff brings to mind a dispute which followed the first war. The question was whether or not soldier patients should be involved as subjects in the teaching program. Resolution was in the affirmative due to an uncompromising stand by "Sandy" Munroe. But it wasn't a problem the second time around. Don Wilson reminds me that Colonel Bill

*The Mewburn Pavilion off to the right. That's where the action is. Forty percent of admissions to the University Hospital are through the Department of Veterans Affairs*

Warner of Ottawa, who set up the DVA medical program, insisted that the veterans be in teaching hospitals.

Mind you, Don was closer to this important phase of hospital history than anyone in my department. Patients in the Mewburn had no need of obstetrical or gynaecological services. We did see a few female veterans, but very few, as they were a healthy lot. Of course Don has insights into many aspects of the story. He was the first of our second-generation medical staff, son of W.A. Wilson, a member of the original cast. Don eventually became Director of Medical Services for the hospital. Right after the war he was assistant to Ken Hamilton,

DEPARTMENT OF ~~PENSIONS AND NATIONAL HEALTH~~ VETERANS AFFAIRS

To

Attention of

Subject          DISCIPLINE

File No.

    Gambling and drinking of alcoholic beverages are prohibited in the Col. Mewburn Pavilion. Offences will be dealt with in the following manner:

    FIRST OFFENCE  -  FINE OF $10.00

    REPEATED OFFENCES -  DISCHARGE FROM HOSPITAL

    Visitors bringing alcoholic beverages into the Col. Mewburn Pavilion will be prohibited from visiting, after their first offence.

    Medical Assistant to the D.A., D.V.A.

P. & N.H. 123S 100M-5 44 Req. 513

*A wall decoration inside the
Mewburn Pavilion. Men who
have been through the war will
not be intimidated by this notice*

who was in charge of medicine in the DVA wards. DVA had a small administrative unit in the Mewburn. Don Easton was in charge before he went to the Royal Alex as Superintendent. George Avison was in the DVA office the longest, from 1945 till his death (in the Mewburn) in 1976.

George's job was Entitlement Officer. Ottawa's policy said that a veteran was entitled to treatment for any war-related illness in a DVA hospital. Obviously the term "entitlement" was subject to local interpretation and George was always on the side of the boys, as was Ken Hamilton. Soldier wards tended to fill up in winter, a fact which had been noted back in the '20s. Amputees who could make it through the summer on the outside found winter hard and exhausting. And Don Wilson notes that life in small towns was dull in winter and some chaps would decide it was time to fight World War One over again and arrive with their pipes and one-pound tobacco tins. The Legion branches were good about tobacco and other items of cheer and the Lady Aberdeen League supplied a library. Ken Hamilton figured they were entitled to stay as long as they wanted, and Don notes that the DVA procedure for discharging patients was so cumbersome a stay might be extended another four or five days.

Pierre Gariepy spent four years in the Mewburn (where he met his wife Gerry) and came back half a dozen times for shorter periods. Each time he returned he noticed that the patients were fewer and the techniques of treatment improved. Some needed improving. Pierre can laugh at his own account of Tommy Robson teaching the boys to use crutches. Tommy was a great masseur but when it came to crutches he had to do the best he knew how, which was a technique he'd used since the first war. Tommy would prop Pierre against a wall, then back away insulting him, making him so mad he walked in hope of wrapping the crutches around Tommy's substantial neck.

I'd never heard Pierre's story about Tommy, but I'm delighted to believe it. And in the post-war much progress was made in Tommy's area. It began with the arrival of Morris Adamson, the country GP who developed rehabilitation into a full-fledged hospital department. Morris came into the Mewburn as an employee of DVA and transferred to the hospital staff two years later. Morris had a feel for working with veterans. In the first war he saw service in both France and Siberia with leave in between to earn his medical degree from Manitoba. Between wars he was a country doctor at Innisfree, Alberta. He worked with a rural health unit. Then, with the second war ending he joined DVA. He went to Mayo Brothers for special training in rehabilitation — I expect it was a three-month course, about par for the time — and in 1945 was stationed at the Mewburn in charge of physical medicine. Anything I'd say about Morris Adamson would have to be good because I admired his work. He was quiet and efficient and I don't think he got a due amount of appreciation.

Over the years DVA just faded away. The Mewburn Pavilion was demolished, finally, in 1983, but by 1951 the veterans had become a minor part of the hospital's total operation. From the opening rush, when 40 percent of admissions were DVA, they dropped in 1951 to just 7.6 percent.

# Chapter 15

# 1945—1951
*All That Pent-Up Energy*

While the DVA era started with a bang and dwindled off to a whisper, the general post-war era, which coincided, was an entirely different proposition.

The post-war was a restless time. Hospital administrators had to adjust to radical changes in attitudes and philosophy. They had no experience from which to know how to live with radical trends and I'm afraid most were not eager to learn. The tumult and shouting of VE-Night had hardly died away before we were apprised that there was no going back to the good old days. Our graduate nurses announced that they weren't going to punch a time clock anymore and there wasn't much anybody could do about it when we couldn't hire enough graduates to fill our establishment. Institutions like ours could no longer count on fear of unemployment as a stabilizing factor. I'm sure many administrators felt threatened.

The opening date of the post-war is obviously May 8 1945 with the celebration of victory in Europe. The closing date is a matter of selection and I've chosen October 27 1951. On that occasion the veterans in the Mewburn Pavilion received a royal visit from Princess Elizabeth and her signature in the guest book seemed to write "amen" to one era as the visit of her parents in 1939 did to another.

Between VE-Day and the visit of the Princess we saw phenomenal growth. Our bed count rose from about 550 to 925 and other indicators kept pace. On VE-Day we had a medical staff of 40 with a dozen interns. We ended 1951 with 40 interns and a medical staff of 70. At war's end we had 25 graduate nurses; at the end of '51 we had 143. We had 108 student nurses on VE-Day and their number exactly doubled. The annual cost of operating the hospital went from $913,000 to $1,621,000. Wages rose from $422,000 to $1,231,000. In 1945 the *dispensary* bought drugs worth $27,000; in 1951 the *pharmacy* bought $118,000 worth. You can go through the records picking out all kinds of comparisons, and see rapid growth. The student population of the university tripled in only two years. On VE-Day we had an enrollment of 1,565 full-time students. Registration for the fall semester of 1947 brought the total up to 4,865, a stunner for those who hoped the university could slide back quietly to the good old days.

The city of Edmonton was growing too — from 111,745 at war's end to 160,000 in 1951. And I have to laugh at the controversy over paving 87th Avenue. It was a country road then. The city wanted to make it the main route for gravel trucks coming up from Hawrelak Park, which was then just an untidy gravel pit. The city was trying to catch up paving all the streets it couldn't afford to pave before, and the gravel was coming from that pit. The board protested the disturbance the trucks would cause the patients, and the administrator of the Mewburn Pavilion was most upset because the gravel route would be closest to the soldiers.

A great pent-up energy was set loose in the post-war. Through the hard times people had made lists of things that ought to be done. A new generation of medical men had been away in the service and seen how things could get done if there was money and a will to do them. The will was there. And money came, unexpectedly, on February 13 1947. On the most dramatic day of the post-war period Imperial Oil made the discovery about riches under the farms around Leduc. Although we didn't realize it at once this was the "wonder drug" of hospital financing. And we needed more money just to stand still.

Thirteen days before the big oil news from Leduc, all our nurses, staff and student, went on straight eight-hour shifts with a guarantee of a full day off each week. Work *days* grew shorter, then work *weeks*. By 1951 charge nurses were on duty five-and-a-half days a week (in another four years it was five days) and in addition they were enjoying statutory holidays, just like everybody else. With fear of unemployment no longer a stabilizing influence, nursing became a highly mobile profession. At one time about the only reason for a nurse resigning was "to get married." Now they were leaving "to see another part of the country." By 1951 we had an average of 143 graduate nurses on staff but had to hire almost that many to maintain the average. With nurses on the move news of working conditions in other parts of the world travelled quickly and our hospital had to compete.

Freeing the slaves required a lot of getting used to. It brought on a new concept, the idea of a nursing *team*. Many argued that there *ought* to be a team, but I reckon that with no single nurse in charge of a patient anymore there *had* to be a team. Work which used to be done entirely by nurses was delegated — or in some cases relegated — to others. The others were nursing aides, ward aides, ward clerks and orderlies.

Looking back, you can see the start of the team idea during the war. In 1943 we began training ward aides (on the job) to relieve hard-pressed nurses of some routine duties. After the war the idea of the ward aide was upgraded to the Certified Nursing Aide, for which a well-organized program of training was organized in Calgary. In 1949 our hospital added CNAs to the staff, along with another category, ward *clerks*, to relieve nurses of some of the expanding paperwork. When staffing was adjusted to operate the big south wing which we opened in 1951 the nursing teams of the University Hospital comprised the following: 143 graduate nurses, 216 students, 48 nursing aides and trainees, 10 ward clerks, 61 ward aides; and of nursing orderlies, still doing their traditional work in male wards, there were 37.

There's an important point to be made about the orderlies. Before they could be integrated into the nursing team the exact role and qualifications for an orderly had to be established. This had always been a vague grey area. And we were fortunate at this time to have "Slim" Lefebvre as head orderly in the hospital.

"Slim" became head during the war when Louis Parkhouse went into the army. "Slim" was turned down because of a bad lung. He took over a collection of medical-side workers, janitors, supply clerks and elevator operators all designated as "orderlies."

"Slim" recalled that medical orderlies worked in male wards because of "the modesty thing." They did many of the same services as nurses, but had no recognized training. In addition they did any work involving physical strength: lifting, orthopaedic work, subduing unruly patients. And their only training came from senior orderlies. "Slim" recalled: "It was a shame the way those guys came off the street and looked after patients."

"Slim" organized classes as best he could and read medical books for information. Some nurses and doctors told him that he had no right to read such things, but "Slim" devoured books the way he used to pack away groceries when he was younger. Helen Peters and Reg Adshead were very helpful. They had him take a university extension course in administration and supervision and he got a final mark of 85 while a BSc in nursing, taking the same course, finished with a 55.

Progress was slow, but the apples were distinguished from the oranges and when staffing was done for the 1951 wing, 20 janitors, supply clerks and elevator operators were shuffled to another department and 37 medical orderlies remained on the nursing team.

Mind you the old regime was highly satisfactory from the doctor's point of view. The charge nurse on the floor was really the doctor's assistant. He confided in her the problems of the patient and what he hoped to see happen. He knew the poor girl would be there seven days a week with an afternoon off. We were never offered the excuse: "I was off that day." As I say, the old regime was ideal for doctors, and some will say for the patients as well, but for the nurses it was slavery. By the post-war, fortunately, hospital administrations had to adjust to the fact that the slaves were free.

All hospitals had to adjust to the nursing team (and travel plans of RNs) but the University Hospital stood alone in having to cope with a new wrinkle in the education of nurses. The change came in 1947 and certainly cancelled out whatever pleasure Angus McGugan felt about the discovery of oil at Leduc.

Since the beginning, nursing in all aspects had been a responsibility of the hospital — contained within the walls. But then nursing training was removed from control of the hospital board and put under the Faculty of Medicine. Helen Peters, with whom Angus worked very well, had been in overall charge of service and training. But in 1947 a professorship was created in the Faculty of Medicine and a new personality brought in with the title Director, School of Nursing. Miss Peters continued as Superintendent of Nursing Services but reported through the new professor.

Angus was always pretty jealous of the hospital's autonomy and of any control by the university. In the annual report which announced the new arrangement Angus wrote: "This change was made against the advice of the hospital administration . . . on the opinion that the principle of authority without corresponding responsibility is administratively unsound."

Angus and the new lady on the block were at daggers drawn for the seven years she stayed. Helen Penhale was her name. She came from Columbia, with the latest ideas on the status of the nursing profession and the position of the professional nurse in the nursing team. Helen was a forthright woman, sister of a general in the Canadian army. She was very sure of her ground and had reason to be with her education and experience. Her ideas had been shaped in the eastern United States — by large populations and large institutions — and she said we ought to be doing these things here. The word *dynamic* would apply to Helen. So would *activist* although the word wasn't in use then.

Aside from the clashes of personality, which were often amusing, Helen and Angus represented two schools of thought. Helen believed firmly that service to the hospital should not interfere with a nurse's education. The old school held just as firmly that a nurse's duty was to serve the hospital and a proper nursing education was obtained through service.

Although Helen's position was in the university she exerted a very strong influence in the hospital — not only in education, but nursing service as well. She and Angus went at it for seven years until she left to take a prestigious job in eastern Canada. At that time the hospital regained control of nursing education in the diploma program, so Angus won that battle, but the things Helen Penhale advocated came to pass at a later date.

While the post-war saw important changes in the education of nurses, it brought even more significant advances in the education of doctors. The advances were made under pressure, the pressure of recent graduates returning from the war service, saying, like Oliver Twist, "Please, sir, I want some more." During the war they had been accelerated to graduation to meet the crying need of the day and had gone into uniform with only six to nine months of internship. All wanted more hospital experience. Many wanted to specialize, and there was the rub.

Across Canada returning servicemen wanted post-graduate development but only McGill and Toronto had recognized programs. Only so many positions could be offered and these of course were reserved for their own graduates. There was no place for Alberta's products to develop the specialties which our own hospital would soon require.

As Ken Thomson recalls, late in 1945 three men held an informal meeting to decide what could be done about the problem which was also an opportunity. Present were Mark Marshall, John Scott, head of the Department of Medicine, and Johnny Ower, the Dean of Medicine.

Johnny Ower became the second dean in 1945, succeeding A.C. Rankin, and served only three years because of declining health. He had a natural interest in promoting young people — a longtime leader in the Boy Scout movement. And he was remarkably practical. He used to impress on the medical staff the importance of keeping each day's work complete and signed out — "so if you die overnight you will not impede the work of the department." He also urged people to write things down. "The greatest memory is weaker than the palest ink."

The trio of Ower, Scott and Marshall had some breathing time in which to come up with a plan because our graduates didn't all come home on a weekend. In fact, medical officers were held in service after most categories had been discharged. Aerial gunners and landing-craft commanders were no longer needed when the fighting ceased but the wounded and sick could not be

*The Four Deans — a famous photograph brings together the foursome who led the Faculty of Medicine and influenced the hospital through the first half-century. At right, Walter Mackenzie 1959-1974. From the left, John Scott 1948-1959, John J. Ower 1945-1948, and Allan C. Rankin, known as "The" Dean because he was the first and served from 1920 to 1945, making his last public appearance. Days before his death which he knew to be imminent he rose and dressed to join his successors for this historic photograph*

abandoned. They recognized a chance to do the right thing for Albertans who had served the country. They also recognized an opportunity to put Alberta on the map of the medical world — with a postgraduate program that would stand alongside McGill's and Toronto's and give the University Hospital a cadre of specialist people, who, if they read the future correctly, were bound to be needed soon.

In times past some of our hardy pioneers, like "Hep" Hepburn, had pursued specialties and been granted certificates by the Senate of the university. These certificates were important historically, but they represented individual efforts and were valid only in Alberta. Faced with the pent-up energy and ambition of the returning servicemen Alberta had a chance to move up to the big leagues with coordinated programs of postgraduate study. It was a golden opportunity, but one which had to be seized with vigor.

The meeting decided that Alberta should have its own program and Mark Marshall would run it. Mark was the logical choice. He'd always been interested in advanced training and individuals "going on." And he had an unbeatable knack for getting things done. Mark devised a scheme which was inevitably dubbed "the Marshall Plan," a play on the American aid program to rebuild post-war economies in Europe.

The plan was straightforward. Programs leading to certification of specialists had been laid down by the Royal College of Physicians and Surgeons of Canada. People in the "Marshall Plan" would do the programs under direction of their department heads.

The programs had to be carried out in a hospital by a resident. There had to be enough beds — that is, patients — in each specialty. And the resident had to be paid. Some indirect help may have come from the federal government plan of 1947 which provided grants for the training of health care personnel, but the main burden was on the budgets of the University Hospital. The university was sympathetic, but unable to help financially. The provincial government, as Ken Thomson recalls, was able to help but not so sympathetic. A top accountant with the Department of Health argued that the doctors on medical staff should pay for the residents since they got the benefit of the work. To which Ken countered that the entire province would reap the benefit.

Of course the most obvious benefit was to the hospital. In the 1950s many products of the program emerged as our specialists and department heads. Without the program they wouldn't have had the qualifications. Jim Metcalfe, for example. Jim took over the Department of Urology when Gordon Ellis retired. He was the first urologist in the program and his recollection is a fine illustration of how it worked. Jim says:

"I graduated from the U of A in 1943. We were privates and then lieutenants in the army and when we came out everybody was looking for more training. There were a dozen people competing for urology courses at the Royal Vic and I didn't have a hope of getting in there. When I was senior intern I hitch-hiked to Minnesota and to Iowa City where Dr. Alcock had pioneered the method of removing the prostate through the penis, but there was no room for

Alberta graduates. I got my chance through the Marshall Plan.

"Dr. Marshall set up a file on all of us. Every two months we'd go to see him in that little building north of the Mewburn. He organized all our programs and had them approved by the Royal College. The College might object that we didn't have the facilities or the charity patients. He'd see that we did.

"He organized a five-year program for me: one year surgery, one year medicine, one year basic, and two years urology after that. In the basic year he'd say to Dr. Shaw: 'Metcalfe's coming to you for three months in bacteriology.' And to Dr. Shaner: 'Metcalfe's coming to you for three months anatomy.' For the final year he came to my chief Gordon Ellis and said: 'Metcalfe should go away for a year. Where should he go?' So I went to Queens and worked with Dr. Nate Berry, the best prostate resectionist in Canada. Dr. Ellis was a very good surgeon, but he had trained at the Royal Vic and didn't have this technique."

After his post-graduate training Jim joined our Department of Urology in 1952, he became head in 1958 and served 20 years.

Ted Gain was the first product of the Marshall Plan to head his department, which he did for 23 years. It happened in 1952 when Ernie Watts had to retire because of rheumatoid arthritis, and there's an interesting family tie-in here. When Ernie left temporarily during the war to go into the navy he was replaced by Ted's wife Effie Dunn. Ted recalls:

"Dr. Marshall pushed me into the postgraduate program. Ernie Watts was the only person in western Canada with specialized training in anaesthesiology. The idea was to do basic and clinical research in each of the specialties and sub-specialties. Anaesthesia rests on the two basic sciences, anatomy and pharmacology. I had to work out a program with Dr. Evan Greene on anatomy and Dr. Floyd Rodman on pharmacology."

Mark Marshall's own successor as head of ophthalmology was a product of the plan. Wint Duggan took over in 1959. Wint had also graduated into the army during the war. He recalls:

"Dr. Marshall was a real force in people's lives. He designed my program. He was a strong believer in not having all training in one location. I did pathology here with Dr. Ower and Dr. Macgregor and then two years at Tulane in New Orleans. Mark arranged for our work in Canada to be recognized in the United States so we could move our programs south of the border."

Cooper Johnston also graduated into the army during the war and became an orthopaedic specialist through the Marshall Plan. Cooper says: "The program gave Alberta something only Montreal and Toronto had before. It showed that Alberta belonged up there, that we could do things. The plan was to spend a couple of years here and a couple of years away, and we all came back to the University Hospital with wider experience. The hospital sent me to St. Louis, but all I got was the appointment, no money. I still had some army money left, so my wife worked and I borrowed."

Donnie Bell was the first to train in gynaecology and obstetrics, spending two years in Cleveland at the University Hospital of that city.

In general surgery Bob Johnston went to Chicago, Al McCarten to

Manitoba, Mickey Michalyshin to the Royal Vic-McGill complex, and Les Willox to Georgetown University. Les's break is a good example of the person-to-person influence required to get our people into senior institutions. It was orchestrated by Walter Mackenzie, a powerful new post-war personality who will be introduced properly later in this chapter. As Les recalls: "He got me into Georgetown over a bottle of bourbon in a Washington D.C. hotel room with his old classmate from Dalhousie, Dr. Coffey. Dr. Coffey was professor of surgery at Georgetown. It had always been second-rate but suddenly got a lot of money, including $17 million from Dr. Coffey's aunt."

In a few years the veterans were taken care of and were contributing heavily to the system, but there was no letup in the Marshall Plan. The post-war brought a rush of beginning students who wanted to follow the same specialist path. Mark ran the program for 15 years, and it continues in full force today. The program has undergone changes to meet new times, but it's essentially the same plan which originated in the post-war turmoil, when the term *specialist* was about to take off into a much wider dimension. A strong tide was running then, one of those "tides in the affairs of men" which are easily missed. Alberta might well have been left stranded, but it wasn't. Only a hospital could have pulled off the Marshall Plan, and only a hospital with a university connection. The University of Alberta Hospital did not fail its responsibility.

Mind you, there was a concern about breaking medicine down into specialties. I have to laugh at "Hep" Hepburn's remark to Don Wilson: "Those guys'll starve to death. They'll never make a living." Although "Hep" had pioneered brain surgery he prudently kept his other options open, including an annual refresher operation removing an appendix.

In the post-war scramble for specialist training one of our graduates managed to get into an old established program in the east. That was Bob Macbeth, who became Director of Surgical Services in our hospital from 1960 to '75. Back from the army, Bob was writing letters of application and getting rejection slips. John Scott, helpful as always, said: "Go see my old friend Dr. Collip at McGill." This was the same J.B. Collip who had pioneered insulin research at the University of Alberta, and was back at McGill. Bob was able to spend two years with Collip, doing research and applying vainly for surgical appointments. Then he got a year in anatomy. One afternoon he was having afternoon tea with the head of that department — it was always terrible tea, Bob recalls — and told him how much he wanted surgery. So the host phoned the head of surgery, who said: "What's his name again? Macbeth? Tell him he's on for next year." There was no selection process, just persistence and lucky connections. So 10 years after entering medical school Bob was able to start a five-year program in surgery. Already we could see how specialization was going to cut into a doctor's earning period. And one of the residencies in Bob's program was considered such a plum he was paid only half the official stipend — which gave him $17.50 a month.

In the post-war drive to develop specialists we got important funding from the same source that financed Sesame Street on TV. It may sound like a joke, but we have the facts direct from Don Wilson, the first Canadian to be awarded a Markle scholarship. John and Mary Markle were outstanding people. They made a lot of money in Pennsylvania coal and enjoyed giving it away to anyone who could convince them of a good cause. Don tells about a lady seeking funds for members of a secretarial association who had fallen on hard times. She was a gushy lady. She said: "Mr. Markle, I'm sure you're going to help us. I can tell by the twinkle in your eye?" "Oh? Which eye?" "The right one, Mr. Markle." He laughed: "That's my glass eye, but here's your money anyway."

Eventually the Markles brought in a professional foundation man to advise them on how to handle the requests. He told them they should not sit back and wait for applications, but identify areas where there was a need. They followed the advice. One area of need was educational programming for children on TV and they bankrolled Sesame Street. Another need was identified in medicine. In the post-war there was a clamor for medical care, so much that good teaching and research men were being lured away from institutions to serve the immediate needs of the public. So the Markles set up a program to keep people in the teaching departments of universities and associated teaching hospitals. The first Markle scholarships were awarded in 1948; there was one for Canada and Don Wilson got it. The institution was guaranteed $5,000 a year to pay for the scholar. He would spend two-thirds of his time in teaching and research, no area specified, and at the end of the five years the institution was honour-bound to take him on full-time staff. Don needed an office and Angus McGugan gave him the old coalbin in the basement. Although the coal was gone the heat lingered on, especially in summer. When Don was able to move to a better location the laundry used it to dry gloves from the operating room. He needed a lab too, and Angus found him a space behind the elevator shaft — four feet wide. There he developed tests for certain hormones, F.S.H. 17 ketosteroids and urinary corticoids.

Another Markle scholarship came our way, to Bob Fraser for work in cardiology. But that was in 1953, beyond the confines of the present chapter.

With the increasing numbers of the postwar period it's obvious that there were many new faces in the medical departments. However the heads of departments remained mostly familiar. Dick Procter, still plugging along in radiology. "Hank" Mewburn in orthopaedics. Gordon Ellis in urology. Harold Orr in dermatology. Doug Leitch in paediatrics. Ernie Watts in anaesthesia. Mark Marshall in ophthalmology. Scott Hamilton in dentistry. Irving Bell in therapeutics. Ross Vant in obstetrics and gynaecology. John Scott as Director of Medical Services — he succeeded "Edge" Pope in 1945 and served 10 years.

There was, however, a newcomer as head of surgical services. When Fulton Gillespie died unexpectedly in 1949, old reliable "Hep" Hepburn agreed to fill in for a year while a permanent replacement was found. And the new man certainly loomed large. The Walter C. Mackenzie Health Sciences Centre commemorates his career.

Walter was a big man with a large appetite for the good things of life. That's how he came to be known as "Fats" in his student days at Dalhousie, and why he and Don Avison (later chairman of our hospital board) and Ingar Telmar, manager of *the Bay*, used to go on diets together competing for a trophy which they put up. I also have to laugh at the story of how the Mackenzies came to Nova Scotia. Walter's great-great grandfather was so incensed when the Church of Scotland introduced song into the service that he uprooted his whole family and moved them across the ocean. Although Walter was certainly more receptive to new ideas than his ancestor, he inherited that firmness of purpose. Walter was a gregarious chap. He made friends. He loved people, he managed to know the right people, and he remembered names. How he could remember names. At medical conventions all over North America he remembered names. Mrs. Jim Metcalfe once asked him his secret. Walter explained that he started early. His parents ran a summer hotel at Baddeck, Nova Scotia, where the guests used to include the Grosvenors, relatives of Alexander Graham Bell. From the age of three his job was to sit on the sidewalk, greeting visitors from the previous year. "Hello, Mrs. McGregor, and how is your dog Patsy?"

Walter was a fine surgeon. He trained at Mayos', then came to Edmonton just before the war and joined the Baker clinic. He went away with the navy and planned to settle in Winnipeg afterwards, but his friendly nature drove him back to Edmonton. Winnipeg in those years was very much dominated by clinics. When it became known that Walter had joined one clinic none of the other men would speak to him, so he said "to hell with that" and headed straight back for Edmonton, where we never had that cliquiness. We always had a true camaraderie here. A lot of it was from the reporting clubs which were organized in the '30s. We'd meet once a month at dinner and then report on something. I was with the senior club, which lasted about 35 years and finally folded when everybody died except me.

The Edmonton atmosphere suited Walter. I believe he was the only Canadian to be president of the two most prestigious medical societies in North America — the Royal College of Physicians and Surgeons of Canada and the American College of Physicians and Surgeons. He did a lot of travelling on society work, with the result that he became well-known, our hospital became well-known and so did the university. Our resources were limited but Walter managed to attract good men here even though financial rewards might be greater in other places.

Though ambitious for the institutions he represented on world tours he was cautious about spending their money. As Don Rees has observed: "He was interested in the new and *tried*." And like all cast in "the great man" tradition Walter's performance drew mixed reviews. One such review is by an acting department head. As dean Walter was a ruthless tyrant, but as clinician he did a bowel resection on the critic's aged mother and for a week after would visit her twice a day, sometimes for 20 minutes and holding her hand.

From the globe-trotting there has emerged a favourite story about Walter and the Taj Mahal. One day the doctors touring India were being taken to view the ancient shrine. Walter told a friend: "Please buy me a postcard. I'm going to see a man in Delhi who's doing excellent work in surgery."

In the late '40s Walter demonstrated his principles and some of the fierce purpose of his great-great grandfather when he wrote the exams for Fellowship in the Royal College of Surgeons of Canada. He was a prime candidate for head of clinical services and if appointed the Fellowship would have been extended to him as a customary courtesy. But Walter wouldn't have it that way. He decided he had to earn it. By this time he was 39 and studying for the same exams as some of his interns. He was teaching the material and studying it at the same time. Failure would have been a terrible embarrassment. He freely admitted afterwards that the equanimity, that was so much a part of his image, was sorely tested.

While the best-laid plans were being developed to give our graduates broader futures, life went on as usual on the crowded corridor above the Wells Pavilion, where interns rushed in all directions — at all hours — in return for room and board and $25 a month. In 1949 Jim Metcalfe was senior resident and attended meetings of the Medical Advisory Board. He says: "Once they debated raising our salaries to $35 a month. But Dr. Hepburn said if they did that we'd just go down to the Lincoln Hotel and drink it. So that was the end of the discussion."

However they weren't dependent on the Lincoln. "We used to steal pure alcohol out of the pharmacy and mix it with lemonade. That was alcohol in its purest form and was a lovely smooth drink."

Cooper Johnston says: "They were still trying to treat us as if we were in boarding school. But we'd been away in the army. We weren't taking it."

As chief resident Jim Metcalfe used to deal with Angus McGugan. "On a Saturday he'd phone and say 'Metcalfe, come in and talk.' He'd have that cigarette hanging out of his mouth and he'd reach in his desk and bring out a bottle of Scotch. Angus made rounds of the wards every day. He cared about everybody. He knew everything that went on in the hospital and he was very understanding. He'd say: 'Metcalfe, when you guys bring those girls up the back stairs at night, try to be quiet, will you?' "

Mind you, there were more nocturnal alarums caused by the ingenious heating system. Bob Cartmell was caught in the eye of these storms, working down in the boiler room at night. The hospital didn't manufacture its own steam. It came from the University's central plant over long pipes, was concentrated in our boiler and distributed throughout the hospital. At times the pipes would shake, rattle and roll and the nurses would beat on them and call down: "Can't you stop that noise?" Bob couldn't, not until the university put in a filter to hold back the silica chips, the same greyish chips you get in the bottom of a kettle. Bob says the pipes would get "all goobed up" with silica and the steam would press through and disturb the night wards. And there were still more nocturnal alarums associated with the pipes from the university. They were in a long warm conduit. Kind-hearted Fanny Hooson would feed all homeless cats who would crawl in and have kittens who would join in a chorus to disturb the dreams of the patients. At this stage in history people expected better of the heating system.

Every group in the hospital was working from post-war viewpoints — patients, nurses, doctors, students, administrators, and in 1949 the so-called "sub" staff gave notice that they too were part of the post-war era. They formed a union — Chapter 23 of the Civil Service Association.

Sam Callan was involved. Sam was an orderly before the war. After service with the air force back problems left him unable to do the heavy lifting on the wards required of an orderly so Angus McGugan created the job of mail room supervisor, by which title Sam was known till 1972. There hadn't been anyone in charge of mail before, but there was more and more of it and a sense that a

In 1950 the hospital makes its first 25 year service awards. Seated are Mary Angus from the linen room, Betty Greig the night nursing supervisor, Jessie Nairn the librarian, and Williamina Nicoll the housekeeper. Standing are Dr. Richard Procter of radiology, "Slim" Waters the orderly, Mrs. Porritt nurse of the old school, George McMillan the x-ray technician and Tommy Robson, therapist and sometime Santa Claus

deluge was not far off. Johnny Beaton sensed it. Johnny came back from service in the far east to run the printing machine, a Multilith which turned out forms and hospital letterheads — very plain of course, no embossing and positively no gold leaf. He says: "I could feel the paper explosion just beginning."

About the union, Sam says: "When the war ended and the boys came home we weren't just prepared to follow the old routine, so we went after a union to negotiate for wages and handle grievances. Dr. McGugan was very receptive. He'd been with the government so long in the public health, he knew what we were working on. He told us to go ahead so Mr. Harrison, the secretary of the Civil Service Association, brought us over a couple of hundred cards and we started signing people up. We got the orderlies and housekeepers and people in the laundry and kitchen and then we opened it up for the nurses and office workers." Dan Schneider, the laundry manager was one of the leaders. Charlie Moore, the butcher in the kitchen, was another. And Joe Kibbler and Bob Roberts.

"We were chartered as Chapter 23 of the Civil Service Association, after the university employees. They were Branch 22. We called the first general meeting in the auditorium in the Mewburn Pavilion, and asked Mr. French, the top man overtown, to explain to us how to get a credit union. It had to be separate because we wanted all the hospital employees to be able to join the credit union and not all could be members of Chapter 23. Mr. French told us 10 members had to sign up. Dan Schneider said: 'Let's do it tonight, there's no better time.' So 10 of us signed and put in 25 cents each to get the charter."

As this was written the certificate of incorporation still hung in the credit union office, dated May 16 1949. The union grew to 230 members with assets of $2½ million. These are the originals, in the order in which they signed:

---

1. *Gus Demro*, assistant manager in the laundry
2. *Maybelle Willoughby*, of the admitting office
3. *Jessie Nairn*, medical librarian
4. *Sam Callan*, mail room supervisor
5. *Ray Warren*, ECG technician (believed the first in the hospital)
6. *Ellis Rose*, maintenance supervisor
7. *Gabriel "Slim" Lefebvre*, head orderly
8. *Jesse Wilson*, storesman (who came to Edmonton as a driver with the U.S. army medical corps)
9. *Charlie Moore*, the butcher
10. *Genevieve Lefebvre*, ("Slim's" daughter, who worked in the laundry)

---

Gus Demro was first head of the Credit Union and the CSA chapter. As this was written account number one was still active in the name of his widow, and the Callan, Rose and Moore accounts were active in the names of the original signers. The Credit Union got off to a good start. Sam says: "We were very proud of our first half-year. We paid one-half percent interest."

I'm sure there were those among us who thought the hospital would fall down if a union ever got in, but in fact the opposite happened. In 1946 fences went up around the construction site of the long-awaited nurses residence, and there's scarcely been a time since when such fences haven't been part of the scene. During the war Tommy Cox and I tried for a nurses home. Back in the '20s "Wash" Washburn had begun urging on the board "the absolute necessity" of one, pointing to the days lost through illness — due to overwork and the lack of any facility for recreation or relaxation. To document the urgency the annual report year after year carried a two-page spread detailing how the days were lost. The summary appeared for the last time in the report for 1946, when some 200 nurses lost 3,486 days to illness. The residence opened May 10 1947, with accommodation for 150 and an extension to house another 125 nurses was added four years later.

With the nurses safely in residence construction fences went up around the site of a major extension to the hospital. It was to add 400 beds, for a total of 925, and make ours, by Angus McGugan's reckoning, the fifth largest general hospital in Canada. It was to be six storeys high — six storeys was high then, let me assure you — and join the existing building on the southeast. It was to accommodate new ideas, as well as some old ideas, which had long been waiting admission to the main hospital. Maternity and paediatric wards were to come in from the wooden annexes. However we hadn't yet reached the stage of knocking anything down and the annexes were to stay — the maternity unit to become the Provincial Cancer Clinic and the children's hut locker rooms for the staff. The extension was the first encroachment on Bob Sherriff's beautiful grounds, but land was still abundant. Out behind, the Department of Public Works was putting up a building for the provincial laboratory, which opened in 1950 and was a plus for our diagnostic services.

Patients were included in the planning. In 1948, as construction began, the board voted to join other Edmonton hospitals in dissolving the group insurance plan pioneered in 1934 by A.F. Anderson, to support a plan on a broader scale. Dr. Anderson's scheme was fine as far as it went but that was only to the city limits. Blue Cross, a name to be reckoned with, was to be province-wide. The decision was proven right but I can't help noting that the vote was taken on April 23, a day sacred to St. George whose flag is the *red* cross.

Our patients could expect better things in the new wing. 20-bed public wards were gone. The largest ward was to hold only four, and was to be known as semi-public. So a patient in the new wing had a choice of semi-public, semi-private or private. Beds were to cost more, reflecting better amenities, such as more toilets per capita and the like. Increases were in the order of a dollar a day — to $10 for private, $7.50 for semi-private and $6.50 for semi-public.

The patient had a personal obligation to pay. If he didn't the hospital's solicitors went after him. That was still the hard reality of sickness, as Peter Owen recalls with reluctance. In the 1970s Peter was chairman of our board, but in 1949 he had just joined the law firm of Woods, Field and Hyndman and the first file he was handed was the collection of overdue accounts. "I felt enraged," he says, "as a young high-minded man. It seemed unfair that we were dunning not only those the hospital had healed, but the loved ones of those who had perished."

Sadly the chairman of our board did not live to see the new wing. Ray Staples died suddenly in 1948 after five years service. Ray's place was taken by Winslow Hamilton, prominent businessman and chartered accountant who was to die tragically some years later in the crash of a Grey Cup charter plane near

The 1951 wing raises an interesting facade towards the south. The maternity ward, in the blackroofed annex on the left, can move inside. So can the children's ward in the closer annex. The original hospital seems smaller somehow, with the Wells Pavilion tucked in behind and the Mewburn Pavilion stretching to 87th Avenue. Out behind, in a spot that will be expropriated one day for the Mackenzie Centre, sits the Provincial Laboratory. Across the gravel of 114th Street is the Varsity Covered Rink. The little building with the dome is the University Observatory, doomed to close soon because the stars are being dimmed by lights of the city

Vancouver. James Walker, retired manager of the Bank of Montreal, was chairman at the official opening in 1951.

But as our six-storey addition came into view over the hoardings we were obliged to beat off a takeover of the board. The "boarder" we had to repel was W. W. Cross, Alberta's veteran Minister of Health, and while we couldn't view it as a "hostile" takeover it certainly seemed dangerous to the long-term prospects of the institution.

Since the government intervention of 1929 we had done rather well on the principle of the balanced board — a chairman representing the broad interests of the community and three members each to uphold those of campus and government.

From campus came the President of the University — Andrew Stewart succeeding Robert Newton in 1951; the Dean of Medicine — John Scott succeeding Johnny Ower in 1948; and the Superintendent of the Hospital, Angus McGugan, who was also Board Secretary.

Government men represented the three departments most involved in the hospital. Malcolm Bow was Deputy Minister of Health; F.G. Stewart represented the Treasury; Arthur Arnold the Department of Public Works, which handled all our building requirements.

As I saw it, the board represented a balance of viewpoints which had to be respected to keep the hospital on course. However, Dr. Cross didn't see it our way, which he frequently didn't. He was proposing to bring to the legislature (at the spring session of '51) changes to our act by which the government would name a majority of members to the hospital board and thus control it.

The rationale was concern about growing budgets. The cost of operating the hospital was increasing at twice the rate of the cost of living. The government felt responsibility for the budgets and we couldn't quarrel with the ancient principle of the piper calling the tune, but we felt the changes would go far beyond the intentions. Provincial appointees, rather than academic and hospital members, would make medical decisions. They would decide which medical men should be directors, who would be heads of departments, what new departments would be established. They would set the direction of medicine.

It was decided that the cabinet should know how we felt. Since Angus McGugan enjoyed, if that's the word, a rather testy relationship in that quarter, it was thought that a delegation should talk to Premier Manning. The task was delegated to Mark Marshall, Walter Mackenzie and Ken Thomson. Angus suggested that Ken go because he and Mr. Manning had served in the same army reserve unit during the war while Ken was waiting to go on active service with the navy.

Ken recalls the meeting with great satisfaction. The committee enjoyed a very good reception and when views had been expressed all around and the session was breaking up, Ken put it right to the Premier: "Does this mean we have a commitment the act will be changed?" "No, Doctor, it doesn't. I have had an excellent discussion, but I have a Minister of Health and I cannot give a commitment on his behalf."

Happily the amendments went to the legislature as we hoped and in a relaxed state of mind the hospital staff planned ceremonies for opening the new wing. The date was set for Tuesday, September 4 in the auditorium of the nurses residence.

On the appointed evening a choir of our nurses opened the program with *O Canada*, and then sat through the speeches waiting to close with *God Save The King*.

Angus McGugan was to give a history of the institution, and I have to laugh at a note in the board resolution approving the program — "not more than

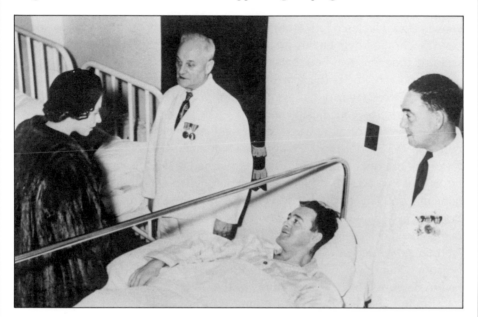

*Royal Visit — October 27 1951 — the Mewburn Pavilion. Princess Elizabeth meets a bed-ridden veteran of the second world war, along with two veterans of the first conflict and of long service in the hospital. They are Tommy Robson, physiotherapist and Christmas party Santa Claus, and Percy Stone, orderly and vigourous presence in the Department of Urology*

five minutes." Whether Angus stayed in bounds I can't say but the other speeches had overtones which were political and amusing.

N.E. Tanner, Alberta's Minister of Mines and Minerals (and oilwells in particular) declared the new wing open. He said the provincial government wanted citizens to enjoy the best hospital facilities and felt the expenditure made in erecting the addition was in order to fulfill that desire. Sid Parsons, the Mayor of Edmonton, congratulated the government for the way it was spending the oil revenue, citing the new wing as an example. But George Prudham, Edmonton's MP in the federal cabinet, saw the thing in a different light. George said the new wing was an example of what could be accomplished by federal-provincial cooperation. He described Ottawa's plan of providing grants to assist provincial governments in their health programs and claimed that 32 Alberta hospital building programs had been so assisted.

Mind you, the polite sparring of the speakers was the shape of things to come. We were entering an age of federal-provincial agreements — and disagreements — over medical care.

As I see it, one more special event marked the close of the era known as the post-war. A reporter for the *Journal* wrote a moving account of it. During the royal visit of Princess Elizabeth, he was assigned to the Mewburn Pavilion. The future Queen was to visit the veterans in our soldiers wing just as her parents had done in 1939. Due to the lateness of the season the affair had to be indoors and Bob Sherriff had no worries this time about photographers trampling his marigolds. The royal party was scheduled to arrive at three o'clock, but the reporter noted activity beginning an hour and a half before, as hospital staff began moving the men into the auditorium. Thirty were in wheelchairs. Eight had to be moved beds and all. Many of the others required some assistance.

Radios were on in the auditorium and the crowd followed the progress of the royal party through the city. They could hear cheering on the radio. Eventually there were live cheers in the street outside the hospital. Then in the corridor. Then they were hearing their own cheers. The Princess stayed 20 minutes instead of the scheduled 10, walking among beds and wheelchairs and asking questions. Then the cheers were outside again. The moment, and the post-war era, were history.

# Chapter 16

# 1952—1957
*The Polio Wing*

Ⅰn the early '50s significant advances were made within our hospital walls, and these events went largely unnoticed by the public, but one intensely dramatic medical happening involved the whole profession and the community as well. It was the last major polio epidemic.

There were, in fact, two epidemics, in successive years, each in turn the worst in the history of Alberta. In the third year the government responded as it had done in the epidemic of the late '20s. It designated the University Hospital the provincial rehabilitation centre and ordered a major addition to the hospital. Construction began when it appeared there might be massive polio for years, but also in the third year the long-sought preventive emerged from the experiments of Dr. Jonas Salk and was given in field trials to Alberta children. In the fourth year Salk vaccine was given widely and the disease appeared to be controlled, but construction was nearly complete on the six-storey addition which has been known ever since as "the polio wing."

In 1952 there was an epidemic of the kind of polio we had known in the past, which affected the spinal cords of children and caused "infantile paralysis" of the arms and legs. Throughout Alberta there were 774 cases with 81 deaths. But then in 1953 came a surge of respiratory polio, which lodged in the brain stem of young adults and paralyzed breathing. We had 1,458 cases with 111 deaths. This polio affected more young adults than children and carried off many parents of young families. For some reason my own neighbourhood of Windsor Park was one of the hardest hit.

We had no local experience with respiratory polio on a large scale but the patients were pouring into the only designated active treatment centre, the isolation unit at the Royal Alex, still essentially the civic "pest house" set up in years past to "contain" infectious diseases like typhoid and scarlet fever by isolating victims from the community. Our paediatricians, who had dealt with "infantile paralysis," had no advice on how to keep alive the young people whose respiratory systems were paralyzed and needed someone to breathe for them.

It was an occasion without precedent but the profession and community rose to it. Although the action took place at the Royal Alex and is a proud part of the history of that institution, doctors and nurses from all hospitals joined in a volunteer effort to keep the patients breathing. Brian Sproule, then a resident in pathology at our hospital, was one of the many. The experience led him to specialize in cardiology and then respiratory therapy after which he set up our first division of pulmonary medicine. Brian recalls: "It was accepted that people could leave their responsibilities and go to the Alex. My salary as resident, such as it was, continued to be paid, but for many it was a significant sacrifice. People at all levels responded. It was a unique and elevating episode."

Russ Taylor (who later specialized in cardiology and headed the department at our hospital), was then a GP, just starting practice with the Allin Clinic. Russ recalls: "An inspiring experience. Here was a community being devastated by a very dangerous epidemic and we couldn't use all the help that was offered. There was so much we didn't know about respiratory polio and the way it was transmitted. The work was dangerous. Several nurses died."

Russ was the second doctor to get involved on a full-time basis. The first was Nelson Nix, whose specialty of anaesthesia gave him insights into the mechanics of breathing, a vital consideration with bulbar polio. Nelson calls the episode "a story of the evolution of specialties, and of inter-specialty communication." In August '53 Nelson's seven-year-old son went into isolation with respiratory polio. As a member of the Royal Alex medical staff Nelson was allowed to go into the unit to be with his son, who, incidentally, made a quick recovery. One day a nurse asked for help with a child in the next bed who was gasping and turning blue. Nelson said: "Get me a bag and some oxygen," and soon had the little victim "pinked up." The bag was the simplest and most-used respiratory support. The doctor or nurse simply took a rubber bag, let it expand and then squeezed air into the patient's lungs. The anaesthesiologist makes an intensive study of controlled breathing. From this incident Nelson got caught up in developing a program to keep the patients alive, and his partners covered his responsibilities in the operating room and supported him so he could stay with it till the following spring.

The Allin Clinic supported Russ Taylor for nine months though he'd only recently been employed to handle the clinic's contract with the new Canadian Chemical plant in Clover Bar. The CCL employees were in the group being hit hardest by respiratory polio. Russ decided he'd have to join the struggle in the isolation ward, but first he was encouraged to go to Minneapolis for two weeks and work in a hospital which was using the Sister Kenny method. As Nelson recalls: "There were too many things we didn't know about keeping people alive."

In the Royal Alex Russ saw the mysterious iron lung unveiled and in action. Back in the '30s he had been in isolation with scarlet fever and he and the other kids were fascinated by the machine which was kept in a corner, draped in sheets and shrouded in mystery. It was a gift from Lord Nuffield, the English industrial magnate, who had presented one to every hospital of a certain size in the British Empire. Now it was in use along with many others. The Royal Canadian Air Force was on voluntary call to fly anywhere in North America where a spare iron lung was available.

Eventually there were 33 and the need was so acute that two little children were in one lung, feet to feet. A newer "tank" respirator had improved on the Nuffield design but worked on the same principle.

The third man in was Frank Elliott. As Nelson says: "The University Hospital was shipping patients in. Frank saw what was happening. He offered to spell us off. More than that, he brought us the skills of an internist. Internal problems were getting away from us — anaemia, swollen livers, hearts. Frank had skills in that area."

Nelson continues: "One day Frank said: 'There are still some things we aren't doing right. We don't know if we're running these iron lungs fast enough. We need a physiologist to tell us.' So Frank brought Harold Rice over. Harold was not a practicing doctor then although he later became one. He was a professor of Physiology in the Department of Medicine. Harold studied our problem and brought us back a simple device incorporating a Van Slyke apparatus. We took samples of breath in glass syringes and read percentages of oxygen and carbon dioxide. The system needs both, ordinarily the body regulates the balance but a person in an iron lung can't do this because the machine takes over. Since then biomedical science has developed a procedure to make this measurement and it's so routine no one even thinks about it. But Harold had to think about it very hard, and his device gave us the answer: 'Are we breathing them too fast or too slow?' "

Brian Sproule sees Harold's invention on another level. On the higher level it was a stimulus to a physiological approach to the management of breathing disorders. Readings of carbon dioxide were more than a series of graphs on a smoked drum. It was important to translate these passive readings into dynamic therapeutic intervention.

Frank Elliott sees the crisis centre itself on another level — as the first intensive care unit. This notion is seconded by Russ Taylor, who points to the minute-by-minute monitoring and the one-to-one attention. And by Nelson Nix who points to the team concept and the fact that patients were under care of the team rather than the doctors who brought them in.

Night and day the iron lungs pumped. Nelson likens the sound to his mother's old Beatty washing machine, with an overriding hum and sort of shush-wop, shush-wop as the bellows reversed pressure, depressing the patient's chest and then letting it expand so his lungs could draw in the air of the room. The patient needed a collar around his neck and this was a problem if he'd had a tracheotomy, an incision in the windpipe into which a breathing tube was inserted. About 150 of those who went through required this life-saving operation. The noise of the iron lungs was wearing, but there was pandemonium early one evening when the noise abruptly died. There'd been a power failure. But reaction was instantaneous. Someone went rushing across the yard to the nurses residence and the nurses, including many students, came running. They disengaged the iron bars attached to the tanks and pumped manually to enable the patients to breathe. Two went blue, but were revived, and after half an hour the current suddenly came back again. But that wasn't the end. The next afternoon Bob Rawlings, the Alex's chief engineer, motioned Nelson to come look through the window. Out in the yard was a big diesel generator for standby power.

There was hardly a department or specialty of the Royal Alex that wasn't involved. The action took place there and is part of the history of that institution so I've limited this account to the highlights. However there's a full story which should be told, giving credit to all who participated. It would include the details of the trip to Consort to bring in a four-year-old boy in an iron lung. "Smitty," the founder of Smith's ambulance, volunteered to drive. On the way back a service station operator in Camrose refused to put gas in the ambulance because he might be fined under the Wednesday-closing bylaw. And at the other extreme were the three Grande Prairie residents who died trying to

*The Polio Wing at night. Occupied in 1956-57 it demonstrates a popular architectural trend — towards the glass box. Sheets of windows promise sunlight for convalescents. The provincial cancer clinic is in the annex, formerly the maternity ward. It looks frail but has a massive core of concrete to shield radiation equipment. When the time comes for this building to go the stubborn core will give the wrecking ball a hilarious tussle*

give a young man a last chance at life in the Royal Alex. On a stormy winter afternoon they set out to fly — the pilot, the patient, the doctor and a nurse. They never arrived. The plane went down in tall timber near Whitecourt and wasn't found for years.

These are all incidents which belong in a full account of the episode which had an important bearing on our hospital. As Frank Elliott says: "When the patients started to recover we pressed for a rehabilitation unit."

They didn't have to press long. On November 26 "Sandy" Somerville, the Deputy Minister of Health, brought to our board notice of the government's intention to provide the hospital with a "polio services wing" for 200 patients.

As you might expect, the board was not about to turn down a free building, but there was a concern, and the concern shows how hospital administrators still regarded the student nurses. The board was told that the size of the training school — how Helen Penhale and her crowd hated that term "training school" — would have to be increased by 25 percent.

The history of the '20s repeated itself — on a magnified scale. In 1927-28 the Department of Public Works put up a wooden hut costing $20,000 in two months to house 60 polio patients. In 1954 that wooden hut was demolished and in its place DPW began raising a six-storey addition of steel-and-brick, costing several millions, intended for 160 polio cases and 100 paediatric beds. But the polio wing wouldn't be ready for two years. Something had to be done immediately to start a rehabilitation program in the existing hospital.

In March a decision was made that 19 patients in respirators should be brought over from the Royal Alex as quickly as possible. Since an iron lung requires two to three times the space of an ordinary bed there was a furious assault on Station 32 (on the third level of the 1930 wing) to remodel it for the purpose. Two of our nurses, Marnie McKay and Betty George, were sent away to gather expertise in polio rehabilitation, but had only two weeks to do it. They went to Winnipeg and observed and helped out at Princess Elizabeth Hospital. Two residents moved into a room right on the ward. Al Mooney still holds the distinction of being the only resident in our history with eight children. (He'd come back to specialize in surgery.) Brian Sproule was a bachelor but that lasted only until he married Nurse McKay. All involved speak warmly of the efforts of Johnny Beaton, our purchasing agent, who managed to provide whatever was needed, though Johnny disclaims doing anything but his job and recalls the period as "the time Frank Elliott worked himself half to death." Certainly everyone, staff and patients, were heartened by the example of Donna Graham, a nurse who had lived in the hospital since she'd been crippled by polio in the late '40s. Though a quadriplegic, Donna learned to paint again holding the brush in her mouth; her lively pictures are treasured by those who have them.

In the summer of 1954, while workmen were busy raising the six-storey addition that was to be the polio rehabilitation wing, there occurred an event which invalidated all predictions about polio. The Salk Vaccine arrived in Alberta. It came then in limited quantities. The National Foundation for Poliomyelitis Research (of New York) which had supported the work of Dr. Jonas

Salk offered it for a field trial in Alberta. 16,167 children participated, half receiving the vaccine. In 1955, as construction neared completion, Salk vaccine was given to 48,984 children and adults and polio declined to 224 cases. Although there was a flareup in 1960 with 103 cases polio ceased to be a worry.

To me the Salk vaccine seemed a real revolution in prevention. I'd first seen polio as an intern in Winnipeg when all we could do was put patients in bed, put hot packs on and pray there wouldn't be too much residual paralysis. Many years later I met Dr. Salk on a visit to Israel, where he was visiting professor at a hospital supported by the Bronfman family of Montreal. Like many

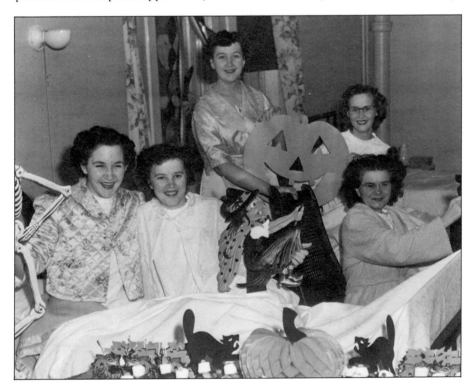

*Hallowe'en comes to the Polio
Wing. Tricks may be limited
but treats abound*

"giants" he was a very ordinary little fellow. I was pleased to tell him that my wife Margaret and I had taken our Salk vaccine before leaving.

For many patients who came to Station 32 in the mid-50s, the University Hospital had to become a permanent home. They became a community within the hospital and theirs is a heartening story which belongs in a later chapter. No more than 50 beds in the big addition were ever occupied by polio patients, though I'm told the electrical outlets in the basements still say *Polio Wing.* However, the addition gave us a total bed count of 1,130 and a chance to create a new main entrance facing south, which was still the chief entryway as this was written.

Fortunately there is a human interest note on which to end a chapter containing so much tragedy. It involved a *Journal* carrier boy. One day, while the polio wing was under construction, he came riding his bike along the jobsite fence as he usually did, when a "cute chick" started crossing the street. She was one of those ladies beloved of poets who go through life causing havoc unaware. The *Journal* boy became so intent on observing the cute chick that he pedalled headlong into a barricade and landed in a bruised heap among concrete blocks and other hard things. The accident made him a patient in our emergency clinic where his wounds were attended to, and Gordon Miniely didn't forget the kind, efficient treatment. Some 25 years later, as Minister of Hospitals and Medical Care he turned the sod for the Walter C. Mackenzie Health Sciences Centre.

# Chapter 17

# 1952—1961
*Money as a Blessing*

The polio epidemic dominated public attention starting the next period of hospital history, a period not so easy of demarcation as others. It doesn't have sharp clean edges like "the war" or the "post-war." So I've chosen to make it 1952 to 1961. I believe there are valid historical reasons for concluding at 1961 — and one compelling personal reason. Shortly after, I gave up an active role in the affairs of the University Hospital and my subsequent knowledge is hearsay — though I'm always glad to hear news of my old hospital.

In 1952 a significant change began to be noticeable. Before that I think it was possible to see the entire hospital at a glance. A shrewd, well-informed glance, of course, but then this began to change. Activity in the hospital started to expand in so many directions — and on so many levels, as Brian Sproule has pointed out — that a single view could no longer cover it all.

In the post-war the place was growing dramatically, but it was still small enough, as Marnie Sproule recalls, that when there was a party everybody went, and Walter Mackenzie would play the drums and "Cappy" Kidd the saxophone. By 1961 this was no longer the case. The intimacy had lost out to what is known as "the numbers game."

In 1952 we had some 700 employees; by the end of 1961 we had run the number up to 1,485. Some of the expansion reflected growth in the community and the university. The population of Edmonton grew from 160,000 to 276,000. The registration of medical students increased from 233 to 283. We started the period with a medical staff of 70 plus 41 house staff and finished with a staff of 169 and 78 residents. The cost of a day of patient care rose from $11.39 to $20.64. The number of patients on an average day rose from 557 to 958. The average stay of a patient increased slightly — 13.6 days to 15.3. However, I'm bound to point out that my department of obstetrics was doing its best to reverse that trend. It had once been the custom that when a woman had a baby she'd get up on the twelfth day, hand the baby to somebody and totter out of the hospital with her husband supporting one arm and a nurse the other. By '61 the mother was leaving after five days, holding her baby with one arm and supporting her husband with the other.

The cost of running the hospital went up rather steeply we thought — from $2.27 million to $6.65 million. Mind you, as this was written in 1986 the hospital was announcing that it had "held the line" at $193 million so perhaps we weren't on such a high mountain after all. But from '52 to '61 there were some interesting shifts in the way the dollars were spent. In 1952 salaries took 54 cents of each dollar; by 1961 wages took 70 cents. Maintenance and utilities remained at about 5 cents. Supplies dropped from 18 cents to 14. Food costs, which had accounted for 15½ cents, took only 8. But one item disappeared altogether. In 1952 there was a provision of 5½ cents for bad debts. There is no such category in the balance sheet for 1961.

That was the result of a revolutionary change on the other side of the ledger, the revenue side. Bad debts — which had plagued the hospital since the beginning — disappeared as by a magic wand. The wand was the federal-provincial health plan, which took effect on April 1 1958.

This scheme had dramatic results for all hospitals across the country, and it was hatched in the nation's capital. Every so often Ottawa says: "I must spread out my arms; I must gather in all my children." It began in 1947 when Mackenzie King announced a scheme for hospital construction grants — Ottawa to match the provinces. Then in 1950 Alberta got into operating costs. A levy of four mills was added automatically to all municipal taxes. The money went into general revenue and was disbursed to hospitals by the province.

Then Ottawa proposed the Hospital and Insurance Diagnosis Act (National). Ottawa would share with the provinces "approved costs" of hospital operation. Essentially it was a 50/50 split, with "have" provinces getting something less than 50 percent and "have-nots" something more. Alberta, at this stage, was about halfway between. To become operative the act had to be accepted by six provinces containing more than half the population. In the main, the provinces rather liked the scheme. On the one hand it appeared to offer more money. On the other hand it appeared to offer a chance to control the operating costs of hospitals, something which was beginning to cause concern. Here in Alberta, two accountants from the Department of Health, Doug Campbell and Bert Foster, were set to work to devise a plan on which both levels of government could sign an agreement.

The Alberta version called on four parties to contribute: the patient, the owner of the hospital — in our case the university, the provincial government, and the federal government.

When the agreement came into effect a dramatic change occurred in the makeup of the revenue dollar. So let's take a 1957 revenue dollar and a '58 model and see how they differ.

In 1957 the patient contributed 23 cents of that dollar, under Alberta's celebrated "dollar-a-day" hospital schemes. If you think of a hospital as a hotel he'd paid one dollar for room and board and a second for hotel services. With the change he paid an admission fee of five dollars for care in a public ward, with the option of paying extra for private or semi-private accommodation. As a result the 1958 dollar contains only four cents collected from the patient.

Blue Cross, the Workmen's Compensation Board and private insurance plans were still major contributors, unchanged at 20 percent.

The men in the Mewburn pavilion were still a direct responsibility of the Department of Veterans Affairs and DVA's contribution dipped marginally from

16 cents to 13.

Then we come to the big 60 cents of the federal-provincial scheme. It was achieved in part by absorbing two existing plans. In 1957 Alberta's provincial-municipal plan provided 13 cents of the income dollar for the purchase and replacement of capital equipment. The province also made direct grants based on actual patient days. These grants amounted to 24 cents. They were also absorbed, except for an important three cents to cover costs excluded from the agreement with Ottawa — for service to outpatients and mental patients. The balance of the 60 cents came from the federal treasury.

Like most grand designs the federal-provincial agreement had side effects which weren't in the calculations. George Sherwood points to one, and George was certainly in the right spot to observe. He had been named Credit Manager during the war, when total deafness in one ear kept him out of the army, and in this job he negotiated with patients over their accounts. George says:

"Any significant illness would saddle a person with a substantial account — say $2,000. That was an awfully big amount. We tried to recover as much as possible. We did everything to arrange some kind of settlement. We took wage assignments, we took chattel mortgages, vegetables, eggs, chickens, sides of beef. Sick people did everything they could to avoid coming in and then did their best to get out as soon as possible. The plan made a drastic change in the way people viewed hospitals. They weren't afraid to come in when they should or stay as long as they should. Some experts compared statistics with previous years and thought hospitals were being over-utilized. The change in public attitude was a hidden cost of the agreement, and not very well hidden either."

When the new order took effect on April 1 1958 the University Hospital became a little more like a regular hospital. We adopted the calendar year rather than the fiscal year for accounts and records so the Alberta Department of Health could obtain statistics to compare with other hospitals. Then we adopted a common language for statistics and a new glossary of terms proposed by the department. As Jack Ellison says: "It was very democratic. We didn't have to use the department's terms but unless we presented our invoices in the common language the department couldn't pay us." Jack Ellison was certainly in an ideal position to observe the changeover. He was our chief accountant and spent more than 30 years with the hospital, retiring as financial comptroller and acting administrator of the Aberhart wing. Jack continues: "On the other hand, accounting procedures were simplified. In billing the government we no longer had to break down the figures so finely. We didn't have to account for the amount of gauze used in a gall bladder operation."

Mind you, although we became more like other hospitals we were still unique in being the only teaching hospital in Alberta. A teaching hospital costs more. Medical students need teachers and facilities which have to be reckoned in dollars, but the needs of the patient are even more costly. A patient referred to a teaching hospital needs medical attention of a specialist doctor. He also needs more nursing attention than would be available in a local hospital — perhaps a constant vigil. To treat such a patient the attending physician needs more diagnostic and clinical laboratory information. To the credit of the provincial government it recognized the differential. Ken Thomson points to discussions with Ottawa over the Laboratory and Radiological Services Act of 1957. Under that plan Ottawa made grants to provinces for those services, but the plan didn't recognize that in a teaching hospital there is a higher percentage of diagnostic investigative tests than in a regular hospital. The Alberta government did and made representations — without apparent success. In preparing our estimates for the coming year we put in for more than other hospitals.

While it was recognized that a teaching hospital should cost more, just how much was an important question. The hospital sent Jack Ellison to visit others and Jack found that it was 40 percent. Coincidentally the accountants at the Department of Health made a survey and came up with the same figure. And that was important because they approved our costs.

Since that time the teaching program has been enhanced by the involvement of other major hospitals in Edmonton, but in the 1950s we were in it by ourselves.

The government gave us new legislation to start 1952 and this period of our history. An Act Respecting the University of Alberta Hospital (Statutes of Alberta 1952 Chapter 99) replaced the much-amended act which had been in force since 1929. The new act reaffirmed the amendments of the previous year, in which we had contended successfully that the board should remain a balance of members appointed from our side of the river and the government's, and that our board would make appointments to the medical staff of the hospital and approve appointments to the Faculty of Medicine in the university. But there was a joker in the new deck that was dealt us.

The act created a position of Business Administrator in the hospital, the holder of the position to be appointed by the provincial cabinet. The administrator would be secretary to the hospital board, a position held since the beginning by the superintendent, and "all the requirements of the hospital necessitating an expenditure of money, or a charge upon the credit of the board or the hospital, shall be requisitioned through the business administrator, and where he approves of the expenditure or charge, shall be purchased or ordered by him."

The functions of the business administrator were carved out of responsibilities held since 1922 by the superintendent, who remained in charge of matters medical. I don't suppose the change sat too well with Angus McGugan, who had managed finances very shrewdly. As the new act was going through the legislature we posted a revenue surplus of $237,000, the result of several years in the black. Hospitals were allowed to retain surpluses then, which seemed only fair when they'd been obliged to retain deficits. Angus managed to put aside something in the neighbourhood of $1,000,000 to grubstake a clinical research program in the medical specialties, which I'll describe in the next chapter.

The act set up a principle of "dual administration" which was unique at the time and has remained so ever since because no one cared to copy it. As you can see, there was a potential for many winters of discontent (and summers too), but dual administration worked better than it should have, principally because the cabinet didn't send in an administrator from outside. The appointment went to Reg Adshead (by Order-in-Council 852/52) who had been around the hospital on the financial side since 1928. Reg had been Treasurer, Business Manager, for the previous three years Executive Assistant to Angus McGugan, and had played an important part in the evolution of our system.

Under the act both Reg and Angus were members of the board to which they reported, another novel twist. Now the chairman of our board was supposed to reflect the community and in 1954 we got a chairman who reflected the fact that Edmonton had become an oil capital. Before this our chairmen had been a wholesale grocer (Harry Cooper), a retired banker (G.R.F. Kirkpatrick), an insurance man (Ray Staples), a chartered accountant (Winslow Hamilton) and another retired banker (James Walker). When ill health forced him to resign we got an oil man. Don Avison was the top man locally with the Imperial Oil Company. To be effective our board chairman has to be an independent soul and that could surely be said of Don, who served 10 years. I enjoyed playing golf with him, a game his ancestors invented, though whether they should receive praise or condemnation for their ingenuity is a moot point. Don had a broad Scots accent, he certainly had a broad silhouette when crouched over a ball on the putting green, and he had a very broad sense of humour which a chairman needs for survival. I've mentioned already how he and Walter Mackenzie and Ingar Telmer would go on diets together competing for a trophy they put up. While I wouldn't say Don Avison was a brilliant man he had a broad vision of the hospital and its special role. And he understood what was going on. The board met once a month and in between Don liked to call around and visit the departments. Asking questions was his forté. One of his favourite questions was: "And how's the morale of the staff?"

The board retained its traditional balance. Three members continued to come from across the river, and although this government presence should be noted, it should not be laboured. The government may have intended only that we get their signals, but it was a two-way street. They got our viewpoints too. "Sandy" Somerville, the Deputy Minister of Health, served the whole time. John McGilp, Supervisor of Hospitals in the department, was succeeded in 1954 by Ed Mather, a senior administrator. F.G. Stewart, the treasury representative, was followed in 1958 by J.M. Currie.

From our side of the river, the president of the university continued to have a seat on the board. When Andrew Stewart went to Ottawa in 1958 to head the Board of Broadcast Governors he handed over to Walter Johns. The Dean of Medicine was still a member, and in 1958 John Scott concluded his long service and was succeeded by Walter Mackenzie. Our third member, like the chairman, was drawn from the community. Winslow Hamilton, who was to die so tragically when an airliner returning from the Grey Cup struck a mountain, left in 1954 and was replaced by Bill Dick. Bill was a long-time Edmonton coal man and fundraiser for many causes such as the Boy Scouts, the Red Cross and the St. John Ambulance. Bill died three years later and Elmer Roper was persuaded to join the board, bringing his experience as leader of the opposition in the legislature and alderman of the city of Edmonton.

The hospital administration developed an unusually large presence on the board. In 1952, Business Administrator Reg Adshead was added, joining super-intendent Angus McGugan. Then the assistant medical superintendent was added. Crosby Johnston, known as "Cob," held the position through 1952-56. "Cob" was very close to the institution and the staff. He'd met many of them in the late '30s when he was a medical student and intern. He came out of war service with TB which held up his career for 13 months. He was in San Francisco when he came to join us in November '52. "Cob" was a very practical fellow. He supported the orderlies, whom he admired very much, and took the lead in increasing their functions in the nursing team — taking pulse and blood pressure. When the orderlies were able to form their own association they made "Cob" an honorary member and sent him a pin which he still treasures. "Cob" helped start the hospital newsletter, which "Slim" Lefebvre put out. "Cob" wanted to call it *The Twelfth Street Rag* — for the street which ran past, but was prevailed upon to settle for *Twelfth Street Beat*, which is still in existence, outliving such publications as the *Saturday Evening Post*. Late in '56 he went south to be administrator of the Calgary General, and the board began advertis-ing for a replacement.

Early the next summer Angus McGugan phoned one day to arrange a golf game so I could meet him. Bernie Snell was a product of the country which invented golf, though as I say it's yet to be established that the sport has been a benefit to suffering humanity. We played at the Mayfair and were to meet many times over the years as Bernie rose to the top of the ladder and spent 18 years as president of the University Hospital. Bernie brought some interesting experi-ence. He'd been at sea during the war as ship's surgeon with the merchant fleet. He had a master's degree in hospital administration from the University of Edinburgh. And for a specialty he told us cheerfully he had chosen infectious diseases, the only specialty of all which seemed destined for oblivion. He was working in Sheffield when he read our ad in the British Medical Journal. At this stage there wasn't a Canadian available with the qualifications. He was inter-viewed in London by one of our professors on sabbatical, and paid his own way to Edmonton. Bernie says it didn't occur to him to ask for assistance and I'm sure it didn't occur to Angus to offer any.

We were interested in his first impressions as a newcomer, and one thing that impressed him was the newness of so much of the hospital. In the old country anything built after the first war was considered new. He was impressed by the number of sophisticated services we offered, and surprised by the peculiar gaps — no virological diagnostic centre and no program for care of spinal injuries. But he quickly spotted the fact that things can't all be developing at the same rate.

We laughed about his invitation to be shown "the social fabric of Edmon-ton." The invitation was extended by one of our British doctors who couldn't adjust to life in the colonies and stayed long enough only to be a footnote in the history. He took Bernie on a tour of beer parlors. There were no lounges yet, beer-only was for sale and men and women drank in separate rooms. Everywhere they went they found men with heads hanging unconscious over their beer and the waiters coming around setting down more glasses — two at a time. "There," said his disenchanted guide, "is the social fabric of Edmonton."

As a member of our hospital board Bernie was impressed by the board's independence and authority, the things it could do on its own. He'd just come from Britain where those freedoms were buried under the National Health Act. However, he now fears that in the long years since, Alberta has gone the same route.

As a member of the administration he was frank about his opinion of "dual administration." With his Scots candor Bernie described it as "a two-headed monster." Bernie noted that the legislation was vague on where certain pieces should fit — under medical or administration — and nursing was one of them. However, Jeanie Clark recalls: "For us it was not a problem. Clinically we related to Dr. McGugan and we met him once a week on Mondays. If our plans involved staffing or expenditure we met with Reg. All three of us had known Reg from our student days and if we had a justifiable story to tell and had our facts we didn't have a problem."

By *all three of us* Jeanie meant herself, as Director of Nursing, and her associates: Jean Lees, in charge of nursing service, and Ruth Thompson, in charge of education. The triumvirate was established on May 1 1954, when the hospital regained control of its own School of Nursing from the university, ending the Seven Years War between Angus McGugan and those who thought university control was a good idea.

But there was a sad note to the year. Jeanie Clark became Director of Nursing during the final illness of Helen Peters, who passed on after 27 years in the hospital. Helen faced her affliction with composure. As Garnet Hollinshead, who knew her from the accounting office, said: "I liked Miss Peters. She gave an appearance of being stiff and formal, but she was anything but. When you got to know her she was a good sport. She was of the old school, very strict with her nurses but fair and nice."

Jean Lees was a true Scot, literally "year in and year out." On New Year's Eve Jean ensured that all bills were paid and she washed and pressed the clothes she had worn that day so the New Year would start in the Scottish tradition with absolutely no business laid over. Jean graduated from our hospital in 1929 and went on staff for 10 years, serving as charge nurse in paediatrics, then general surgery and orthopaedics. She went to the University of Toronto for a certificate in teaching and administration. Early in the war she was matron at Medicine Hat General, the first municipal hospital in Alberta. Then she spent four years in the army medical corps, coming home with the Royal Red Cross Medal, First Class. Jean returned to her alma mater in 1947 as night supervisor at the Mewburn, and then was appointed Associate Director, Nursing Services, a position she held until retiring in 1965.

While Jean Lees was a product of our hospital's diploma program, Ruth

Thompson took a BSc through the University. This meant a year of arts, three years in the hospital, then a final year back on campus. But by 1929, when Ruth was ready for her final year the U of A had abandoned the program because of the cost and she had to finish at Toronto. That seemed to establish a travel pattern. She was instructor at the Lamont General, matron of Belleville General in Ontario, and spent much of the war at sea as a nursing sister on hospital ships. She returned to Edmonton as Administrative Assistant at the Mewburn, then went for a master's at Columbia, and was Director of Nursing at Victoria General in London, Ontario, when the call came to rejoin her alma mater as Associate

*Helen Peters*

*Ruth Thompson*

Director in charge of Education. She had good rapport with the nursing instructors (of whom there were a dozen and growing) and until she retired in 1972 was chairman of many committees around the hospital, both business and social.

Like Ruth Thompson, Jeanie Clark followed the BSc program, but financial conditions had improved at the University of Alberta and she was able to complete the course here, graduating in 1941 in public health nursing. She worked in High River, Calgary, with the AARN, earned a master's degree in public health from Johns Hopkins, had experience with the Alberta govern-

Jeanie Clark

Jean Lees

ment, and had just completed a year of midwifery in Edinburgh, Scotland, when the call came to rejoin her alma mater as assistant to Helen Peters.

We were all pleased to have three of our graduates in charge when the hospital regained custody of the diploma program. Hospitals liked to hire their own people for the sake of employment alone and when they could be employed for the top jobs it showed that the institution had the right stuff. From a purely practical point of view your own people had experience and understanding of the way things were done in the hospital.

Mind you, breaking up with the university took some un-doing. There had to be a rather complicated agreement. Perhaps the main points were that entrance requirements should remain the same as for the university's BSc program, that is, high school matriculation, and that courses in the diploma program should be similar to the BSc though they needn't be identical. We also set up an advisory board for the hospital school, a body of 12 well-wishers including myself. The Director of Nursing was Chairman and we met about three times a year, usually when a class was coming up to graduation, to discuss standards for promotion and admission, and handling the degree students who still took service training in the hospital.

The main hospital board then established a unique relationship with the nursing sector of the hospital. Once a quarter, the Director of Nursing met with Don Avison and company and made a direct report of activities in the nursing area. This one-of-a-kind arrangement apparently originated with "Sandy" Somerville. I suppose it was an attempt to compensate for the loose terms of the provincial act which left nursing partly in the medical area, partly in administration. Anyway, it worked well because the personalities involved knew and understood each other and the hospital.

The students lived in their own residence across 114th Street, and a glance at this neat brick building opened in 1948 would assure the passerby that student lifestyle was nothing like the old days.

Mind you, the only students who could fully appreciate the new lifestyle were those who had experienced the old. Two such were Muriel Gibson (Gillespie) and Margaret Exham (Aistrope) who had been in training from 1946-49 when they moved from St. Stephen's College to the residence. They were impressed at finding everything so new and shiny, and proud to be in the best residence on campus. The floors didn't creak. Neither did the box-spring mattresses, which were brand new like the desk and dresser which two students shared. When a boyfriend called (and the boys seemed to find the nurses wherever they went), it was no longer necessary for him to stand at the front door while someone yelled up the stairs. A receptionist at the main entrance called the young lady through an intercom which ran to each room, and the lad waited in a parlor with comfortable chairs and a fireplace. The girls could stay out a half-hour later — till 10:30 — because there was no late bus in the area. And when going on duty the tunnel made a great difference. No more bundling up on cold mornings. The tunnel ran to the main hospital. According to legend it was conceived originally for steampipes and enlarged for pedestrians. Mind you, most of the students came from small towns or farms where a pedestrian tunnel would be considered something of a marvel. At least 75 percent were from outside Edmonton. Living in the atmosphere of a boarding school for three years the classes were very close, and have remained so in the years since.

Living in residence was compulsory then, though it's changed now. Each year students marked their progress by moving to the next floor up, and progress was also reflected in their uniforms. A patient who understood the system could tell at a feverish glance what level of experience he was getting at the bedside. Students began the first year in a blue dress (with a white apron) and black shoes

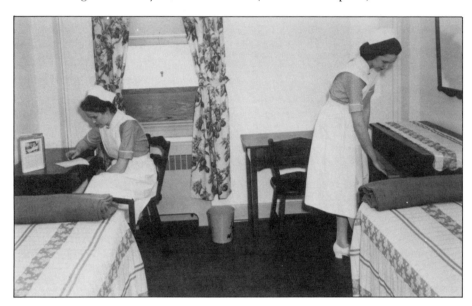

*1950s lifestyle for the student nurse. It wasn't always like this.*

and stockings. If they passed the six-month probation period a cap and bib were added. In the second year they were awarded a pink uniform — with the initials UAH woven into the cloth — and at the end of that year they got rid of the black shoes and stockings. By tradition the black objects were tied together in a long chain and chucked off the High Level Bridge. As seniors they wore white shoes and stockings and in the final six months, as a badge of rank, were awarded long white cuffs. (Cufflinks were a favoured graduation present.) Many strictures covered the wearing of the uniform — de-regulation had not yet reached the nursing industry. The girls were forbidden to wear the bib or apron while

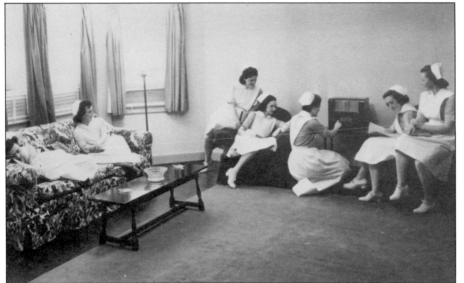

*Before television the most interesting entertainment comes via radio, though apparently not interesting enough to keep all the girls awake*

smoking. And the uniform was never to be worn to the Varsity Tuck Shop, still a focus of campus life.

Jeanie Clark makes an important observation about the changing mood of the '50s. The strong role models of an earlier time, the Mrs. Porritts who terrorized students on the second floor, were fast disappearing. Staff nurses were melding into a pattern. Many were recent graduates, not much older than the girls they were instructing and supervising.

The concept of the nursing team was also gaining headway. Just how much becomes clear when you line up the staff numbers at the start and close of the period. The following box score is much like a picture:

|  | 1952 | 1961 |
|---|---|---|
| Graduate Nurses | 143 | 342 |
| Students | 286 | 385 |
| Certified Nursing Aides | 48 | 109 |
| Ward Aides | 81 | 118 |
| Orderlies | 37 | 81 |
| Ward Clerks | 10 | 27 |
|  | 315 | 1062 |

The personnel of the nursing teams increased some 240 percent while the number of patients increased only 40 percent. In this differential are many factors. Shorter work hours, emphasis on education rather than service, and complexity brought about by technology and specialization.

When we'd completed an apartment house for our nurses we proceeded to do the same for our interns and residents. Like the nurses they were in quarters all over the place and their number was doubling. Something had to be done. Most were living on the top floor of the pavilion built for convalescing soldiers of the first war, and one bunch was directly over an operating room. Six were living in "the cottage," off the covered walkway from the original hospital. And in a shack on the roof of the original a married intern was living with his bride.

The problem was brought to formal notice of the board in February 1955 in a presentation from the late Ted Donald, chairman of the intern committee. The board proclaimed itself sympathetic.

A few years earlier the medical advisory committee had rejected a proposal to increase the interns' stipend $25 a month, accepting the argument of "Hep" Hepburn, who reasoned that the interns were carefree bachelors who would only spend it in the beer parlor of the Lincoln Hotel. But by the mid-50s wedding bells had played havoc with the tradition of sneaking nurses up the back stairs for parties. Half the once-carefree young rascals were married.

That was a significant development dictating action on housing. But the imperative was a change in the entire system of residency. In the old days, before specialization, the fledgling doctor would spend a year in a rotating internship (later two) before going out into the world to do general practice. But with the Marshall Plan, and other postgraduate programs, the system became more complicated. A man would spend a year in the standard internship and then another two or three years in residence, developing his specialty. The doctors needed the experience in their specialty, and the hospital needed their services to maintain the teaching program in a specializing age.

In 1957 a report prepared for the provincial cabinet emphasized this point. "If the University Hospital is going to maintain its position with the advanced teaching hospitals of the country . . . an increased house staff is essential." (For good measure the report mentioned keeping ahead of the Soviet Union.) In 1951-52 we had an establishment of 35 interns and six "residents" doing advanced work. For the 1958-59 year the administration and medical advisory board recommended an establishment of 30 interns and residents to the number of 44.

A year in cramped bachelor quarters above an operating room was one thing, but three or four was another. The hospital pressed for the higher establishment and a new residence to accommodate the "house" staff. Public works designed the building and it opened in June 1958.

It faced the nurses residence across 114th Street, and contained married quarters in which a couple and one child could live. (Today it's a hostel, for country people who come in for tests but don't require admission to the hospital.)

In the new residence bachelors no longer had to share rooms, and the accommodation was altogether so much finer that the administration was emboldened to charge residents $10 a month. For board they could continue to have a meal ticket for the cafeteria (like the student nurses) or take $30 cash. There'd been a fundamental change from tradition in the cafeteria. Tradition was shattered as of April 3 1957 when a new dining hall was opened in the lower floor of the polio wing and the Red Cross Hut-cum-diner converted to a badly-needed store room. Meals went on a cash basis. Coffee was 5 cents. Breakfast 35 cents. Noon dinner 60. Evening supper 55. Night supper 60 cents. To put these prices in perspective, the base salary for a graduate staff nurse was $275 and the hospital was buying the handsome home of Edmonton's late Mayor John Fry (just across 112th Street) for $15,000. Fanny Hooson was still in charge of the night kitchen and Fanny didn't approve of charging. However she left the cash drawer open for those who did.

As Sam Callan relates, the staff, represented by Chapter 23 of the Civil Service Association, had voted in favour of the arrangement. That was because of a change in income tax law. From time out of memory the hospital had provided meals which were reckoned to be part compensation for working there. But in the mid-50s the national revenue service announced that the meals had a cash value which must be reported as income. There was to be no free lunch, no tax-free lunch anyway. So the employees negotiated to have the money added to their salaries. They weren't permitted to bring brown-bag lunches into the new premises, but so many could see the economic advantages that an auxiliary cafeteria was opened in the Mewburn where they could take a brown-bag from home and buy coffee and dessert.

The CSA branch carried on negotiations with Reg Adshead, the business administrator of the hospital, but it was not yet a true union. Johnny Pedden has pointed this out, and he was a close observer. Johnny came to the hospital in 1949 as accountant in the payroll section, when personnel work was thought of as a function of payroll. By 1959, when payroll had come to be viewed as a

1958 — hospital administrators of the old school wouldn't approve of this scene. Interns and residents move out of their rabbit warrens to a new "house staff" residence on 114th Street. Eventually they will be paid enough to set up their own homes and the residence will become a hostel for patients who don't require a hospital bed

function of personnel, he was appointed the first personnel officer.

Johnny says no one was sure whether the Public Service Act or the Alberta Labour Act (or any act) applied to University Hospital employees. Angus McGugan, who had encouraged the formation of Chapter 23, saw it as a means of communication. The chapter made presentations, but decisions were made unilaterally by the administration and board with no further steps.

Non-medical employees doubled in number to 1,500 and very early in his job Johnny Pedden noted significant changes. There had been a time when names on the payroll were almost exclusively from the British Isles, and the

*Three Scots share a joke. From the left are Medical Superintendent Angus McGugan, his assistant Bernard Snell and Bob Sherriff, the man responsible for the beautiful grounds*

names indicated further whether the employee would want Christmas off or Hogmanay. With the influx of newcomers from Europe, Dutch, German and Italian names appeared. As Johnny says: "They were called Displaced Persons and they were displaced in another way. Most had done white-collar jobs in their native surroundings. When they landed in Canada they came into service jobs in hospitals — janitors, dietary workers, ward aides. Their children took these jobs too. But with knowledge of the language and familiarity with the new country they quickly reverted to their previous occupations. The newcomers took part in the high turnover too. The annual turnover rate was around 50

*Sam Callan and the staff of the mail room*

*Dan Schneider ran the laundry*

percent."

Construction crews from the Department of Public Works seemed always to be busy somewhere on the grounds — and when you see an aerial view of the time we seemed to have unlimited open space for Bob Sherriff's gardeners to keep green and trim. Eventually DPW turned its attention to our need for laundry. 1952 was the last year laundry activity was measured by the piece — 3,685,000 pieces of which 10 percent were uniforms and gowns to be pressed. The next year, when productivity was reckoned by weight the laundry processed 2.3 million pounds, and in 1961, with use of a brand new plant, the output nudged 6 million pounds.

The manager of the service in this period, as he had been since 1936, was Dan Schneider. Dan was a good friend of mine, and of everyone in the hospital, including his own staff. Dan was active in employee affairs, the United Way, his church, and he and his wife liked to travel.

Dan and I once collaborated on a paper for the Alberta Medical Association. For some reason they asked me to give a talk on "The Value of a Laundry to a Hospital." I brought out the value of our laundry during the staphylococcus outbreak of the early '50s. It was noticed first in the obstetrical department when women who had been delivered developed breast abscesses. Staph infections had to be prevented mainly by old-fashioned scrubbing and cleanliness and the laundry put in special measures to help. I was also able to tell the AMA about the praise Dan's operation had received from the American Institute of Laundering.

This Institute had an interesting gauge for quality. It sent out five samples of things which were to be laundered 20 times and then returned for testing. The Institute reported that in our plant the fabrics lost only five percent of tensile strength and whiteness retention was 99 percent. (95 percent was "excellent".) In a hospital whiteness was rated perhaps even closer to godliness than cleanliness. And to top it all, among large hospitals, Dan's laundry had the lowest unit cost per rated day.

The Scots on our board had to appreciate that touch. The Institute's praise was bestowed in 1958 and Dan was soon engaged in the design of an entirely new laundry facility which the Department of Public Works had ready in 1960. Like service buildings since the beginning it was behind the hospital and incorporated other services which had been out back in that quaint collection of shacks. Mind you, one service was omitted from the new building though its name was legend. The roothouse was gone. We no longer bartered hospital care for potatoes. In essence that might be the story of the time.

# Chapter 18

# 1952—1961

*What Specialization Did*

The size of our medical staff increased dramatically, from 70 to 169. That happened at other hospitals in Edmonton as well.

The boys of the old brigade pretty well disappeared in the wave of new faces. That happened at other hospitals.

But there was a change at our hospital which was unique to us, and came about because of our connection with the university's Faculty of Medicine.

This change concerned doctors treating patients. (I'm not including people in support services such as radiology, anaesthesiology and clinical laboratories.) In 1952 we had 67 doctors treating patients. They were all part-timers, earning a livelihood seeing patients in offices overtown and in the beds of the hospital, and teaching medical students in accordance with professional responsibility. By 1961 we had 150 doctors treating patients, and some 22 were full-timers, on salary from the university and conducting limited practice from offices in the hospital.

This was a revolutionary change at an institution which had always been run by part-timers and I would be "doctoring" the truth if I said the change was welcome. Don Wilson was the first to receive a "geographic full-time" appointment, on September 1 1954, and I enjoy his story of being invited for a friendly drink by a prominent member of the medical staff. Over the friendly drink Don was told: "This is wrong. I intend to destroy you." Obviously the senior man didn't destroy Don or the new trend. I'm told that in 1986 the hospital had 350 doctors treating patients and 155 were geographic full-time.

As I say, the revolutionary change came because of our connection with the Faculty of Medicine. In the mid-50s the university had a visit from a very powerful bunch of fellows, the accreditation body for medical schools of North America. The LCME, the Liaison Committee on Medical Education, was an American body with a Canadian representative. Canada did not yet have its own. The interest of the LCME, please note, was entirely with undergraduates and not to be confused with the interest of the Royal College (of Physicians and Surgeons of Canada) in postgraduate programs of our Marshall Plan.

The accreditation committee had a powerful message for the university: your Faculty of Medicine doesn't have any full-time teachers. You'd better get some or your school will lose its accreditation and your graduates won't be licensed to practice in other provinces or the United States.

The message was received with shock and disbelief. Because of the great personalities it had been assumed that Alberta had a fine medical school. However unwelcome the message, it was received. Tim Cameron (our fifth Dean of Medicine) believes we may have been the last university medical school in North America to get geographic full-time instructors. John Scott, the third dean, was a dedicated part-timer, but he wrote of the change: "It was recognized that while part-time teachers will always make a major contribution, the need for full-time clinical teachers became a necessity."

With the help of the provincial government's oil money it was possible to hire qualified people to satisfy the accreditation committee, which solved one problem but created another. The university recognized the danger of a professor who gave medical lectures out of books and had no clinical reputation. It also recognized that earnings in private practice were greater than the salaries the university could offer. To attract the right people they were given simultaneous appointments to the medical staff of the hospital, where they could supplement their earnings from practice. That solved the university's problem but raised one in the hospital.

The medical staff had always been a part-timers club. Now there was to be a geographic full-time club as well, occupying the same clubhouse. Don Wilson is well-qualified to comment on the resulting friction because he was for some years a part-timer and then the first charter member of the GFT club. Don puts it this way:

"Part-timers viewed geographic full-time appointments as a threat. The part-timers argued that they had to rent an office overtown, buy furniture, hire a secretary and nurse and pay for the rest of their lives, while GFT poeple got offices and secretaries at no cost, did too much practice and took patients away from them. On the other hand the GFT people thought: 'The part-timers are trying to dominate us, gobbling up beds and gobbling up income and they can't be relied on for enough teaching.'"

Opposing viewpoints haven't budged one inch in 30 years and I don't think they ever can be *rapproched*. With apologies to Rudyard Kipling for dragging him into our internecine dispute I fear that "never the twain shall meet."

Lionel McLeod, an early member of the GFT club, says: "We were a new breed inside the building. The concern was: Would we do the things we were really paid to do? Teaching and research. Would we take practice away from the part-timers who had carried the load through the difficult years? There was a ceiling on how much money we were supposed to make from practice. The usual idea was that it should be 50 percent with anything over going to the departments. But no one was really assigned to watch it."

Both clubs agree that in the hospital the patient is number one, and in the classroom the student is first concern, but the full-timer argues that they get better served by him, and the part-timer argues the opposite. Some part-timers contend that they actually spend more hours in the wards than official full-timers and thus know more of what's going on in the hospital. And who am I to contradict? However, there's a growing squeeze on the hours a part-timer can give to teaching. It's explained by Tim Cameron (one of our graduates who served as Dean of Medicine from 1975 to '84). Tim says: "In the fine old days a practicing physician could budget his time to give the faculty a half day a week and compensate himself by charging the patients, Robin Hood style. But as time went on this became a very expensive contribution only a wealthy man could make."

Well those are the arguments on both sides. They were put forward on the appointment of our first geographic full-time man in September 1954 and have been advanced ever since without bringing the sides one inch closer to agreement. So we'll leave the matter there and suggest that perhaps patients and

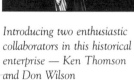

*Introducing two enthusiastic collaborators in this historical enterprise — Ken Thomson and Don Wilson*

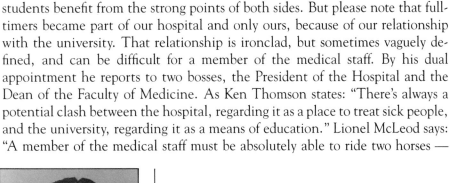

students benefit from the strong points of both sides. But please note that full-timers became part of our hospital and only ours, because of our relationship with the university. That relationship is ironclad, but sometimes vaguely defined, and can be difficult for a member of the medical staff. By his dual appointment he reports to two bosses, the President of the Hospital and the Dean of the Faculty of Medicine. As Ken Thomson states: "There's always a potential clash between the hospital, regarding it as a place to treat sick people, and the university, regarding it as a means of education." Lionel McLeod says: "A member of the medical staff must be absolutely able to ride two horses —

*Lionel McLeod*
*Endocrinology*

even in midstream with the waters running fast. When he's forced into an adversary position his loyalty will be to the program he's trying to run, rather than either institution. The pendulum swings. Sometimes the hospital has greater sway, sometimes the university has. But in spite of the pushing and pulling it works out because one is nothing without the other."

The first batch of full-time appointments came in the Department of Medicine. We had three clinical departments. During the '50s there were no full-timers in my area of gynaecology and obstetrics. In surgery there were two. In medicine were some 20. Mind you the priority was not established by the hospital but by the university, which had to find money for the full-time salaries and judge which areas of instruction were under most pressure from the accreditation committee.

The full-time program was implemented by Don Wilson. In 1955 Don was named Director of Medical Services in the hospital and Clinical Professor of Medicine, and this was an important historical event. One of our graduates became the third person to hold the position, in succession to "Edge" Pope (1922-45) and John Scott (1945-55). The job came open when Dr. Scott decided that being Dean of Medicine was sufficient activity and relinquished the clinical professorship.

Don ran an efficient department for 13 years. He was quiet, he didn't advertise, but I'm pleased to say he's been named an Officer of the Order of Canada. So his work didn't go unrecognized.

Full-time appointments were used to create new divisions in the Department of Medicine and upgrade existing ones. In fact, three divisions were upgraded so much they broke off as autonomous departments. 1957 may be better remembered as the year the Russians launched the Sputnik and Diefenbaker unhorsed the Liberals, but it was also the year that psychiatry, rehabilitation and paediatrics became autonomous departments. If I may, I'll deal with each in turn.

*Psychiatry*

As you'll recall, our original psychiatric unit fell victim to the depression, but in the wing which opened in 1951 the loss was recouped. A 30-bed ward was provided in the basement. Patients were treated by Ken Thomson, who'd been a reluctant witness to dismantling of the original unit, and Sid Spaner.

Sid ran a small unit for the veterans in the Mewburn Pavilion and was a delightful character. He was the son of a general store keeper in Grande Prairie and we all enjoyed his stories about his only vice, if it was one. Sid bet on race horses who seldom repaid his trust. He entertained us more than once with the story of his honeymoon. He was in the Air Force during the war and stationed for a time at the Montreal Neurological Institute. He met Sylvia in Montreal and between the time they were married in the Windsor Hotel and the time for the honeymoon train to depart Sid managed to fall in with a bookie and make a losing investment with the money for the wedding trip. He had to scurry around to his friends, of whom he had many, to cover the loss. Poor Sid died eventually of a heart attack on his way home from the races, but he was with us a long time.

In 1953 psychiatry was upgraded from a *service* to a *division* in the department of medicine, with Sid in charge. But he had so many irons in the fire that he became a leading promoter in a campaign to make psychiatry a separate department and bring in a full-time head.

Keith Yonge, was a very likeable chap with a pioneering bent.

Keith arrived in 1957, after taking a roundabout route to medicine. In 1934 he had been sent to Newfoundland by the commission which governed the bankrupt British colony to manage "an experiment in commercial welfare." The

Keith Yonge
Psychiatry

commission persuaded a Welsh company to start a lumber operation, involving a new town with all services provided, including medical. Keith found the last part so interesting that after seven years he went to McGill for an MD and then went home to London to specialize in psychiatry. He was in Saskatoon, clinical director of a new psychiatric unit in the University Hospital there, when he accepted a call from Edmonton.

You'll enjoy Keith's first impressions of our hospital. He says: "I found the Edmonton setup a bit of a shock, a step back in time. The Saskatoon setup was modern and open. This was brand new, but constructed on the model of a mental hospital, an outpost of Ponoka. In the basement. Heavy doors with peepholes. Windows with shotproof glass so the patients couldn't see out. Doors with big locks and huge keys. The only treatment room was for hydrotherapy, an outdated method for calming people. It was built as though mental patients were entirely different from medical patients.

"I had to campaign hard to replace this heavy construction because it was relatively new, and built, as the administration told me, 'on the best advice.' But we did put in ordinary doors and windows and we obtained a ward on the sixth floor to increase our capacity from 30 to 60 beds.

"I argued that psychiatry should function in close integration with other fields of medicine, not in isolation. To give an example, we worked with paediatrics to develop a unit for emotionally-disturbed children. It opened with 10 beds in 1959.

"The department had no structure as we understand the term today. I had a part-time secretary, but she worked at a desk in the hall. But there were two resident doctors on staff. That was consistent with the idea of the teaching hospital and it was built up."

There are statistics to show how quickly Keith built up the psychiatric service. In 1953, the year the division was created, the hospital admitted 17,223 patients, but there's no record of psychiatric cases. By 1961, when we admitted 22,059 the Department of Psychiatry accounted for 1,093. There were also 730 outpatients. And there were social service consultations involving 216 adults and 71 children. As Keith says: "We became a consultative service to the hospital as a whole." Keith Yonge served 18 years and when he retired to Vancouver Island he took as a memento one of the giant keys he'd found on the patients' doors when he came in 1957.

The department has certainly grown since Keith broke down the doors. In 1986 it comprised some 68 people, including 5 full-time psychiatrists (and 5 part-time), 15 psychologists, 12 nurses, 8 secretaries, and in addition an establishment for 24 residents.

*Physical Medicine and Rehabilitation*

This department became autonomous in 1957.

The evolution started during the first war when the hospital was under the army and Tommy Robson arrived to exercise his broad-shouldered therapy on behalf of injured veterans. The service grew in response to the polio epidemics of the late '20s, and grew again with the need to treat injured veterans of the second war. In 1947 the hospital established a division of physical medicine (within the overall department of medicine), with Morris Adamson in charge. Then the polio epidemics of the early '50s provided another push forward. Qualified physiotherapists were in short supply, the only ones available were in the old country, and there was no school west of Toronto. In 1953 the hospital was working with the university to set up a School of Physical Medicine (like a school of nursing) to train therapists. We had in mind a two-year program leading to a diploma, but a lot of meetings were needed. The program had to be designed to meet our requirements as well as those of the CPA — the Canadian Physiotherapists Association — which granted certificates valid anywhere in Canada. The program had to meet requirements for funding by the provincial government as well as the federal.

In a venture of this kind it's useful to have a key man who's somewhat ahead of his time. Our man was J.R. Fowler, better known as "Rip." Rip was a rare bird then — he had specialized in physical medicine. *Physiatry* is the professional term for it. It's concerned with neuromuscular activity, restoring muscle function by both physical and psychological methods. Rip became interested during the war. After graduating from the U of A in 1942 he went overseas and worked in military hospitals. Afterwards he specialized in Toronto, sponsored by the Department of Veterans Affairs, mostly at Lindhurst Lodge, a halfway house for paraplegics and others with damaged neuromuscular systems trying to make their way back to work, or into society, or just to live at home. Returning to Edmonton he became involved with the Workmen's Compensation Board, planning the rehabilitation centre at 71st Avenue and 119th Street. It opened in December 1952, with Rip in charge and the next project was the School of Physical Medicine.

It was obvious to all that Rip should run the school as well, and the way the school came into being shows the collegiality which has bonded together the medical profession in Edmonton. An advisory council was set up, mainly from the medical staff of our hospital. I was a member, I'm proud to say. When the school got into business in 1954 the members of the council, along with others, supplemented the instruction by trained physiotherapists. The school began with a dozen or so students. Like student nurses they spent time working directly with patients at our hospital, the Royal Alex and the Compensation Board's rehab centre. The WCB also played a supportive role in the school project. With increasing activity in the oilfields and construction we were seeing the dim beginnings of a specialty which has come to be known as "industrial medicine." The first students were trained in *physio*-therapy, the urgent need of the moment. Occupational therapy was added later. In the '60s speech therapy was included and Rip Fowler's school went on eventually to become the School of Rehabilitation Medicine, granting degrees as well as diplomas.

There was much in the future, but at the time the school opened our immediate concern was with the respiratory polio epidemic, which was passing from the acute stage described in Chapter 16 to the long recovery phase. The second phase began for us in March 1954 when 19 iron lungs were transferred from the Royal Alex isolation unit to Station 32 of the University Hospital.

There was so much polio about that hospitals could handle only the most serious cases. This created a roving outpatient assignment for Elizabeth Wood, who had joined us in 1927 during the first occurrence of polio. Miss Wood was the first Canadian physiotherapist to train under Sister Kenny. The provincial government had sent her to Minneapolis for a course during the war. She went out on house calls, showing families the Kenny method of hotpacks to start retraining polio-damaged muscles.

While our medical staff and nursing teams were doing everything possible for the iron-lung patients on Station 32, some of their problems were beyond medical science. Only our hospital handymen could help, and they certainly did. Bob Roberts, the engineer, was a noted Mr. Fix-It. Bob rigged up signalling devices so the most paralyzed patient could activate his own buzzer. One patient might be able to move a hand. Bob would attach a buzzer where he could push it. Another might be able to move only his head. Bob took care of him too. Bob's gadgets helped patients do something for themselves and that was a very big thing.

Johnny Gibson, the carpenter, devised another aid beyond medical science. As Johnny recalls: "Dr. Huckell had trouble with patients lying there who couldn't read. So I concocted a business that attached to the headboard. It was a tilting table where the patient could set the book where he wanted. Some couldn't turn the pages so I concocted a business for that. It was a stick he put in his mouth with a rubber ball on the other end. The ball would turn pages. Dr. Huckell told me: 'This is the best goddam thing I ever saw.'"

In 1956 the service got a boost in status. It became the division of physical medicine *and rehabilitation* with a geographic full-time head. The new man had specialized in rehabilitation at St. Thomas's Hospital, London, just across the river from the Houses of Parliament. Mike Carpendale was a quiet, likeable chap. He didn't seem like a driver but he ran a very efficient service for 10 years. He tells about his move here in characteristic fashion. Mike says: "I was at the Mayo Clinic in Rochester and looking at places I might like to go. I rather liked the sound of the name Alberta, so I wrote Angus McGugan a letter and inquired if there might be a position. He wrote back that there might and invited me to visit. I wasn't sure Alberta might not be all Red Indians and cowboys, but it proved a very pretty place and the hospital was attractive. I started July 1 1956 in the basement of the Mewburn. The next year we moved into the new polio rehabilitation wing and the division was raised to a department."

Mike continues: "The respirator patients were moved to the sixth floor of the polio wing. On the ground floor we were treating 60 polio patients. Another floor became an orthopaedic ward for reconstructive surgery. We were operating the biggest rehabilitation centre in North America, 300 to 350 patients a day. The Mayo Clinic was the largest in the United States and was treating 250 to 300.

"One of the things we did was establish a clinic to design braces for the upper limbs. We got grants to send three people to UCLA. There was Gordon Wilson, an orthopaedic surgeon. Jim Littlefair, our chief physiotherapist. And Wally Stauffer, who ran an artificial limb company.

"The Edmonton Transit System helped out in a remarkable way. They gave us a life-size model of a bus, with doors and a ticket box and seats. so patients could practice getting around indepently on public transportation.

"Rehabilitation cases take so long that students can't observe recovery and think patients are going to lie there forever, taking up space in the hospital. We got grants from the Canadian Legion to make films with time-lapse photogra-

Morris Adamson
*Physical Medicine and*
*Rehabilitation*

Mike Carpendale
*Physical Medicine and*
*Rehabilitation*

phy. Lionel Brown was the star of our favourite film. Lionel was six years old, and about to enter school, when he got polio. He was completely paralyzed and in a respirator. But we took film of his progress each week and in a year he was able to start school. We called our film *Late For School.*"

A favourite of all the staff was a little boy with Down's Syndrome who developed his own program of therapy. Merle was about nine. When he was able to walk again he would make his way to the elevators and push the button to make them stop at his floor. When the doors opened passengers would look down and see Merle smiling happily up at them. Merle's program combined physical, occupational and psychological factors. An expert could hardly have done better.

Merle was able to go home eventually like most patients, but for some this was never possible and the hospital became their permanent home. Despite their handicaps they formed a unique and lively community. They have organized many things for themselves including a charter flight to Hawaii. They are sharp students of sporting events and the economic implications of the results. As someone has said: "They know the betting line better than Jimmy the Greek." Gary McPherson became an expert at playing horses and ran his own for a time. A person in a bookstore encountering "Ghost Towns of Alberta" would never suspect that author Harold Fryer was a paraplegic able to drive his own van and visit historic sites. The community includes victims of a brief resurgence of polio in 1960. The population has remained at about 20 since it formed in the early days of our department of physical medicine and rehabilitation. But the department has grown. By 1986 it numbered 96 full-time people.

*Paediatrics*

Paediatrics broke off to become an autonomous department in 1957 and the push came from the university, where the Faculty of Medicine was being pushed by the powerful Liaison Committee on Medical Education. Paediatrics was a particular concern because it was the only specialty for which the chief teaching hospital was the Royal Alex, not the University. Facilities had a lot to do with it. For many years our children's ward had been an annex on the grounds while at the Royal Alex the children and attending physicians enjoyed a sunny ward stretching along the top floor. So few doctors had specialized in children's medicine that Doug Leitch, who was head of paediatrics at our hospital for 30 years, was also kingpin at the Alex. He wasn't too happy with our setup so he did most of his work and teaching overtown. So did his pal and partner Jimmy Calder, and when Doug retired in 1953 Jimmy carried on as chief in the same way. Doug and Jimmy were great clinicians, but had no interest in the politics of administration, and that was coming to be required of a department head. By the mid-50s conditions were ripe for a change. There was the push from the accreditation committee and the post-war specialization was bringing some young people into paediatrics and on to our medical staff. Lloyd Grisdale, Brock Armstrong, Lou Beauchamp and Kay Swallow come to mind.

The obvious move was to bring in a geographic full-time head and the choice was Ken Martin, an English chap who had specialized at Great Ormond Street Hospital in London and came from the Children's Hospital at the University of Manitoba. Ken was surprised at the sudden invitation. He recalls:

"I had written to the Dean of Medicine enquiring of possible openings for a paediatrician and was assured there was no future for me. On one occasion I passed through Edmonton and enquired of Dr. Leitch, telling him I was mainly interested in work involving teaching. Plied generously with Dr. Leitch's whiskey, embroidered with his superb humour and inimitable silent laughs, the impression I gained was a negative one."

Ken Martin
Paediatrics

Bill Taylor
Paediatrics

But the climate was changing rapidly. Ken Martin took over paediatrics in January 1957, to serve nearly 15 years, and as he says: "It was an ideal time for any individual to be appointed head of a department. It was a time when no one could say *no*."

Mind you, sometimes they said *yes* rather grudgingly. Ken says: "It was necessary to care for the child as a whole and include the family. This meant radically changing the restricted visiting hours. Parents and siblings had been looked on as something of a nuisance, interfering with strict nursing care, a hazard to hygiene and likely to introduce cross infections. Much against 'the better judgment' of administration and care staff parents began to be included in decisions and care."

Ken has written a history of the department and has given a big chapter to the first 18 months of his tenure, which were full of decisive changes. The number of beds was increased dramatically — from 60 to 125. There was a 20-bed section for school-age convalescents and long-term patients. And, to quote Ken: "It was with extreme misgivings that Angus McGugan allowed me to separate off eight beds as an infectious disease unit. Angus had been reared in the days of isolation hospitals, before antibiotics, in which a cross-infection could have a dread outcome in a ward." An outpatient department was set up, which saw 150 children a month. With a grant from the Coordinating Council for Crippled Children, Neil Duncan was able to visit children's cardiac centres in Canada and the United States and set up a monthly outpatient clinic in cardiology.

It's been said the new department "took over the newborn nurseries," but I think it's more correct to say that Ken "brought the doctors together" on the nurseries. Babies had always been under direct care of an individual doctor, usually an obstetrician though in the early '50s some strong young paediatricians were getting involved. It's obvious that at some point in a person's life responsibility passes from the obstetrician to the paediatrician and at some later point the paediatrician says "you're too old for me, you're ready for the family doctor," but no one can say exactly when. To "bring the doctors together" on the newborn nurseries the department was authorized to hire a second geographic full-timer and the choice was Bill Taylor, an Aberdonian by way of Winnipeg.

Bill's delightfully dry Scottish humour survived the ocean crossing. As he recalls: "In 1957 I claimed to be a neonatalogist, though by today's standards I was just an enthusiastic amateur. You didn't have to know how to do much then except how to feed the little beggars, keep them warm, give them some antibiotic and a whiff of oxygen. Now we have all sorts of little machines that blow your mind, and sometimes it takes two nurses to mind one baby. At that time we had two nurses looking after 10."

Neonatal nursing was recognized as a specialty, and the department organized six-week courses open to graduate nurses. Before that a small area of the nursery was set aside for premature babies. This was the first attempt at a neonatal intensive care unit and the provincial government was so impressed it financed a larger unit in the polio wing and another at the Royal Alex. In setting up the prototype Bill Taylor got help from a specialist outside of medicine. Al Stewart, a biochemist, presented the premature nursery with a small micro-lab in which the staff could test tiny amounts of blood — .1 or .2 cc's. Equipment available previously required 5 cc's which was a lot of blood to take from a three-pound human being. Bill has been kind enough to say that I was always supportive of the nursery plan, and I'm pleased to be able to reciprocate by stating that care and teaching in the newborn area benefited greatly. Ken Martin notes: "What impressed me most about Edmonton and our hospital was that although medical people had differences of opinion — Walter Mackenzie and I often disagreed violently — they were never allowed to get personal."

There were also differences of opinion with the government. Ken says: "I had many talks with the minister of health, Dr. Cross. He had been a general practitioner and couldn't see any need for the specialist or going outside the system as it had been. At one meeting we were trying to show the need for specialized teachers for children in hospital wards and Dr. Cross kept saying: 'I don't get it.' Finally he said: 'You may think me a stupid old bugger, but I still don't get it.'"

However, the case was eventually made and the Department of Paediatrics grew. By 1986 it had grown to 140. Included were 22 secretaries, 15 technicians, 6 nurse-practitioners, 35 full-time doctors, and on part-time staff almost all the practicing paediatricians in Edmonton, a total of 49. We've come a long way since Doug Leitch and Gordon Swallow were the only paediatricians in town, which gave them material for a humourous lecture they called "Two Old Goats and the Kids."

Those were the three divisions of medicine which grew up and left home in the 1950s. Mind you, the department of medicine did not go into decline. Quite the contrary. New divisions were created. Divisions got full-time directors. The department was set firmly on the road to the organization that's found in the hospital today, and if you walk the halls you can read the signs. Let's take a look at the organization as it stood in 1986 and then check on the progress that was made in that direction in the '50s.

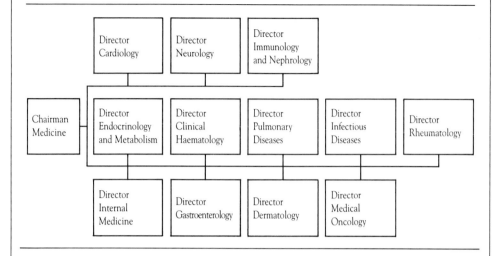

The divisions established or recognized in the period 1952-61 were cardiology, neurology, endocrinology and metabolism, pulmonary diseases, dermatology, therapeutics and internal medicine. Each is highly individual so let's consider them that way.

*Cardiology*

Cardiology became a full-time division in 1953 with the aid of a Markle scholarship. It was the second Markle to come to Alberta, which was nice, and the second to come to all of Canada, which was splendid. With the Markle money — $6,000 a year for five years — we were able to set up a cardiovascular diagnostic unit with a full-time director.

Bob Fraser got the appointment, the first of several in the hospital and faculty. He was Director of Cardiology (1953-69), Chairman of the Department of Medicine (1969-74), Associate Dean of Medicine (1978-83), and Acting Dean (1983-84). Bob Fraser can take credit for a number of things but credit for the cardiovascular unit he gives entirely to Joe Dvorkin.

Joe is no longer with us, but until his early death in 1975 he was very influential in the hospital although he remained a part-timer by choice. For a time he was chairman of the medical staff committee. Bob Fraser remembers Joe Dvorkin as "a doctor's doctor," a first-class teacher and role model for students. I got to know Joe in his student days, when we got to know all the students because they were so few. Joe was relatively quiet, but he had some positive ideas of his own and there's no doubt he blossomed as he went along. Joe graduated during the war and after his army service he went to New York to specialize with Arthur Master, one of the leading cardiologists of the day. When he returned to our hospital as a member of the medical staff he promoted for a cardiovascular unit to investigate heart disorders with the catheter technique.

Just at this time Bob Fraser, one of our class of '46, was completing a postgraduate program at the University of Minnesota. Bob's experience included a year of clinical research among people who had suffered heart attacks. The department built its own treadmill and put heart attack survivors on it with little catheters in their arms and legs. Bob says: "Looking back now, it's rather frightening. I didn't know very much, but the thing was I knew more than anybody else."

You'll enjoy Bob's story of how the unit started. Angus McGugan found $5,000 for a state-of-the-art machine to record heart sounds and arterial pressures. But the unit had no fixed address. Hec Duggan agreed that Bob and Joe could use the x-ray lab when the radiologists were finished for the day, but that wasn't till around 4:30 in the afternoon. They could handle only one case at a time, and each was a hot, sweaty, hour-and-a-half. They wore leather x-ray aprons in addition to gown and mask. And to read the pulses on the machine Joe had to wear red glasses and put a towel over his head. They would float a catheter into a vein in the left arm of the subject, then through the heart chambers into the artery going to the lung. If extra heart beats showed up Joe would shout a warning because they had no means of slowing down a heart which began to race. The catheter withdrew blood samples from the heart chambers and arteries. These were analyzed afterwards and comparative oxygen readings showed whether the heart was functioning normally. Ted Bell lent them his new clinical laboratory in the basement, along with technician Anne Shaw, daughter of Bob Shaw, the legendary Professor of Bacteriology. The lab work took so long that on many evenings the phone would ring and a stern voice would say: "Dr. Shaw speaking. Is my daughter still there?"

The cardiovascular unit was ready to welcome its first patient in November 1953, after a final rehearsal carried out under protest from Angus McGugan. Angus vowed that "no darn dirty dogs" were coming into *his* hospital, and gave in only when Bob and Joe said they couldn't undertake to work on humans until they'd tried an animal under hospital conditions. They'd been practicing with dogs in the MacEachern Laboratory on campus, where conditions were better than in the hospital.

Despite the difficulties they carried out catheterizations on 100 people in the first year and 500 patients were referred to a weekly "round," or meeting, at which doctors were invited to discuss patients with heart diseases. There was uneasiness expressed about these "rounds" by no less a progressive than John Scott. He thought Bob and Joe might be *fragmenting* medicine. There were other objections. Bob says: "Some people considered us dilettantes. We could prove a patient had a hole between connecting chambers of the heart but nobody could do anything with the information. Then John Callaghan arrived on the scene with cardiovascular surgery. That gave us a raison d'être."

The work load got so heavy that Bob persuaded the powers another full-time cardiologist should be engaged. I like Bob's story of how he countered the traditional argument about lack of funds. The Markle Foundation was paying the university $6,000 a year for Bob's services but he was only getting $4,800. The rest was being held "in reserve" for some future need. The reserve would help support another full-timer so advertisements were placed in the medical journals and in November 1956 Dick Rossall arrived from Leeds University in England.

Dick had to cash in his pension to raise the airfare, perhaps that's why he didn't move again. He kept busy in many areas. When Mark Marshall retired in 1962, Dick took over our postgraduate training program. In 1969 he succeeded Bob Fraser as head of cardiology and was still there in 1986. From 1971 to '75 he was also Assistant Dean in the Faculty of Medicine.

In 1961 cardiology had two full-time medical staff, two part-time and a technician. By 1986 the division had an establishment of 16 technicians, 12

*Bob Fraser*
*Cardiology*

*Joe Dvorkin*
*Cardiology*

cardiologists, 5 cardiology fellows in training, 4 residents, 6 nurses, 11 secretaries and an administrator. A total of 56.

*Neurology*

The dictionary calls it "the medical science of the nervous system and its disorders." From about 1930 neurology in our hospital was practiced by an internist (Ken Hamilton), a neuropsychiatrist (Ken Thomson) and neurosurgeons (Hep Hepburn and Guy Morton). In 1957 our first designated neurologist was appointed to the medical staff when George Monckton came

*George Monckton*
*Neurology*

from England to head the new division.

George trained at the National Hospital in London. As he says: "There were about 30 of us who had specialized ourselves out of employment. I wrote to people in Canada. One gave me Don Wilson's name. He invited me and I think he was rather surprised when I came."

George came as a part-timer and shared an office overtown but the next year the position of division head was made full-time with a major grant from the Muscular Dystrophy Association of Canada. George engineered the grant on his own initiative, with a proposal for a research lab to study muscle enzymes. The lab was set up in three rooms of the Wells pavilion where interns and residents had recently lived their lives of quiet desperation. The next year the lab was granted the services of a full-time biochemist. By 1986 the division had grown to include three biochemists, five technicians, six secretaries, two residents, and 12 full-time neurologists including George Monckton who remained as director till 1980.

*Endocrinology and Metabolism*

This division perpetuated the pioneering inquiries of Heber Jamieson, who started back in the '20s to explore the mysteries of metabolism through reading and observation. In 1948 Heber's work passed to Don Wilson. Don set up a metabolic laboratory capable of assessing patients with endocrine (or glandular) disorders, made possible by the first Markle scholarship to come to Alberta. In 1957 the third Markle grant enabled Lionel McLeod to take over.

The opportunity couldn't have come at a better time for Lionel, one of our graduates (class of '51) who went on to become Dean of Medicine at the University of Calgary, Chairman of the Alberta Heritage Foundation for Medical Research, and along the way, President of the Royal College of Physicians and Surgeons of Canada. Only four Albertans have been president of this august body, all associated with our hospital — Fulton Gillespie, John Scott, Walter Mackenzie and Lionel McLeod. And none of the foregoing might have happened for Lionel if he hadn't developed a sudden allergy to animals.

The allergy surfaced at McGill, where he was doing basic research in his postgraduate program. Just when the animals got to be too much for Lionel, running both the metabolic lab and Department of Medicine got to be too much for Don Wilson. Lionel came back to Alberta to operate the lab, and at times acted as personal physician to Heber Jamieson, the founder of the movement. Heber must have been interested in Lionel's reason for leaving McGill, because he was the local pioneer in researching allergies. Heber gave Lionel a small library of publications he had read and saved on renal analysis, historical records of the distant time when he had pursued metabolic research all alone and tried to create a scholarly atmosphere among clinicians.

In 1958 Endocrinology and Metabolism was made a division of medicine with Lionel as head. In the early '60s money became available for expansion, and as this was written in 1986 the division had a staff of five secretaries, six full-time endocrinologists, each with a lab employing half a dozen technicians.

*Pulmonary Disease*

This division was created in 1959 as Chest Diseases and Pulmonary Function when Brian Sproule returned with four years of expertise from Parkland Memorial Hospital in Dallas, the medical branch of Southern Methodist University. In addition to expertise Brian brought back two machines, one for each of the services the division was to provide.

The hospital had to pay for the Haliburton respirator, the basic equipment of a respiratory therapy clinic for victims of the bulbar polio epidemic, but the other came free. Ted Gain, from anaesthesiology, helped assemble the respirator. Ted had an IPPB — an Intermittent Positive Pressure Breathing machine — to reverse the negative mode of the iron lungs. This cooperation was typical. Specialization was breeding interdependence.

The free machine, which was certainly welcomed by the hospital board, was the basic equipment for a pulmonary function laboratory. It was a parting gift from Brian's old boss in Dallas. Brian had designed and seen to the fabrication of a polaragraphic oxygen electrode, which measures oxygen in the blood. The hospital board was glad to get a free machine, but was beginning to realize that every machine needs a technician who doesn't come free. The technician who ran this one came from the ranks of hospital orderlies, and Gunther Sintzinger was the first of many. As this was written in 1986 there were 50 respiratory technicians, eight lab technicians, two research scientists, nine physicians, and Brian Sproule was still Director of the Division of Pulmonary Diseases.

*Dermatology*

This specialty has grown away from the hospital. Patients with skin diseases are treated in offices and those with venereal disease in provincial clinics. In 1952 dermatology admitted 250 patients to the hospital, in 1961 only 122, and by 1986 hardly 10. There have been no full-timers in the division and very little turnover. Harold Orr was director from the beginning of the hospital. When Harold died in 1952 he was succeeded by his younger partner Paul Rentiers, and when Paul retired after 23 years he was followed by *his* younger partner, Jack Brown.

Paul Rentiers graduated in Alberta during the war and specialized afterwards at Mayos. When Harold Orr died Paul was for some years the only dermatologist in the city.

In the 1950s steroids completed a revolution in dermatology which was begun by antibiotics. At times there might be as many as 10 patients in hospital with psoriasis. Eczema was a common and very mean disorder which could cripple a patient because he was wide-open to other infections. The previous remedies were tars and greases which could make the condition worse, x-ray and arsenic which were sometimes effective but hazardous. Steroids went to work on inflammations. A skin ailment which could take weeks to control with old methods might be cleared up in hours. So dermatology moved away from the hospital.

*Therapeutics*

This division has the distinction of being the only one to disappear. Irving Bell was the authority from the beginning until his death in 1955, and then Floyd Rodman took over. Floyd had the ideal background for therapeutics — a pharmacologist who had returned to university and obtained an MD. When Floyd left in 1961 the handwriting was on the wall, and writ large. With the multiplication of specialties and sub-specialties — approaching 35 in number as this was written — no one person could teach therapeutics. The teaching and practice were scattered through Internal Medicine.

*Brian Sproule*
*Pulmonary Disease*

*Floyd Rodman*
*Therapeutics*

*Internal Medicine*

Doctors have an idea what is meant by the word "internal" in this context though they concede that "internal" is not a very good word, and would welcome one which expresses neatly and exclusively what it is if someone could find such a word.

Frank Elliott says all the term "internal medicine" ever did was express what it is not. Until the 1950s it was not dermatology, surgery, obstetrics or paediatrics. But then the Department of Medicine began to split off into sub-specialties and the meaning was expanded. Internal medicine didn't mean cardiology, neurology, endocrinology nor pulmonary function.

As I see it: In former days you had the GP. He was a sort of internal medicine man, and he looked after everything. As time went on people were studying more and more about less and less — medicine was becoming fragmented and compartmentalized. It's getting to the point now where the Royal College is wondering how many sub-specialties it should allow.

In the late '50s internal medicine was recognized as a division within the Department of Medicine. As Don Wilson says: "There was a group of people who didn't want to go into what they saw as a narrow field. People like Frank Elliott, Ken Thomson, Stan Greenhill and Al Gilbert. Knowledge became so vast that no one person could cover it all but there was a real need for the general internist — and now more than ever."

By 1986 it had become a small division of only four or five. One faction in the hospital contends that there is no longer a place for it, others that internal medicine is still the basis of everything. Happily I can take refuge in the old saying that the truth probably lies somewhere in between.

*The Special Services and Research Committee*

Before going on to explore the divisions which specialization caused in the Department of Surgery, I'd like to introduce the above-named committee, which held its first meeting on November 23 1955, and directed the testing of new ideas for inclusion in regular hospital services — and regular hospital budgets. Budgets are awkward. They are built of items of proven worth. It may be difficult to justify an item from historical experience, but a committee with its own money can justify a trial with the possibility of error.

You can see this committee coming with Angus McGugan's annual reports. Beginning with 1949 he'd have a proud paragraph devoted to *special services*, such things as neurosurgery, metabolic medicine and orthopaedic rehabilitation developed within our hospital, which others didn't provide. One year he wrote: "It is no longer necessary for the people of Alberta to go to large centres in the east and south for diagnosis and treatment except in rare instances." Again I'm reminded of Sir Walter Scott's immortal words: "Brave words, bold youth." The paragraph changed little from year to year but in 1954 there were new services to report — the radioisotope unit, the cardiovascular unit, the expansion of occupational therapy. Then in 1955 came our Special Services and Research Committee.

The committee was, in effect, a foundation, operating like others bearing famous names such as Rockefeller, Ford, Markle and Muttart. Our committee observed two guiding principles valid for foundations.

One was stated in the official philosophy: "The committee may initiate research and special projects in the diagnostic treatment area, but will not be able to provide long-term support." If an idea is worthwhile, it should be able to fly on its own after a reasonable time — Markle scholarships were for five years. And if a foundation gets involved in permanent support of a service its hands are tied.

Principle number two was enunciated by the head of the Ford Foundation, McGeorge Bundy. A foundation can afford to take risks and afford to fail. Governments can't afford failure because they are accountable for spending. This applied to us because the provincial government had a very large stake in our operation.

A foundation needs its own money. The Rockefeller family made their money from oil, the Ford family from automobiles, the Markle family from Pennsylvania coal, the Muttart family of Edmonton (of which more shortly) made their money from home-building.

Our committee used the interest on money from two sources, one of which was the original Rockefeller grant of the 1920s. When time came to repay it the university was told to keep the $500,000 and spend it wisely. The other source was the fund Angus McGugan had squirreled away from operating surpluses of the hospital, an amount in the neighbourhood of $1,000,000. Of this we spent the interest only — because it was conventional wisdom and because of a nagging fear that the government might want it or tell us how to spend it.

I had the honour of being a member of this committee, as clinical professor and head of Obstetrics and Gynaecology. Other members were the professors of Medicine and Surgery (Don Wilson and Walter Mackenzie), John Scott the Dean of Medicine, Ted Bell, the head of Clinical Laboratory Services, Reg Adshead and of course Angus McGugan.

We proposed spending $50,000 a year and our thinking was project-oriented, to show results for evaluation. At the same time we began receiving support for specific programs from outside organizations, the most important of which was the Muttart Foundation. The Edmonton success story of Merrel and Gladys Muttart has a prominent reminder in the river valley, in the glass pyramids of the conservatory. It's regrettable that their contributions to medicine are not equally recognized. In the '30s they got their start in business selling scrap lumber. In the post-war building boom they got into prefabricated houses. Houses need heating so they got into furnaces. And plumbing, so they got into that, until they had 55 companies from Newfoundland to Hawaii. Mrs. Muttart was diabetic and a patient of Don Wilson, whose specialty was endocrinology and metabolism. Doctor's appointments would turn into three-hour sessions in which she talked about the Muttarts' desire to support medical research. They went to the Markle family for advice, which was freely given, and the Muttart Foundation was incorporated by a private member's bill in parliament. Over the years the Foundation has provided $3,000,000 for research and diagnostic treatment in the University Hospital and Faculty of Medicine. The first contribution came when the Markle Foundation's five year support of Bob Fraser's cardiovascular program ended. And Bob's program was the essential medical-side component of open-heart surgery.

So now let's cross over to the surgical side of the house and see what was happening there.

*Department of Surgery*
This chart shows the structure of the department in 1986.

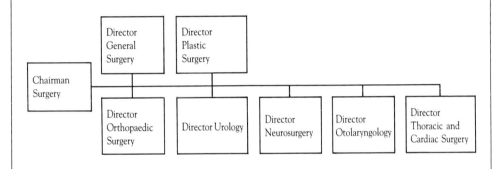

Evolution towards the current structure of surgery was completed in the period 1952-61. The department of medicine took longer, but surgery developed specialized divisions earlier and I'd like to consider each in the order in which it came on the scene. However, before anything else, I must point out that 1952 witnessed a significant change in the theatres where our surgeons plied their art. After a quarter-century in charge of the operating rooms, Christina MacKay moved to night supervisor. There are many stories of Miss MacKay's faithful stewardship and Les Willox tells one of the best. Scalpels were still like old-fashioned straight razors and had to be sharpened each time. Les was doing one of his first operations on a little kiddie, and the scalpel, in Les's judgment, was no better than a file. So afterwards he went out on the balcony and pitched it as far as he could into the snow. Les had been heavy-weight boxing champion of the Canadian army so it was doubtless an impressive throw. But it didn't awe our Miss MacKay. She was watching and saw to it that Les got that scalpel for his next operation.

Les laughs: "We ended up the best of friends. She wanted to establish herself as boss right away."

Mind you, when Tina retired from the scene Walter Mackenzie emerged as undoubted boss in all matters pertaining to surgery. Walter was young and vigorous and building the department with a new generation of surgeons coming out of the war and the Marshall Plan.

Les was in the first group to train under the Marshall Plan. Les says: "We came back imbued with the idea that every man had to be a triple threat — like the ideal football player who could run, pass and kick. We had to be good at clinical practice, good at teaching and good at research. We did research one afternoon a week at the lab. John Scott came in one day and watched what I was doing and said in his joking way: 'Willox, you've set research back 10 years!'"

The lab opened in 1952 and is a good example of a Walter Mackenzie promotion. He wanted to establish a division of experimental surgery, but that word *experimental* makes people uneasy. The board was really uneasy when he asked to build a penthouse on the roof of the hospital. It was turned down flat.

Bob Macbeth
Surgery

Les Willox
Surgery

Dogs and people in the same building? Never. So he talked the Alberta Division of the Canadian Cancer Society into building it on the understanding the Department of Surgery would make use of it. It was named for Dr. J.S. McEachern, a Calgary physician who had been licensed in the days of the Northwest Territories and was still in practice. The lab was physically on the university campus, but our hospital staff worked there with the help of post-graduate students on research fellowships. And the fellowships were a fine example of the cooperative spirit in the medical profession here, the spirit which had caused Walter to choose Edmonton over Winnipeg. The funds were engineered by the head of the Royal Alex, Walter Anderson. The other Walter persuaded the Edmonton civic employees welfare fund that a grant for research in surgery was a sound investment in the health of the community. The first grant was made in 1952 and in the next 20 years some 83 research fellows were supported by Edmonton civic employees.

Les Willox makes an important point: "This was the age of publish or perish. You got recognition and grants if you made the right presentations and did enough publishing in the surgical journals. Everybody knows Walter Mackenzie was a master of that game and they assume he was born with the gift of gab, but he wasn't. Walter was a terrible speaker when he started out but he struggled to become a good one, and pushed the rest of us. He made students and junior staff men rehearse their speeches over and over. We were all doing research part-time, on our rounds, in our own group, and then polishing up reports for forums. Once John Callaghan and I went down to Seattle to a forum where there was a 10-minute time limit. You had a light on your table. With two minutes to go it went amber and when it turned red it turned you off. The first men up rambled on and only just succeeded in introducing themselves when their time was gone, so they were hostile as hell when John got up. John's original presentation was full of Irish blarney and went for an hour. But Walter got him to work it down and down, until he gave it in Seattle in nine minutes and 50 seconds. He got a big hand."

It was in connection with the lab that the Department of Surgery made its first geographic full-time appointments, mostly to satisfy the demands of the all-powerful Liaison Committee on Medical Education which accredited the university medical school for surgery. They were Bob Macbeth and Cam Harrison. Bob succeeded Walter as head of surgery in 1960 and Cam went to BC in the same capacity.

Bob says: "The geographic full-time principle was a lot slower developing in surgery than in medicine. Walter Mackenzie saw the benefit of full-timers but he never gave up clinical practice. Surgery is mainly clinical, a skill. If you stop doing surgery you lose the dexterity. Later on, when Walter was dean, he was the only dean among the 14 or 15 Canadian medical schools with a practice."

Surgery blossomed in this time, but as I always told my students: "The scope of surgery depends on anaesthesia." So before we look at the divisions in surgery perhaps we should see what was happening in that essential support area.

*The Department of Anaesthesiology*

There are many figures which could be invoked to show trends in this department, but there is one which tops all others for significance. By 1961 the length of the average anaesthetic had increased to 80.2 minutes. In that year alone it lengthened by 10.1 minutes.

There are two main reasons, which we can cite on the authority of Ted Gain, who became head of the department in 1952 and stayed till 1975. Surgery was becoming more complex; open-heart surgery sometimes went eight hours. That was one reason. The other was that the surgeon now had the luxury of

*Ernie Watts*
*Anaesthesiology*

*Ted Gain*
*Anaesthesiology*

taking his time. In the past the mark of the surgeon was speed. The anaesthetic was planned on his estimate of how long the business would take and he had to rush to complete his work before it wore off.

A Canadian medical discovery changed all this. Dr. Harold Griffiths of McGill showed that curare, a muscle relaxant used by Indians of the Amazon jungle to tip their hunting arrows, could benefit humans in the operating room. As Ted notes: "Curare became widely available in the late '40s, but not widely accepted till the early '50s, our profession being conservative. Curare relaxed not only the muscles of the patient, but the surgeon as well."

George Moonie was a postwar graduate who joined the department as curare was coming in and eventually succeeded Ted Gain as head. George notes that one of the benefits of curare was the ability to control respiration. The anaesthetist could slow the patient's breathing right down and take over for him so he wouldn't develop too much carbon dioxide in the blood and then require oxygen. Curare was not used by itself, but in conjunction with pentathol or nitrous oxide. The use of two old-fashioned agents, ether and cyclopropane, dropped off and this was welcome because they were inflammable.

Anaesthesiologists on staff increased to nine and there were also four residents in the postgraduate training program. Curare posed only one disadvantage to a teaching hospital. There was a decline in spinal anaesthesia which was still useful though it had a time limit. Students had less opportunity to gain experience with it.

In the '50s developments in medicine reduced some areas for surgery, but anaesthesia opened others.

*General Surgery*

From the beginning the term general surgery had the dictionary meaning of *applicable to the whole*. The grand definition was upheld right through the time of Hep Hepburn who did an appendectomy once a year just to keep his hand in. But by the '50s general surgery was being perceived as what was left after deducting the specialties, and the list was further reduced as medicine controlled conditions which used to lead to the scalpel.

Walter Mackenzie directed the division of general surgery in addition to heading the entire department. Bob Macbeth explains one of the reasons: "We were training surgeons. There is a disadvantage to training students in a referral hospital. If surgery gets too specialized they might not get experience with ordinary afflictions."

The responsibility of general surgery narrowed down to the areas of head and neck, breast and abdomen, including operations for cancer, gall bladder, appendix and repair of hernias. There was a parallel with internal medicine, but internal medicine remained broader than general surgery because of the element of diagnosis. Bob Johnston says: "Ulcer surgery used to be very common. We still operate for obstruction, perforation and hemmorage but in conservation management all we had to offer in the '50s was antacids. Since then medicine has provided drugs that suppress acid production in the stomach."

It can be argued that medicine removed from the list a surgical skill that was early on recognized as a specialty. Jack Fife was the hospital's expert on goitres. He'd studied under the great Frank Lahey at the Lahey clinic in Boston. Les Willox recalls: "Goitres were a horror. With a toxic goitre there was a devil of a time to get the patient in shape to operate. You had to bring down the activity. Sometimes Jack would have to operate four or five times, reducing the gland a little each time. Then in the '50s we got radioactive iodine to cool the patients off. At one of our meetings we had a great discussion on the subject: 'Is I-131 going to replace surgery?' I said I-131 was not competitive but complementary and blessed it for relieving us of some very bad cases."

## Urology

This is the senior sub-specialty in surgery, dating from 1923. Into the '50s it was dominated by two highly original personalities, Gordon Ellis and Gordon Tucker, who felt that all work and no play was a barren policy that could not commend itself to men of reason and taste. Gordon Tucker, on leaving a party, was fond of announcing that he would drive since he was unfit to sing. The Gordons were old guard, of course. In 1958, Jim Metcalfe, one of the new wave succeeded Ellis as head of the division.

That was a year of sharply-increased activity for urology. The number of patients went up nearly 50 percent, to 1,088.

In addition to new techniques of surgery urology pioneered renal dialysis in the hospital. At the very first meeting of the Special Services and Research Committee (on November 23 1955) Walter Mackenzie raised the idea of buying a kidney machine. Jim Metcalfe recalls how it came about. One night he and some residents were coming out of a room where a man was dying from an overdose of poison. Jim said, "If we had a kidney machine we could save that man." Walter happened to be in the corridor with his usual retinue. "What's this about an artificial kidney? Should we have one?" A dialyser was being produced in Cleveland and the Mayo clinic had brought one in. The committee sent Jim to observe the Mayo operation and spend a week in Cleveland with a co-designer of the Skaggs-Leonard machine. $1,935 was appropriated to buy it and the parts arrived in March 1957. Assembled in the McEachern lab for practice on animals, it was the size of an old-fashioned TV and worked on the principle of osmosis, with toxified blood being pumped out of the patient, passed between layers of cellophane to remove the toxic elements, and then pumped back in. The first hospital patient to benefit was a young woman in a coma from a deliberate overdose of drugs. She woke the next morning without even a headache.

Peter Allen participated in this ground-breaking, though as a resident, in a rather humble capacity, mostly hauling the machine from the lab. Perhaps it helped him decide to specialize in neurosurgery rather than urology, at which he did very well, becoming chairman of that division in 1969, and Vice-President (Medical) for the entire hospital in 1986. "It was a great big thing," Peter recalls with feeling. "If they hadn't invented something better we wouldn't be using kidney machines today."

    Of course they did invent something better. In 1960 Bill Lakey (later head of urology) brought one back from Michigan. Though an improvement it was still too drastic for repeated dialysis of one person, but a gentler version would make that possible in the early '60s. The art of dialysis would then be advanced by nephrology — a fledgling medical specialty of which the oldest surgical specialty of urology is the operating cousin.

Jim Metcalfe
Urology

Gordon Ellis
Urology

*Orthopaedics*

This is the second-oldest division, dating from 1924 when Hank Mewburn returned from a year-and-a-half in Boston with credentials to be certified as the first orthopaedic surgeon in Alberta. I'm told that nowadays the division has a five-year postgraduate program. Five years would certainly have tried Hank's patience.

In the 1950s the aftermath of polio dominated the attention of orthopaedic surgeons. Hank had retired before this (in 1948) and Graham Huckell was head of the division when polio struck. Fortunately, some younger men had come in. Ollie Rostrup. Cooper Johnston and Gordon Cameron from the Marshall Plan. And Gordon Wilson, another son of our pioneering surgeon W.A. "Whispering Willie" Wilson to establish his own name in the University Hospital.

Reconstructive work was concentrated in the so-called "polio wing" and at one time orthopaedics had 120 beds assigned. As Ollie Rostrup says, the responsibility for patients was something of "a mixed grill." Most of the treatment was done by the new Department of Rehabilitation Medicine but except for a few cases the patients were under an orthopaedic surgeon or internist.

Doctors and residents grew skilled at assembling casts on the patients and mostly on the joints of knee and foot. Though made of Plaster-of-Paris they were different from the sculptures which provide so much humour for cartoons. More properly they were removable splints which had to support a joint but had to come off each day for exercise therapy, lest the patient suffer a complication called contracture. If polio left a knee with strong muscles on one side and little muscle tone on the other the stronger muscles could twist the knee out of alignment.

So many splints were required that our hospital abandoned a quaint custom which had lingered with us while others were buying tailor-made casts from suppliers. We were still "rolling our own." Bill Bryan the orderly used to make them in a basement room. Our purchasing agent, John Beaton, bought him Plaster-of-Paris and crinoline mesh in varying widths, and Bill made them up when he wasn't helping Tommy Robson with physiotherapy. Hank Mewburn was a firm believer in Bill's casts, saying they had "more substance" than tailor-mades. But Bill couldn't keep up with the demand of the '50s, and nowadays such splints are plastic — lighter, harder, and the kids can use them for war games in the wards.

Reconstructive work on polio patients was the absorbing business of the orthopaedic surgeon and remained so into the next decade. Medicine produced the Salk Vaccine to eliminate further epidemics of polio, but medicine also opened up great advances in orthopaedic surgery, as antibiotics removed the fear of infection which had made surgeons reluctant to go into joints. Surgery and medicine came together on arthritis. Arthritis is a medical disease, in which the orthopaedic surgeon got involved in the later stages trying to correct deformities and restore function after the disease had done its damage. At our hospital medicine and surgery linked up in the persons of Edward G. "Cappy" Kidd, the first man from Alberta to be sent away for postgraduate work in rheumatology, and of Gordon Wilson, who had a particular interest within his chosen specialty of orthopaedics.

"Cappy" was on our Marshall Plan, but Gordon pursued his special interest the old-fashioned way. After wartime service with the British navy he went into practice in Edmonton and each year would arrange on his own initiative for a week or so at some medical centre where he could observe work on traumatized and arthritic hands. He spent time in Boston, San Francisco, New Mexico, and two weeks at the University of Iowa medical centre where Dr. Flatt was starting

*Ollie Rostrup*
*Orthopaedics*

to replace joints in the hand.

Nowadays rheumatology is a division of the Department of Medicine with four full-time doctors, but in the '50s "Cappy" was a one-man band, operating our Rheumatic Diseases Unit a half-day a week.

Likening "Cappy" to a one-man band is appropriate because he played the saxophone at staff dances. He was one of our wartime graduates. He says that growing up in the depression he had so little experience spending money that when he served in the army medical corps in England he was unable to get rid of his salary and came home with a secret shame — a bank account. On a more serious topic he notes that every so often medicine seems to take off — everything happens at once. The postwar was one of those times. "Cappy" was studying internal medicine at the university of Minnesota on our Marshall Plan when a further year in rheumatology was financed by a dynamic new force on the medical scene — the Canadian Arthritis and Rheumatism Society. Founded in 1949, the society was sparked by Mary Pack, a Vancouver physiotherapist, and Edward Dunlop, a fantastic fellow, totally blind from a war injury, who went from coast to coast raising hell and raising money for the cause. The society's first objective was to provide fellowship money for postgraduate research. With money in hand, John Scott arranged for "Cappy" to spend an extra year in rheumatology. He went to New York City where Cornell University operated the Hospital for Ruptured and Crippled Children. ("Cappy" says it's a shame they changed the name to the Hospital for Special Surgery because no one could forget the original.)

There he worked with Dr. Richard Freiberg, who had pioneered the only known remedy for rheumatoid arthritis. Arthritis is a disease which comes in more than a hundred varieties. Rheumatoid is the crippler. Dr. Freiberg's remedy was injecting a solution of gold salt into the muscle. It worked only on rheumatoid and if it worked it stopped the disease cold though no one knew why. When "Cappy" returned to Edmonton in 1952 the society sponsored a Rheumatic Diseases Unit in our hospital where he tried to convince doctors of the gold salt solution. There were great hopes for cortisone at this time, but it turned out that cortisone was only a pain-killer, marvellous though it was, and that the disease went on unchecked and too much had unfortunate side-effects.

The unit was overtown as part of the Outpatient Clinic, and operated a half-day a week. It stayed there until the outpatient service was moved to our new Clinical Services Wing in 1961.

In the meantime Gordon Wilson's special interest led to another special service in the hospital. This was the Paralytic Hand Clinic established in 1959. The clinic was a travelling unit which met once a week in a ward where there were reconstructive cases resulting from polio or arthritis. Any doctor could attend. The clinic was headed by Gordon and included a plastic surgeon — usually Mac Alton — and a representative from the Department of Rehabilitation.

Everybody was looking for research money then and Ollie Rostrup tapped the Edmonton Eskimos for $5,000 in return for his volunteer work as team physician. The grant paid a resident to do research on injuries to the knee. Gordon Cameron helped Ollie with the Eskimos and took over when Ollie gave it up. And in recent years Gordon has added the Edmonton Oilers and Trappers baseball team to his responsibilities. Of course we had another surgeon in sport — Les Willox was for many years medical officer of the Edmonton Boxing and Wrestling Commission. And Rex Boake, a urologist who came a little later, has been president of the Eskimo football club.

The division of orthopaedic surgery got a new director in 1958. Graham Huckell retired and Ollie Rostrup served for 18 years — until Graham's son John was ready to take over.

### Neurosurgery

Guy Morton says modestly that when he took over the division from "Hep" Hepburn all the pioneering had been done, brain surgery was no longer the glamour specialty it had been in the '30s and '40s and was about to be upstaged by open-heart surgery.

Glamourous or not the work certainly increased. Back in 1941, when the division was formally recognized, "Hep" performed 65 major operations. In 1952 Guy was joined by Tom Speakman and together they performed 202 major operations. In 1961 they did 374.

Tom Speakman was an Icelander from Manitoba, like the Vants, and was a nice chap as you'd expect. He and his wife Pat had a lovely family and I remember delivering five of their children though I'm told there are six so I must have missed one. Tom took his special training in Montreal with some of the top men of the day — Wilder Penfield, William Cone and Boris P. Babkin. He earned an MSc with his research into the influence of the cerebral cortex on the central nervous system. Bob Macbeth points out that Tom never lost his interest in research, even in periods of crushing clinical responsibility. Bob also notes: "On matters of principle he was no fence sitter. He took on Donald Gordon and the CNR, the medical advisory board of the hospital, the operating room committee, and myself." Sad to say, Tom Speakman lived only 45 years.

Through this period the burdens of the division fell entirely on Guy and Tom. Other centres were developing new procedures in neurosurgery which had to be evaluated. As Guy points out, new things are introduced all the time, and some are perfected and some disappear. One which was abandoned was surgery of the basal ganglion for Parkinsonism. It was intentionally destructive surgery and such procedures seldom last.

The heaviest burden was in diagnosis. It was almost entirely on the surgeon. The brain is hard to x-ray and the only procedure Guy and Tom had to rely on was the one "Hep" Hepburn had used back in the '30s. Air was introduced into the spine so he could obtain a pneumo-encephalogram. Diagnostic help for the neurosurgeon came eventually from the direction of the x-ray department. In 1961 radiology produced 400 arteriograms, a procedure in which dye in introduced into the bloodstream to provide the necessary contrast. Radioneurology flowered in the 1960s. As Guy says, the air-in-the-spine procedure is as good as it ever was, but there is now something better. Very much better.

The nursing aspect of neurosurgery was becoming a specialty too, as Pam Allan recalls. Pam was charge nurse in the neurosurgical ward from 1954 to '61, and I like her story of how she accepted the offer to come here. She was at the Royal Vic in Montreal in a good position. Our offer contained more in the way of prestige than salary, but Pam was intrigued enough to flip a coin. If the nickel had come up "tails" she would doubtless have enjoyed an interesting career elsewhere, but it came up "heads" — for Edmonton. She was charge nurse in

*Guy Morton*
*Neurosurgery*

neurosurgery. From 1961 to '68 she was in emergency with time off for a BSc from McGill. From '68 through '84 she was Director of Nursing Service and capped off her career as Vice-President of Nursing.

Pam recalls that although she wasn't making much money "specialist doctors" didn't get rich in neurosurgery either. They might operate eight to ten hours and the patient would still die. Patients came as a result of motor vehicle accidents, brain tumors and aneurisms, and they came from all western provinces because it was the most advanced facility in western Canada. Station 54 was a nice-size ward — of 23 beds — and Pam and her staff cleaned out a utility room and transformed it into an intensive care unit. "Early ambulation" was a fashionable new term in hospital circles, and some patients would wander away. Pam recalls a Danish fellow with the bluest eyes. He was recovering from a head injury and still confused. "So we put a sign on his back — *Please return to Station 54."* Twice he was returned from the university campus.

*Plastic Surgery*

Plastic surgery was not set up as a formal division until 1965 but it was a recognized hospital service before that. It started right after the war when Ted Hitchin returned from the navy and restricted his practice to this specialty. Others had done a little of it, like "Hep" Hepburn who felt an obligation to repair cleft lips and palates for children, but Hitch went all the way. He was of the pioneering school of specialists who just went ahead and did it, pursuing an interest and picking up tips where they could. During his navy service Hitch spent a brief time at Valley Forge, Pennsylvania, with Dr. James Barrett Brown, the most eminent plastic surgeon of the day, and was very proud of it. Hitch was into his specialty before the Royal College of Physicians and Surgeons had qualifying exams for fellowship in plastic surgery. When the exams were instituted in the '50s he declined to take them, and nobody was surprised.

He was a colourful character, crusty and outspoken. He would swear in the operating room and throw instruments, but he suffered a great deal from asthma and eventually died of it. Towards the end he'd say: "If I'd known I was going to live this long I'd have taken care of myself." Patients either loved him or the opposite depending on whether they knew how to take him, but he was a very kind-hearted fellow and quite concerned about them. There was a skit in one of those annual shows the medical students put on. A voice came over the loudspeaker: "Calling Dr. Hitchin. Calling Dr. Hitchin. You should hear what they're calling Dr. Hitchin!" But that wouldn't bother Ted. He just laughed.

The second plastic surgeon to come aboard was of the new generation. Although Mac Alton served in the navy all his medical training was post-war, and when he joined the hospital staff he brought with him his FRCS. Mac was from Lamont, where his father was a prominent physician. He got his MD here and then Walter Mackenzie encouraged his interest in plastic surgery. Walter could see gaps in hospital service and recognized that specialists would be needed with more training than Hitch. Through his personal contacts Walter arranged a program in the United Kingdom. In Walter's case, Mac defines "a personal contact" as backing a prominent surgeon into a corner at a medical convention cocktail party somewhere, planting his thumb under the victim's nose and saying "I've got a man available. You've got to find a place for him." Walter actually obtained an appointment for Mac at East Grinstead, the famous hospital south of London where Sir Archibald McIndoe had worked wonders with allied airmen burned in crashes, not only in treating them surgically, but getting them out into society again. But Mac could see he wasn't advanced enough for East Grinstead and trained in Glasgow. And when he came back to our hospital in 1958 he was the first man in Alberta to be qualified in plastic surgery by the Royal College. As this was written the number of fellows had risen to 27.

With two specialists on staff group things could happen. In 1959 a Cleft Lip and Palate Clinic was set up. It was a multi-discipline team, comprising a plastic surgeon, a dentist, a speech therapist and a social worker. The team looked beyond treating the condition to the management of children with problems caused by it. It was the first of several teams which have caught public attention and brought recognition to the division of plastic surgery. Everyone has heard something of the burn unit team and the microvascular surgery team which reattaches severed limbs. These, of course, came much later.

*Otolaryngology*

This medical term refers to ear-nose-and-throat. For many years there was a marriage of convenience between otolaryngology and ophthalmology (the eye) and the combined work was perceived as belonging within surgery. But in 1960, with Mark Marshall about to retire, the arrangement was ended. As a result of post-war training programs there were vigorous new practitioners in both areas. In dissolving the marriage it was felt that work on ear-nose-and-throat should continue as a division of surgery, but that ophthalmology should be an autonomous department, though it did not become so officially until 1968.

Ken Clarke was named head of otolaryngology in 1960 and served 16 years. Ken was the first of the new generation. One of our graduates, he was inclined towards ear-nose-and-throat by military experience overseas with the Southern Alberta Regiment and by family tradition — an uncle and cousin in Glasgow were both in the field. Ken specialized at the University of Toronto and joined our medical staff in 1950 — a great help to Bill Armstrong who had done almost all the work since the outbreak of war.

The next year the hospital opened the southeast wing and EN & T emerged with its own ward of a dozen beds. The year after that the board endorsed a change in viewpoint which was to affect profoundly the practice of otolaryngology. Tonsils, long regarded as a threat, were to be seen as a possible benefit. The change is recorded in the board minutes for February 22 1952: "Dr. Mackenzie felt that the routine removal of tonsils of nurses in training was not justified. Unless a frequent history of sore throat or quinsy is obtained from candidates . . . tonsillectomy should not be required as a routine procedure." As Ken Clarke explains: "Immunologists argued that tonsils are an essential part of the body's immune system and by taking them out we were doing people a disservice." Quite a change from summers when Jack Bridge used to tour the countryside with the provincial clinic lining up children and lifting tonsils by the hundred. Some surgical procedures were being eliminated by drugs. Mass tonsillectomies were eliminated by the weight of opinion.

In 1954 otolaryngology was made a division of ophthalmology with Bill Armstrong in charge. More young men came in. Tom Wilson. And Peter Quinlan, an English chap who had pursued an interesting specialty. Peter introduced the microscope into surgery in Edmonton. He used it to operate for a

Ted Hitchin
Plastic Surgery

Mac Alton
Plastic Surgery

Ken Clarke
Otolaryngology

form of deafness called otosclerosis, in which the three little bones of the ear get fixed and won't vibrate to relay sound. With a microscope Peter could magnify the trouble area and loosen the last little bone. His equipment was elementary by current standards. Now there is a Diploscope, by which two surgeons can work simultaneously while the picture they see is shown magnified further and shown on closed-circuit television. But Peter's microscope was a significant advance.

*Ophthalmology*

The "eye" department emerged with its own building in this period. It was a one-storey effort, on the north end of the property, facing 87th Avenue, and came as something of a surprise to everybody, including the hospital board. There were mixed feelings about it, but all conceded it was a good example of how Mark Marshall could get something done. It was put up by the provincial department of public works in 1954 with money from an anonymous donor, and stood for 30 years.

Mark moved his practice over from the Tegler Building and did his teaching there. And our first cornea implants were done there by two younger men who had gone away to train under the Marshall Plan. Wint Duggan, as mentioned, went to Tulane. Don Rees went to Northwestern for three years and whenever Mark went east he'd stop overnight in Chicago and take Don to a football or hockey game. That was Mark's style.

At this time the eye department took off unexpectedly in a broad new direction, due to personal intervention of Alberta's Minister of Health. The story is unique in the history of our hospital and Alistair Boyd can tell it at first hand. Alistair came from Scotland in 1958 as the first full-timer in ophthalmology and was to head the department from 1963 to 1980. From the moment he arrived he found himself working closely with the newly-appointed minister, Donovan Ross, a general practitioner from the Stony Plain district.

He tells a background story to illustrate Don's concern about sick people. "His wife was a nurse. I used to sit with her at CNIB banquets and hear about epidemics when there was no more room for kids in the Stony Plain hospital and Don would bring them home. Once they had eight sick kids in bed — all other people's."

He brought this intense concern to the problem of blindness in the province. Glaucoma was then the commonest cause — an imbalance between interocular pressure and the local blood pressure. Too much inflow or too little outflow can cause it. One of the sufferers was Walter Mackenzie.

With financing direct from Don Ross's department a clinic to study glaucoma came into existence in January 1960. The opening was something of a scramble. Barbara Salter has been the orthoptist in charge since the start, and she recalls: "I'm not a nurse. I came from England as Dr. Boyd's secretary. Don Hassard and Andy Patrick (our first residents) gave me a 10-minute course in tomography and we were away." Fortunately a state-of-the-art device to monitor the fluctuating pressures was available. That *Goldman Perimeter* is still in service.

Barbara continues: "The idea was to provide research, teaching and patient care — in that order — but patient care just swamped us."

Under pressure from the medical community testing soon expanded beyond the original intention. Glaucoma patients had to be referred by an ophthalmologist, but any practitioner could send a patient for a report on "visual fields."

Coincidentally there developed a strabismus — or "squint" — clinic. "Once you used to see kids with a crossed eye that would go blind," Alistair says. "Now we can start work on a strabismus at one year. We like to get them no later

*Alistair Boyd*
*Ophthalmology*

than Grade One. In the '70s we got a program going in the Edmonton schools and it's gone province-wide."

The strabismus clinic is run by Gillian Budd, an orthoptist who has been with it since the beginning. "There is no national body registering orthoptists," Alistair continues. "We have our own training program. Don Ross helped dream that one up and the money came direct from his office."

The money is now lost in the global budget of the hospital, but the clinics continue. You might call them a personal legacy to the children of the province from a country doctor who cared about them very much.

*Thoracic and Cardiovascular Surgery*

Open-heart surgery was certainly the new kid on our block, or any block for that matter. The first successful open-heart operation was performed in Chicago in 1952. The first in Canada was performed at the University Hospital on September 17 1956.

The heart is in the chest (or thoracic) region of the body. In the late '40s thoracic surgery was acknowledged as a specialty. Herb Meltzer did surgery on the lung for tuberculosis. Colin Ross, Colin Dafoe and Carl Whiteside were on our staff as thoracic surgeons and Carl also performed a cardiac operation. Carl could "split" or widen the mitral valve — without opening up the heart. This was an acknowledged procedure. Carl was very confident and willing to talk about it to the press. Poor Carl had a flair for the dramatic and died quite young — of a heart attack while addressing a medical forum in Ottawa on heart disease. Carl had acquired his specialty from clinical experience. Walter Mackenzie felt that the hospital needed someone who had done experimental and research work as well. He knew the top men everywhere and through them knew about young men with promise. His choice to develop as cardiac surgeon was John Callaghan.

John was a graduate of the University of Toronto and was doing postgraduate work there on hypothermia with Dr. Bigelow. Walter had met John and heard him give a paper on electronic pacemakers to a forum in Boston. Walter and John Scott, our revered head of medicine, put a deal together to get John Callaghan here. They could see that he would qualify for a McLaughlin travelling fellowship — provided by Colonel Robert McLaughlin, the Canadian automobile magnate who had also owned Canada Dry Ginger Ale. The only condition was that he would need an appointment to the staff of a hospital, so that was arranged and John was off travelling for three years. To London for work with Lord Brock and Sir Clement Price-Thomas, then to Stanford in California to study with Dr. Frank Gerbode (pronounced ger-BOE-dee). His travels led him back to Edmonton in August 1955, to establish a program of cardiovascular surgery.

That took another year, conducting experiments on animals in the McEachern Lab, setting up procedures involving other medical departments — and building the pump. The heart-lung pump was the technological key to open-heart surgery. It provided a temporary bypass of circulation through heart and lungs so the surgeon could repair heart defects which had not been reachable before. There was no commercial pump available so John, and interested allies like Joe Dvorkin, set out to produce locally a replica of a machine developed at the University of Minnesota by Drs. Lillehei and DeWall. John says the design was "pre-Model-T." Les Willox described it as a Rube Goldberg invention, although Les regrets that nowadays he has to explain that Rube was a newspaper humourist who entertained readers with marvellous inventions made of miscellaneous hardware. Les assisted on the first two dozen operations. He had been sent down to the DeBakay clinic in Texas and came

*John Callaghan*
*Thoracic and Cardiovascular*
*Surgery*

back with the bypass procedure. John recalls that most of the machine work was done by an outfit with the intriguing name of Gopher Engineering. The university workshop made some metal wide-tube connectors which had to be highly polished. And the program got a boost one Sunday morning when John Beaton's car broke down near Vet's Sheet metal shop. When John went in to phone for rescue he saw a young fellow polishing copper tubing with jeweller's rouge. He recognized the polished pipe as something John Callaghan could use and in his capacity as purchasing agent bought it on the spot. John says: "Pipes had to be smooth to the nth degree. Dr. Callaghan would put a microscope on them and if there were any burrs he'd throw them out. He told me: 'What I'm trying to do is cut out all the variables.'"

The pieces of the heart-lung pump gradually fitted into place, along with the pieces of the diagnostic and operating procedure. Open-heart surgery depends on a complex intersupport system of specialties. Anaesthesiology, radiology and clinical laboratory services are obvious. The pieces of the diagnostic base were put in place while John was on his travelling fellowship. In 1953, as we've seen, Bob Fraser established the cardiovascular clinic in the Department of Medicine. On the surgical side, the following year, Bob Macbeth established a peripheral vascular clinic, which met each Monday to discuss surgery in the periphery of the cardiovascular system. In the meantime the first open-heart patient was waiting.

When Susan Beattie was a year old her family physician, Dr. Pat Rose, recognized a congenital heart defect. He suspected it was in the membrane separating the top chambers of the heart. When Susan was five her case was referred to Bob Fraser's clinic and the diagnosis was confirmed. Susan's problem would become acute when her body grew bigger and the heart couldn't keep pace. In 1954, when John Callaghan was on his travels, Susan entered Grade One. When Susan was eight, and about to enter Grade Three, she needed the operation. John says he and his team really weren't ready — "you're never as ready as you'd like to be" — but Susan couldn't wait. So the first open-heart surgery in Canada was scheduled for September 17 1956.

Susan's family doctor was by the operating table. Pat Rose says: "My part was just to watch. When John had the heart exposed there was a very strong sensation. None of us had ever seen a functioning heart that way. John turned to me and said: 'Well, Pat, do we go ahead? We think we know what's wrong but we don't really know because we haven't been inside.' Of course it was just a rhetorical question. We knew we had to go ahead."

The first operation achieved all that was hoped for. Susan grew up and married and had two children and nearly 30 years later attended the ceremony opening the cardiac surgery room in the Mackenzie Centre.

In the next 18 months 50 operations were attempted. Another surgeon joined the team. Cec Couves came as a clinical fellow, after residency at the DeBakay clinic in Texas. The Rube Goldberg pump provided moments of unscheduled drama, one of the reasons Les Willox likes to describe cardiovascular surgery as cardio-*theatrical*. When the pump overloaded blood would start spewing onto the floor and Les would have to carry on the operation while John Callaghan attended to the hardware.

Inevitably the pump dictated the gazetting of a new breed of technician, but at the start it was the responsibility of a nurse. Anita Wilde is surely one of the most thoroughly-travelled of that profession, having seen duty in Hamburg, Ottawa, Spokane, Juneau, Bangkok, Beirut, Belgrade and Conakry — which few can identify as capital of Guinea in west Africa. From 1956 to '58 she served a hitch in Edmonton as her husband Henry did a fellowship in cardiology at the University Hospital, just when a resourceful nurse was required to run John

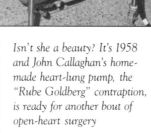

*Isn't she a beauty? It's 1958 and John Callaghan's home-made heart-lung pump, the "Rube Goldberg" contraption, is ready for another bout of open-heart surgery*

Callaghan's pump.

Mrs. Wilde has vivid memories of the contraption. It required six hours to set up — and had to be sterilized after that. In addition to the permanent polished-metal tubes more than 30 plastic tubes of varying lengths and diameters had to be cut and attached for each operation. She recalls: "Plastic tubing is not flexible. To slip it on the connectors, wetting of the tubing ends made the job easier. This I found out one day by accidentally depositing tears of frustration on to my thumbs which inadvertently transferred the liquid to the tubing ends."

Tubing had to remain transparent through the operation. If discoloured or cloudy, air bubbles in the arterial stream could not be seen. Clarity was achieved only by steam sterilization, which required prolonged venting to get rid of the moisture and only in the night hours was there room in the operating rooms for this procedure.

Anita had to give up this grinding work after two years by reason of becoming a patient in our department of obstetrics, and the specialist technician who came aboard to man the pump brought the title "the perfusionist." In the dictionary of medicine *perfusion* means "the injection of fluid into an artery in order to reach tissues," and the pump certainly injected a very important fluid into the body when it wasn't pumping it onto the floor of the operating room. The pump was electrical, though its appearance seemed to predate electricity and when the power failed, as it did on occasion, the perfusionist maintained the flow with a crank.

There was a more subtle problem with the blood supply and this was solved in typically quiet fashion by the Red Cross transfusion service and its genial director, Don Buchanan. Don was also helping those of us in obstetrics to combat the Rh factor in pregnancy. The Red Cross here in Edmonton was making up half-litre bottles of a formula developed by experience in wartime England. The bottle contained 380 millilitres of donor's blood — the rest an anticoagulant comprising distilled water, dextrose and disodium citrate. This formula was fine for a normal transfusion, but a patient in open-heart surgery required an average of 18 bottles, in one case as many as 60. In such large amounts the formula was upsetting the body's balance. We're into a very complicated business here, but to put it simply — by experiment and consultation with John Callaghan the local Red Cross reduced the disodium citrate and arrived at a ratio of 400 to 410 millilitres of donor blood to 90 to 100 of anticoagulant. This went on for a couple of years until an eastern laboratory began to supply pre-packaged units. And although I've often noted a reluctance in Toronto medical centres to be guided by western wisdom the lab certainly recognized our experience with open-heart surgery. Don and John did a paper on the subject which was presented in Rome to the Congress of the International Society of Blood Transfusion.

Pioneering a surgical specialty is fraught with setbacks and disappointments. Nurses got a pretty good view of this aspect and Jennie Flowers was charge nurse on Station 53 — actually the urology ward — where John Callaghan was given one room for his open-heart patients. After surgery they were brought there directly rather than to the general recovery room and a special post-operative team took over. Once a parent ran screaming from the room because she wasn't prepared for seeing her child under intensive-care conditions. Jennie recalls that successful operations ended in the death of the patient because disease was far advanced and surgery was a last chance. She says: "It was very hard for a young man, especially from Toronto, to come into this hospital and start such a big program. Whenever the operating room is involved there's competition and tension and heart operations took up a lot of hours. Dr. Callaghan was a young man and some days you could almost see him age before your eyes. But he could really talk — he could sell ice to Eskimos. He once told a friend of ours: 'If something goes wrong people can sue me. But I can't stop. This is how it has to be.'"

In a couple of years things got easier. The specialty moved into its own ward on Station 55. Operations were proceeding at a pace of two a week. A factory-made heart-lung pump came on the market — a Pemco K-Cross Oxinator from Cleveland. It was used for the next 400 operations and the Rube Goldberg contraption was put into storage waiting for a museum to display it — a museum which was still pending as this was written. A plastic fibre called Ivalon came on the market, to replace artery segments obtained from cadavers. Fabric was better and safer with no rejection and no degeneration. At this stage the surgery was confined to repair of congenital heart defects, but replacement of valves would begin in 1962, another Canadian first.

In 1960, thoracic and cardiovascular became a division of the Department of Surgery with John Callaghan as director. John was still there as this was written, and the division had a data bank with information on 7000 cases — beginning with the first open-heart operation in Canada.

The Department of Surgery climaxed this busy period of progress by moving into a new suite of operating rooms. They occupied the fifth level of the Clinical Services Wing, which opened in 1960-61. The Wing deserves a chapter of its own, which will follow.

The new suite had 14 operating rooms compared to six, and other important comparisons are noted by Bob Johnston:

"The lighting was artificial. There were no windows and this was considered a drawback by some. When surgeons needed daylight for operations there used to be a lot of talk about the best direction to have the windows facing. Humidity was a constant 50 percent. In the old OR's the only way to change the air was by opening a window, but here we were air-conditioned and the air was changed 10 times an hour. (In the Mackenzie Centre it turns over 25 times.)

"Two of the rooms had glass domes and this was a big improvement for teaching. Twenty students at a time could sit around and observe by looking down. In the old OR's they had to scrub and dress with the surgical team and often saw very little. (Shortly after the opening Premier Manning came for a look through the dome. Accompanied by health minister Don Ross he observed John Callaghan performing open-heart surgery on a little girl from Leduc.)

"Even our floors were the last word. Explosive gases were still used in anaesthesia. Floors were grounded to carry off static electricity.

"Another important point — rooms were all the same size. I remember Walter Mackenzie insisted on this so they could be switched around among all services. The system of major and minor rooms was a nuisance. Somebody lost sight of this laying out the Mackenzie Centre."

Another new feature was the recovery room, which much impressed Les Willox. Les says, in his forceful way: "It cut down on the agony in the wards. In the old days we'd wheel the patient back to his room and a nurse would sit with him till he came out of it. By this time we had a shortage of nurses. Surgery was getting more complicated, so was anaesthesia. The anaesthetist would have to chase down a mile of corridors to check on the patient. In the recovery room he was held until he could look after himself. It was just a big barn of a room with half a dozen bins and a charge nurse sitting on a dais to keep an eye on things, but we had oxygen, and if something went wrong after an operation the patient could be wheeled right back in again."

Les missed only one feature of the previous arrangement: "About the time we'd finished our operations in the old place the internists would wind up in the room outside for coffee — Frank Elliott, Ted Donald, John Scott. We could have informal consultations on what was wrong with somebody. The only one who objected was Johnny Macgregor the pathologist. He liked to do frozen sections in that room and didn't like getting bits of sugar mixed in."

Olive McLennan witnessed the transfer from the vantage point of the Operating Room Technician, a recent addition to the OR team. Walter Mackenzie, who didn't miss much, had observed that as fast as he could train graduate nurses for surgery they felt an uncontrollable urge to travel. He'd also observed that Certified Nursing Aides were not so peripatetic, and decided he could train CNA's for certain functions of the nurse and they would stay around longer. Walter was certainly right about that. Olive McLennan was one of four to complete the first three-month course in 1956 and was still on duty in the mid-80's, along with her friend Lydia Mireau who took the course shortly after.

(In connection with this program a footnote of interest to male chauvinists is found in the board minutes of September 13 1957: "It has been found necessary to train females rather than males because of the problem of the general salary schedule of the hospital." In other words, women could be paid less.)

Olive recalls: "We thought it was a beautiful place to work. It was so much drier. One job technicians had taken over was sterilizing the instruments, and there was a steam autoclave between each room so we weren't running in and out with dripping trays and pitchers of boiling water. We said goodbye to the solution room. It was terrible. Someone would get called away with a tap running and the floor would be awash.

"It was certainly nicer for the patients. In the old place the corridor ran right through the middle with operating rooms on either side. Patients on stretchers had to lie outside with people walking by. Afterwards they were wheeled out into the same corridor — and you never look your best coming out from the OR."

This suite was to serve for the next quarter-century.

*Obstetrics and Gynaecology*

This was the third of the triumvirate of departments dignified by a professorship when the hospital was organized. The others were medicine and surgery and O and G is a combination of these, about equal. The practice concerns medical conditions exclusive to women. That means of the reproductive system, including pregnancy, which was certainly a major concern in the baby boom of the '50s.

I had the honour to be professor of Obstetrics and Gynaecology from 1942 to 1962. My department didn't experience the subdividing that went on in medicine and surgery, but when people would ask me if there was any specialization, I'd tell them that when a doctor got too old and tired to go out at night and deliver babies he confined his practice to gynaecology.

Our department participated fully in the baby boom. From 1952 through '61 we delivered 18,000 of the little ones, including 220 sets of twins and four of triplets. Other departments kept pace with the rising population, but we contributed to it as well. At one stretch Ron Horner held the dubious honour of admitting more patients than anyone else on the medical staff — 50 a month for delivery. Ron was the first of the new generation of obstetricians and we were certainly ready for a new wave. Ron had graduated from the U of A in 1939 and done three years postgraduate work in Cleveland before joining the RCAF as a medical officer. Even then Ron got some unexpected obstetrical experience when the armed forces set up a maternity ward for women members who had loved well, perhaps, but not wisely.

We escaped from the annex out back just in time to meet the baby boom. In the fall of 1951 obstetrics moved into Station 44 of the new south wing. (Gynaecology went into Station 43.) "The new maternity section seemed very posh." This was the assessment of Margaret Munro (Mrs. Donnie Bell) who had worked as a nurse in the annex and had enjoyed the atmosphere so much, she returned to the new wing to have her first child. As a professional she was impressed by the nurseries on each corridor, the small "premature" nursery, large labour and delivery rooms, two rooms for emergency admissions, consulting rooms, examining room, rooms for students and staff. "Room" was the overriding difference. We even had a medical stenographer to make notes on deliveries — this was certainly progress. Shortly before, I'd lobbied for a part-time stenographer for our whole department and all my arguments failed.

The baby boom was a period of increased safety for both mothers and children. For the mothers antibiotics reduced the danger of infections and fevers and there was better and more extended care both pre- and post-natal. Back in 1935, when we had 15,000 births in Alberta and 85 maternal deaths, the Royal College of Physicians and Surgeons of Alberta established a maternity mortality committee to promote better care during pregnancy — go every month to the doctor, check the blood pressure, don't put on too much weight. Maternal morbidity declined, and we began to classify not only mortality but morbidity.

Then, in 1953 Dr. Herman Siemens of the Leduc-Strathcona Health Unit said to us we were doing such a good job with mothers, why didn't we do something for babies? So the college set up a Perinatal-Mortality Committee, the first in North America.

In raising the baby's chances of survival the most important event of the '50s was treatment of the Rh factor. Ron Horner calls it "aggressive" treatment and that's certainly the word. We couldn't have done it so aggressively without the help of Don Buchanan and the Red Cross blood transfusion service.

I've already mentioned this service in connection with open-heart surgery.

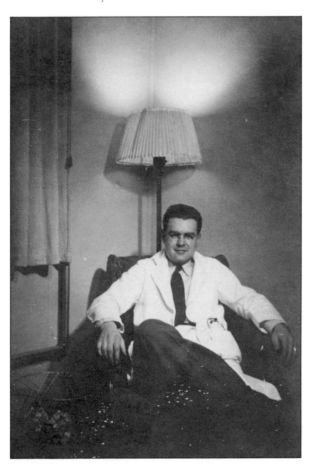

*Ron Horner*
*Obstetrics and Gynaecology*

Perhaps I should explain its origin. When the war ended the Red Cross was left with a lot of funds and expertise in gathering blood. So the national director went across Canada offering to set up blood banks. If a provincial government would provide a building the Red Cross would provide a service. Not surprisingly, only the two provinces farthest removed from Ontario showed interest, and in 1947 blood banks were opened in Vancouver, Edmonton and Calgary.

Stan Greenhill opened the Edmonton office. Don Buchanan came in 1949 and was in charge for some 30 years. Don is no less a Scot for having been born in India — his father was with a Highland regiment guarding the British Raj. During the war Don was out in Alberta as a medical officer with the RAF and got to know Ron Horner. Finding post-war Scotland an unfavourable environment for a medical man he spotted an advertisement in a medical journal seeking qualified doctors to run blood banks in Canada. When Don arrived in Edmonton and went to call on Angus McGugan, Angus gave him a typical welcome — offering to help him with his English!

The key to averting Rh-negative brain damage to babies is monitoring the blood condition of the parents, and if the baby is likely to be Rh-negative to be prepared for transfusions. Before Don came we had to send blood samples to Winnipeg for analysis. Dr. Bruce Chowne, who had made Winnipeg the centre for Rh treatment in North America, was always very helpful. But with Don Buchanan we could have it done here and consult with him on a near-at-hand basis.

My departmental report for 1958 can show how the program worked. We delivered 1,969 babies. During pregnancy the Red Cross tested the blood of the mothers and 304 showed Rh-negative. Only an Rh-negative mother will produce an Rh-negative baby so further testing was done with the fathers involved to spot combinations of positive-negative factors which might endanger the baby. This screening reduced the potential problem cases to 46. Thanks to the Red Cross we were able to offer these mothers immune globulin. Women who'd developed antibodies were recruited to donate blood which was then sent to the Connaught Laboratory for an extract of the globulin factor. Potential problems were monitored closely. In the eighth or ninth month, if the antibody titre rose sharply, we might induce labour. Eventually 25 babies were born jaundiced and we transfused them with blood from the Red Cross. Another five needed new blood for ABO compatibility.

Also in 1958 we were all pleased that Don Buchanan was appointed to the hospital and faculty of medicine to work in pathology and clinical laboratory services.

Caesarean section became routine for the safety of the baby in an Rh-negative situation. It was a safety routine for both when the mother developed toxemia — a rapid rise in blood pressure before delivery. In the '30s we had done Caesareans only as a last resort — in less than two percent of deliveries. By the '50s we were running at about five percent, but only for the safety of mother or child. As this is being written the rate is up around 15 percent — for the safety of

243

1952—1961

the doctor. These are litigious times in which everybody wants a scapegoat. If a baby doesn't survive the parents look for someone to blame. It has to be the hospital or the doctor. It's my opinion that doctors today have to practice "defensive medicine."

The '50s brought at least one unpleasant surprise. We had hardly settled into our commodious new quarters on Station 44 when we experienced a surge of staphylococcus infections. As Ron Horner says: "Staph infections just took off and multiplied like rabbits in Australia." The operating rooms were bothered by staph, but the maternity wards were hit hardest. New mothers were breaking out in boils and breast abscesses. We could culture staph from finger marks on a bedside table or dust on a wall. We could even culture it right out of the air. Ron was holding forth on the problem at one of our meetings so I said: "All right, you're head of the committee to do something about it." Ron's committee beat staph the old-fashioned way, with simple cleanliness. Walls, floors, beds and furniture were washed down repeatedly, the housekeeping staff cooperating with customary dedication. Nose cultures were taken of hospital personnel to iden-tify carriers, and a fine paediatrician had to be told to literally keep his nose out of the maternity wards until the infections were controlled.

Ted Gain and the anaesthetists helped us introduce the new developments in medicine and surgery. They also helped us keep up with fashions in having babies. Women gossip about their deliveries. In the '30s they said: "My dear, you must be asleep." So the anaesthetists produced a condition we called "twilight sleep" in which the mother did little pushing and the baby often was delivered with forceps, sometimes with damage. By the '50s women were saying: "My dear, you must be awake." So Ted and his department were ready with the pudendal block, a local anaesthetic which reduced sedation and made for a happy atmosphere in the delivery room. I'm glad I retired before the current craze, when women started saying: "My dear, you must have your husband in the room." I wouldn't want "that fellow" around. It's making too much of togetherness. Besides I've heard young women swear in labour — and they've come up with words I'd never heard before. Two related trends of the '50s were pre-natal exercise and early ambulation, and as I've mentioned already, the average "confinement," as the term used to be, was reduced to five days, a benefit to the entire hospital during the baby boom.

In the area of gynaecology one of the biggest advances was pap tests for detecting cancer in the cervix. I kick myself I didn't keep a diary because I'd like to know exactly when some of the following events happened, but in the early '50s a chap in New York named Dr. Papanicalaou (and another chap, Dr. Trout) were looking at cells from the cervix and discovered odd-shaped cells, which they identified as cancerous. I was down in the state of Washington the year after the test became known and heard more about it. I talked it up around Edmonton but couldn't get anyone interested. As Ron Horner explains: "Pathologists were trained to work with blocks of tissue and couldn't see the value of a few cells." Then one of the lads came home from the war — Lee Brown — and started doing some tests. The method was to take a smear on a slide and fix it with a mixture of alcohol and ether, very time-consuming. I remember being away somewhere on a trip or a conference and reading an ad in a medical journal for some stuff to squirt on slides. I ordered some from a surgical supply company. We sprayed it on the slide to fix the smear — then in the lab we dissolved the agent and left the swab free for testing. Eventually the pathologists came around and pap tests were an accepted thing in the '50s.

If surgery was required we did it. If radium was the treatment we referred our patients to the annex out on the grounds which, until recently had been our maternity ward. (No building was wasted then. When we moved up to Station

*Reminding us of that gallant crew, without whose able support the medical advances of any age could not be brought to suffering humanity, "Slim" Waters operates on a wheelchair*

44 of the extended main building the provincial cancer clinic moved from overtown to the old maternity cottage.) In the University Hospital all cases requiring radium treatment were eventually referred to Dr. Victor Wright's clinic — we called him "Daddy" Wright — although the Royal Alex continued to use its own supply. There is a widespread belief that no committee once formed ever ceases to exist, but this was the fate of the radium committee, a powerful group in our hospital since 1925.

Like the Department of Surgery we climaxed this period of busy progress with a move to the Clinical Services Wing. In 1961, as I've mentioned, surgery took over the fifth level of this welcome addition to our plant. Obstetrics took over level six, while gynaecology remained on the fourth floor of the 1951 wing — where we had been for 10 years — and took in the space vacated by obstetrics.

We had three case rooms in the new venue — case room is professional jargon for delivery room — and two labour rooms with two beds each. We had 58 beds for maternity, with a daily occupancy rate of about 55, and introduced a routine called *rooming in*, by which babies could remain with their mothers. We delivered more of them, 2,211 in 1961, up from 1,512 10 years before, and gynaecological admissions increased from 719 to 1,709. Mind you we had a growing staff to handle all this work. There were seven of us in 1951. Ten years later there were 12, with nine courtesy staff and three residents.

Years went swiftly and happily. It was stimulating to work with new ideas and younger colleagues, but as time went on I began to notice something. At consultations and committee meetings all my colleagues were younger. Some were very much younger.

# Chapter 19

# 1960—1961
*Clinical Services Wing*

This welcome addition to the work space deserves a chapter of its own, as I mentioned earlier. It sought to correct an imbalance which had built up over a long period. As Angus McGugan wrote: "For many years beds had been added without making provision for expansion of support units." In April 1956 the board approved the idea of a major addition which would enable support services to catch up. Initially it was titled "the *service* wing," but that name was clearly short of the mark and it was elevated to *Clinical Services Wing*. To plant the footings the cornerstone of the main building, which the founders had laid with great expectations on June 25 1913, had to be removed, and there was some consternation when the historic stone was mislaid and then found again. Work ceased briefly in July 1959 when Queen Elizabeth, on her second visit to Edmonton, came to see the veterans in the Mewburn, but the project proceeded on schedule and the Clinical Services Wing was occupied over the winter of 1960-61.

The interior arrangements were most satisfactory though, mind you, the externals made people nervous and bricks began to pop. With your indulgence I'd like to conduct a tour of the interior.

At the conclusion of the previous chapter we were on the sixth level in our new obstetrical section.

Going down one level we'd find the brand-new operating suite of the department of surgery.

Down one more to the fourth level and we'd find Ted Bell setting up the entire floor as the clinical sciences laboratory.

Down to the third level and Hec Duggan would be spreading out the equipment of the department of radiology.

On the second level we'd find the outpatient and emergency service.

On the first level Jessie Nairn and the medical librarians would be moving in the patient records, and all records would be inside for a change. For some time any "remembrance of things past" had to be fished out from under the Wells Pavilion, chilly work in winter and a clammy enterprise in wet weather. Elsewhere, chapel fittings and four dental chairs would be going in and books would be going up on the shelves of the John Scott medical library. This was a fitting tribute to a true gentleman and scholar who had retired by this time from his responsibility as dean of medicine, but still went out visiting auxiliary hospitals, explaining gently that "my patients are there and so are most of my friends." He was still reading, and I have to laugh at Marnie Sproule's story of coming to visit the Scotts on a Saturday morning. John was in his den, deep in a book. Marnie remarked that it was "The Story of Philosophy" by Will Durant. "Yes," he said, "I am reading it for the fifth time and I never cease to enjoy it."

The levels of the Clinical Services Wing require a note of explanation because 112th Street slopes uphill from the south. The main entrance to the hospital at the south end was from the first level, but by the time you walked to the north end the first level was partly-submerged and entrance was through the second level through a department with an interesting history.

*The Clinical Services Wing — the box all that beautiful space came in. The windows along the top level make it bright for the newborns on the maternity floor. The floor below, with almost no windows, has the new operating suites, a source of pride and satisfaction. Below the operating rooms the clinical sciences laboratory spreads over an entire floor. Below that is the radiology department. The entrance door with the ramp leads into the emergency and outpatient area. Half-submerged in Level 1 are the medical records, library, chapel and dental clinic*

*The Outpatient Department*

Until 1960 the outpatient service was an outpost of the hospital. In 1924 it had been moved overtown to the Kenny McLeod house — at 9912 - 103rd Avenue. In 1940 it shifted a few blocks to a building the provincial government bought from Eaton's department store at 10048 - 101A Avenue. In 1954 it went to another downtown provincial building, the Williamson Block, at 9815 Jasper. It finally came home when we put up the Clinical Services Wing.

Outpatient service has been called the laboratory of the school of medicine. Every teaching hospital had one. In the days before Medicare it was a good

*July 1959 — Royal Visit III takes precedence over construction of the Clinical Services Wing. Queen Elizabeth meets the veterans on the grounds of the Mewburn Pavilion. Dr. Frank Ramsey, DVA superintendent, is in the picture along with the Duke of Edinburgh, and Angus McGugan, in the background at right, looking very pleased*

deal for all parties involved. The hospital got patients for student doctors and nurses; patients without funds got the service of a hospital; and civic and provincial welfare departments had a central depot to which they could refer clients. It certainly provided cases for my own department of obstetrics. In the period 1952-61 nearly a quarter of the babies we delivered had their mothers referred from the outpatient service.

From the welter of figures compiled by this department perhaps we can pick three sets to indicate the growth of activity. In 1952, 1,061 outpatients made 7,063 visits. In 1959, the last year overtown, 3,654 patients made 16,666 visits. In 1961, the first full year back home, 4,419 patients made 25,000 visits.

Another point should be made here. Each medical division in the hospital had its own outpatient program. In 1961 these programs accounted for a further 100,000 visits. So the ancient equation — one patient equals one hospital bed — was long passé.

Our renowned "Ma" Porritt ran the outpost from 1942 to '55. When she retired at very long last the position was taken by Clare Carlyle, who served 14 years. One of our graduates, class of '36, Clare took part of her training at the McLeod house location and is well qualified to compare the working of the clinic at downtown and campus sites.

The Jasper Avenue establishment was small. In addition to Clare, Sylvia Saville was the secretary, Edythe Markstad was instructor for the student nurses, of whom there were two at a time. A resident was stationed overtown and doctors from the medical staff came over on rotation for morning and afternoon clinics. Clare recalls that almost all the patients were indigent. Many were sent from the provincial single men's hostel and bus loads came in from the work camp at Gunn. When the move was made to the campus an editorial in the *Journal* gave the opinion that some of the clients would no longer find their way to the clinic. And although no one could say so this was certainly part of the idea. Almost every day Clare had to call the police to remove a difficult case. She called so often that a running joke developed. The police used to go through a routine of questions: Name? First name? Year you were born? It finally go so that when she said "Mrs. Carlyle calling" the operator would come back: "First name Clare. Born in 19--." Well, whatever is was. Clare isn't obliged to tell anyone but the police. There were some regular visitors. One was an epileptic, a nice lad, but always in scrapes. Whenever he was due to be released from lockup he wrote Clare a letter. She had 18 letters from him. The clinic was an equal-opportunity setup. A lady client once socked Clare on the jaw when the drugs she demanded weren't handed over. Edythe Markstad, who was taller, stood in the way, and the lady abandoned the engagement.

Apart from being out of the combat zone the campus location offered the advantage of close proximity to all the services of the hospital. To specialist members of the medical staff on geographic full-time appointments. To x-ray service. To the pharmacy — the nurses had dispensed drugs overtown. And the dietary and social service departments assigned full-time workers to the outpatient clinic. The majority of patients were still referred from welfare agencies and their needs often went beyond simply medical.

But the most important advantages were to the students in our medical program. Adam Little explains: "The feeling was we were catering to a small but steady group that needed financial help. The clinics weren't attracting the variety of patients our students needed to give them a balanced experience with what a normal practice would be."

Adam is the authority on this subject although his specialty in medicine is haematology. When the move was planned he was asked to direct outpatient service in addition to his regular duties as geographic full-time member of the

*Clare Carlyle*
*Outpatient Department*

medical staff. Adam's MD is from the University of Manitoba — he came to us in 1955 — and I would have to say that you can't have too many graduates of Manitoba if you want a hospital to run well.

There was another aspect to the move — our emergency service was upgraded and combined with outpatient service. Adam explains the emergency aspect too: "The feeling was that residents and interns should be exposed to more of that work. It would offer them a more varied clientele on which to gain experience for a practice."

Since the beginning of the hospital "emergency" had been one room — at three locations on the first floor. As Bob Johnston recalls: "In it there was a chair, a table and a cabinet. The only thing in the cabinet was a thermometer and that was used for one purpose — for the duty intern to take the temperatures of children being admitted for tonsillectomies."

The room was unstaffed until late in the '50s when a nurse was on duty during the day. She would decide whether the case needed medical or surgical attention and attempt to contact the appropriate member of the medical staff. There was once a wild night of medical drama in that room. A railroad worker lost both legs in a switchyard accident. The staff was determined to save his life and succeeded, although they used 40 bottles of blood and left a scene of carnage that took days for maintenance men to restore.

The Clinical Services Wing was designed with the ground floor reserved for emergency and outpatient work. The design included a ward of six beds for acute cases, six examining rooms, three minor surgery rooms and an orthopaedic plaster room.

*Radiology*

Hec Duggan and the x-ray people moved on to the floor above the outpatient-emergency section.

Hec succeeded "Pop" Procter, the last of our original department heads in 1953, on returning from a year's fellowship in Europe provided by a grant of $3,600 from the Alberta division of the Canadian Cancer Society.

The x-ray film is the basic coin of radiology. In 1952 the department processed 45,000 films. In 1961 films totalled 132,900. Of greater significance are the figures on arteriograms. These have been noted already for their contribution to neurosurgery — a dye being introduced into the bloodstream to produce a successful x-ray of the brain. In 1952 the number of arteriograms was nil, a condition that persisted through 1959. But in 1961 there were 400 arteriograms, the work of Henry Pribram, an English-trained radiologist who made a brief career stopover in Edmonton.

Radiology was operating on a different plane. The prime example was the radio-isotope lab. Hec Duggan recalls the story:

"We set it up in 1953 when I came back from Europe. There were four of us who wanted to treat patients with disorders of the thyroid — cancer and parathyroidism, better known to the public as goitre. But no one of us knew how to go about it. It took a partnership of four viewpoints. Don Wilson for medicine

— Don was in direct contact with patients. Myself for radiology. Ted Bell in clinical laboratory services. And Don Scott. Don wasn't in the hospital or even the Faculty of Medicine. He was in physics at the university and we needed his special knowledge — the way Harold Rice, the physiologist, was needed to measure patients' breathing during the polio crisis. Later on a biologist, Dorothy Weber, joined our team, because when you're injecting patients you have to know how much to give.

"We had a grant of $9,000 from the Alberta Division of the Canadian Cancer Society. What we contrived was equipment to calculate doses of radio-

*October 14 1955 — Hec Duggan demonstrates the radioistope lab for a medical symposium. Viewing the picture 30 years later he laughed that the hand-lettered panels contained most of the information then available on Nuclear Medicine*

active phosphorus. Our major piece of equipment was the first scanner in Alberta, a primitive one-inch model put out by Tracer Lab. There wasn't much literature to refer to or places to write to. There were few papers and we had to travel to get information, or learn from demonstrations by companies which made lab equipment. We got a "professional training" grant from the province so Don Scott and Don Wilson could spend two weeks at an isotope clinic in the eastern states. I was a member of the Society for Nuclear Medicine, but it was only founded in 1953, the year we started our isotope lab. About all we could get from the society was signs. They were yellow and magenta and read *Radiation Hazard — Danger*. We tacked them on the lab door and they certainly scared people off.

"Our first patient was a girl from Calgary who had a goitre from hyperthyroidism. We used radioactive gold which had a half-life of only 2.7 days. It came from Fort Knox, Tennessee, and with airline schedules what they were a shipment often took 30 hours en route. I'd meet the planes at the airport."

The radio-isotope lab enjoyed the moral and financial support of a body to which I've already made reference. This was the Special Services and Research Committee, grubstaked initially with $1,000,000 Angus McGugan had managed to salt away.

The committee always reported glowingly on the achievements of the radio-isotope lab. Everyone was impressed with it. Well not quite everybody. When the cornerstone was being planned for the Clinical Sciences Building (not to be confused with the Clinical *Services Wing* though it often is) Hec and his co-conspirators were asked to put in the research papers they'd developed with isotope experience. The news brought a typical teen-age reaction from Hec's son: "You mean it smells so bad they have to bury it?"

*Clinical Laboratory Services — Since Renamed Department of Laboratory Medicine*
This department, which moved on to the fourth level of the Clinical Services Wing, did not exist until Ted Bell returned from postgraduate training in 1949.

Ted was one of three sons of Irving Bell in the hospital staff — Donnie was an obstetrician and Gordon a cardiologist. Ted started postgraduate training in England when he was still in the army. From here he was sent to the University of Minnesota to work with Dr. Gerald Evans, a dominant figure in laboratory medicine. Throughout his association with the hospital Ted had a knack for getting what he wanted, and he certainly showed this talent when he went to Minnesota. He took Mary Wholey, the head of our pharmacy, as his bride.

Since the beginning the hospital had depended on the university for pathological lab work and on the provincial lab for bacteriology and serology. And while cooperation from people like Johnny Macgregor and Bob Shaw was unstinting the time had come for us to stand on our own. As department head Ted inherited a single room on the third floor of the old hospital next to the elevator, where, in his student days, he and others had done clinical laboratory analysis under direction of a technician — blood sugars, blood urea nitrogens, gastric titrations, that sort of thing.

The hospital was certainly correct to identify laboratory services as a growth area. Ted started out providing a dozen procedures — each done manually, step by step. As this was written the department could do 2,500 procedures and turn out 3,000 individual tests per hour.

Harold Bell (no relation) became chairman after Ted's untimely death in 1973. Harold joined the department in 1957 after Ted was stricken with polio. He recalls: "Ted was wheelchair-bound but it was hard to keep up to him. He could make that wheelchair move. He was a hard-working guy, in every way.

*Ted Bell*
*Clinical Laboratory Services*

And a voracious reader."

In the late '50s automation came to the aid of the lab. The first *Technicon Autoanalyser* was obtained. It could handle 12 procedures at a time with the technician simply putting samples in at one end and taking them out the other. As Harold Bell says, Ted was a master at knowing how to justify what he needed, and the administration was very supportive. They could talk to Reg Adshead or George Sherwood at any time and could even phone direct to the Deputy Minister of Health and argue for what they felt was necessary.

Ted was also a leader in training. When Harold arrived the staff was 18 technicians, most of whom Ted had trained on the job on a one-year apprenticeship. He was involved when the university set up a degree course and NAIT started its own two-year program. Graduates of both programs were in the employ of the department of laboratory medicine as this was written. And that's quite a number. The department had 16 MDs, seven PhDs, 175 qualified technologists and 60 support staff.

*Dentistry*

With the advent of our Clinical Services Wing, dentistry gained a permanent presence in the hospital. For many years Scott Hamilton had brought patients into the operating rooms for oral surgery or assisted at injury operations where dental trauma was a factor. But dentistry was never on the premises of the hospital as it was of the university. That changed with the new wing. A clinic of four chairs was established on the first level. Hec McLean says: "It gave experience to our students and residents. Most of the work was done for the hospital. I argued that patients coming in should have a dental inspection to give the attending physician a report on the health of the mouth and had a lot of support for it." Gradually the clinic took on an outpatient function and with the later move to the Mackenzie Centre dentistry gained a very obvious presence in ambulatory care.

*Pharmacy*

This department certainly ranks as a "clinical service" and would logically have been housed physically in the wing of that name if it had not already attained room to breathe. In the shuffles of the mid-50s the pharmacy acquired the entire basement of the 1929-30 addition. However it maintained an outpost in the Clinical Services Wing for clients of the outpatient and emergency department.

The pharmacy is one of the very oldest services of the hospital. Back in the 1906 version there was a dispensary identified by a picture of a pestle-and-mortar on the door.

When the hospital moved to the campus the dispensary wasn't much bigger. It was put in the basement under the x-ray room and got stuck for nearly 40 years. Three ladies were in charge down there, commencing in 1923 when the university recaptured the hospital from the army. All had BSc's from the U of A and all gave up pharmacy for matrimony. Margaret Russell was first. When she left in 1928 Bill Goldberg filled in briefly before going into business on Jasper Avenue. Ethel Norris was next but when she married in 1932 she was succeeded by J.M. Sisson, a gentle old-timer who'd had enough of Jasper Avenue and wanted a slower pace. Mr. Sisson retired eventually in 1945 and was followed by Mary Wholey, a lively girl who made lots of friends, but departed in 1948 to become Mrs. Ted Bell.

Walter Maday came next. Walter was in charge for 28 years and maintains that he is grey-haired now only because the walls of the x-ray room were shielded with lead, but the floor wasn't.

*Walter Maday*
*Pharmacy*

*257*

*1960—1961*

Even with his original dark hair Walter was a pharmacist of the old school, beginning his career when a candidate had to work two years in a drugstore before he was accepted into a university course in pharmacy. He apprenticed at Armstrong Drugs, a celebrated establishment on 97th Street, and earned his degree in 1943.

When he took over the pharmacy Walter maintained the special relationship Mary had established with the interns. In Walter's judgment the overworked denizens of "Hogan's Alley" were holding the hospital together in return for lodging and food. The pharmacy added spirits, subtly of course. In the labs 7-percent alcohol was kept for fixing slides. Walter put up signs, understood by the interns, which read: "If you must take it don't refill with water." Walter also aided and abetted a St. Patrick's Day ritual. "Cappy" Kidd liked to give selected patients capsules of methalene blue, a powdered dye which can be used to mark money. Taken in capsules it resulted in green urine. The camaraderie of these high jinks had a useful carryover into the '50s when the carefree interns returned from postgraduate training as leading members of the medical staff.

Using as a measure the number of prescriptions issued, the pharmacy doubled its activity from 1952 to '61 — 62,159 prescriptions against 124,444. And the department wasn't merely "dispensing," it was manufacturing. As Walter explains: "The pharmacies in all teaching institutions were into manufacturing. We had to give the teaching staff what was needed even if it wasn't available. And the medical staff was into more and more specialized work. For many years Gary Longford was in charge in the manufacturing area."

Alistair Boyd, the ophthalmologist, presented Walter's group with a real challenge. He wanted to use fluorocene to trace blood circulation in the eye. But fluorocene was available commercially only in a 2 percent solution. He needed 25 percent. Pharmacy residents were put to work on that tricky requirement.

The surgeons needed oral electrolite solutions — of three potassium salts. These were made to order. Each member of the medical staff had his own preparations — Harold Orr and Paul Rentiers had special ointments for dermatology.

When open-heart surgery started the pharmacy had to import drugs which were not in use in western Canada. It also participated in clinical field trials of new commercial drugs — keeping records of the doctor, the patient and the results.

Sometimes the pharmacy had to scrounge other people's equipment. A little later, when Lionel McLeod got into advanced kidney work, solutions for dialysis were made up in the autoclave in the infant care area. The neonatal people would be finished making up the babies' formulas by noon and the pharmacists could use the autoclave after that.

Some of the ingredients in these compounds could be pretty potent, so much so that in the early '50s Angus McGugan came close to advertising for a new pharmacist. It seems that workmen were replacing the roof on the laundry. A big rain and windstorm came splashing in from the west and rain poured down the elevator shaft into the basement of the laundry, the "volatile storage" area for the pharmacy. One of the most volatile was acetate, which came in 45-gallon drums. Walter was about to remove the seal from a drum of acetate so it would fit on a makeshift hoist when he noticed a workman smoking. Under protest the smoker doused his flame. When the seal was lifted an ominous sh-h-h-h broke the attentive silence. The acetate had gone gaseous, a spark could have created a vacancy in the pharmacy. After that the acetate was stored outside, in a lean-to against the outer wall of the laundry. The lean-to was of wood so an explosion would blow away from the main building. It was a safety solution that would hardly find favour today, but then we usually settled for something less than the ideal.

By avoiding explosions Walter Maday was able to work right up till 1976, when he retired as head of a department with eight graduate pharmacists. In making his exit Walter put out the fourth formulary in the history of the hospital. Previous editions were issued in 1936, '44 and '58. The dictionary defines a formulary as "a *book* containing the names of pharmaceutical sub-stances and their uses." But the '76 version was developed to go on the computer. And through all this time the department maintained an historic activity dating from the hospital's first participation in "leading-edge" medical research. For half of each day an assistant was engaged in measuring and mailing weekly doses of insulin to some 325 diabetics around the province. So was perpetuated a service founded in the 1920s with a personal gift of $5,000 from John D. Rockefeller Jr.

*Dietary Service*

I find that the food a patient receives in hospital often makes the first and the lasting impression. You can talk to a man who's just been released after a complicated emergency operation that took 10 hours and 12 doctors and backup from all the departments listed earlier and ask him what impressed him most and he'll likely answer: "The food was lousy."

A great deal is expected of the dietary service, the only service of the many required in a hospital which is equally important to patients and to staff.

Every day of 1952 the dietary service had to serve 1,813 meals to patients and 1,465 to staff. Every day of 1961 it had to provide 2,706 meals for patients and 1,497 staff. The staff figure did not increase in proportion to the patient (which doubled in that time) because of two fundamental changes. Work periods, weeks and days, were shorter. And as of April 1957 "board" was no longer considered part of remuneration. Salaries were adjusted and the hospital cafeteria offered meals on a cash basis.

The inflation of the time showed in costs. The cost of the average hospital meal rose from 24.86 cents to 30.45. And in those basics, meat and potatoes, the price of meat rose from 35.4 cents a pound to 55.78 cents, potatoes rose from $1.326 a bushel to $1.73. And specialization, that other feature, was apparent too. In 1961 four percent of meals were made to standards of the Canadian Diabetic Association, 13 percent were deemed "therapeutic" and 83 percent were standard or "house diet."

The hospital board gave the service an approved establishment of 10 graduate dietitians but these were in big demand and short supply and the department was rarely up to strength. However there were also six interns, in which regard the hospital enjoyed the benefits of its own pioneering. The dietetic residency program started back in 1928 when my late wife Margaret Malone trained two students in a four-month course. In 1929 the course was extended to six months to conform with standards of the American Dietetic Association and in 1934 was extended to a full year. In 1940 our program earned final approval of both the Canadian and American dietetic associations. Through 1984 a total of 372 students had passed through the general dietetic internship program and another 29 through a clinical program.

The kitchens where the food was prepared started the '50s in brand new quarters. The new kitchens were described as "light and airy" which couldn't be said of the location they'd occupied since the founding of the hospital — in a stub wing at the rear of the main building with the boilers in the basement, the laundry on the first level and the kitchens above. As of May 16 1951 the dietary service prepared meals in all-new facilities in the southwest wing, also new, which opened that year. There were actually two kitchens — a general kitchen and a servery for therapeutic and special diets.

When budgets allowed the service acquired new equipment in tune with the times. An electric meat cutter for the butcher. A Qualheim electric vegetable cutter. A Champion dish-washing machine. In 1957, when the new staff cafeteria opened in the polio wing and staff meals went on a cash basis, the servery was relocated and redesigned.

The dietary service worked with the medical staff on research — with Don Wilson on metabolic problems, Ted Bell and Jack Gilbert on fat absorption, and Joe Bertrand on a study of blood sugars in mothers with larger babies. Eventually in 1962 the hospital assigned beds specifically for treating patients with dietary problems.

In addition to providing meals for patients and staff the dietary service was a part of all hospital "occasions" and "events" as caterer. An interesting history could be constructed around the events in the diaries of Margaret Lang (who was Director of Dietetics from 1948 to 1959) and her successor Irene Torrington. About 150 per year, they ranged from meetings of the hospital board for which a tea tray was required to receptions following the graduation of a nursing class, which Margaret Lang described as "verging on a mass feeding" and she certainly put it well. For ceremonial occasions there were even 36 place settings of 1847 Rogers Brothers silver plate. Such an occasion was the luncheon provided on November 7 1953 to celebrate the opening of our radio-isotope laboratory.

There was brisk turnover in the dietary service. But through all the comings and goings one factor remained constant. As she had been doing since 1929 Fanny Hooson the night cook walked from her home in the Highlands every afternoon to cook for staff on the 3 p.m. to 11 shift. For hospital staff who felt pushed off balance by the rush of new forces and bigger numbers it was a comfort to know that Fanny was on the job in the night kitchen, ready to provide a sandwich or meal with the traditional personal touch.

*Social Service*

In 1953 the hospital engaged Mrs. Shirley Phillip to work with patients who needed personal counselling or help in adjusting to life after discharge. As a form of social service it was essentially discharge planning. In 1961 the hospital set up a formal department (of half a dozen) based on an enlarged concept of the *medical* social worker, involved with patients from admission to outpatient status.

The first medically trained social worker in the hospital was Imelda Chenard, a spritely lady who had come west originally from French Canada to learn English. (DVA had Mary Davis stationed in the Mewburn Pavilion to work with veteran patients.) In 1959 Keith Yonge brought Imelda from Saskatoon to work in his department of psychiatry.

Keith laughs: "There were always problems with the administration where staff — and therefore budget — were concerned. What you got, you got grudgingly. But once convinced you could depend on support from that quarter."

Keith saw the medical social worker as part of the diagnostic team, involved in the original diagnosis by obtaining information on the home milieu of the patients, in therapy which was not strictly psychiatric, and in facilitating on-going treatment of patients after discharge. Keith says: "This person takes some irksome responsibilities off the doctor, who is geared to deal with the specifics of an illness."

When Mrs. Phillip left in 1960 Stan Greenhill of the medical staff was asked to oversee social service for the hospital. Stan had a good view of the situation. He was director of a discipline known as Community Medicine, concerned with research into sociological and psychological factors in community health and was also involved in the student health service. Stan engaged Mrs. Goldie Furman as medical social worker for the hospital and asked her to prepare a report on how a social service department might be set up. Goldie was a UBC graduate, recently arrived from Chicago where she'd done social work with the Illinois Epilepsy Institute. She gathered information by listening and finding out what was done in other places. There was a feeling that the accreditation committee — the "Big Brother" of teaching hospitals — thought such a department was desirable. Keith Yonge says: "I think there was a general recognition that it was 'behind the times' to not have one."

So we had one, as of 1961, with Imelda Chenard heading a group of half a dozen, working in all departments where they were welcome. Initially some doctors were less convinced than Keith Yonge and Stan Greenhill and a social worker could approach a patient only on referral from a doctor. But the idea took firm hold. As this was written the social service department had grown to a staff of 30.

*Pastoral Care*

The design for the Clinical Services Wing included a significant feature on the lower floor — a chapel. This recognized one of the needs in patient care. To be ill and in hospital is a bewildering experience and in many cases one feels that "the hand of the Lord smote him sorely." Emotional and spiritual comfort is needed. In our institution this was a greater problem than in other city hospitals because more of our patients were country people referred by their local doctors. Throughout the '50s the percentage declined somewhat — from 60 percent to about half — but was still high.

In 1960, the year the Clinical Services Wing opened, the Edmonton Council of Churches made possible the appointment of a chaplain on an ecumenical basis. Reverend Frank Jennings served the University Hospital (as well as the Royal Alex) and also acted on behalf of the hospital in liaison with other clergymen. Poor health soon forced Mr. Jennings to give up the work and he was succeeded full-time at the University Hospital by Reverend Ronald Dougan who served 10 years.

The chaplain visits patients on referral; does consultative interviews with patients in cooperation with doctors, lawyers and nurses; participates in educational programs and acts as chaplain and counsellor to the hospital staff.

As early as 1961 the annual report stated: "The chaplaincy service is an integral part of patient care."

*The Auxiliary*

In a period dominated by things new, it was interesting to note the vigorous revival of something old. The Women's Auxiliary had been essential to the original Strathcona Municipal Hospital — financially and in other ways. When the institution was taken over by the military commission in 1916 much of the furniture and equipment actually belonged to the auxiliary. The ladies had to consent to turning it over to the army, which they did except for furnishings in the maternity ward.

An auxiliary was started in the late '30s, but didn't last. Then in 1955 the idea was revived on a determined basis by some of the volunteers who worked in the hospital, many of them wives of the staff. Their initial interest was the nurses residence. With money from bake sales they furnished a "green room" where students could entertain friends and families, and provided a silver tea service for state occasions. The ladies had a feeling that Angus McGugan regarded the auxiliary as a necessary evil and perhaps not all that necessary but their own assessment of the need was destined to prevail.

In 1960 the 90 members incorporated under the Societies Act, with three defined objectives: promoting community understanding of the hospital, giving volunteer service wherever required in the hospital, and maintaining a supervised volunteer department. The last objective was going to require a paid supervisor, and to engage Jeanne Rymal the auxiliary staged the first of 13 annual charity balls.

The next year 1,334 volunteers contributed 8,946 hours of work and Bill

Taylor the Scottish paediatrician provided the auxiliary with a money-making proposition which became a happy hospital tradition. Bill obtained a research grant for a project involving newborn babies and wanted photographs to go with his reports. He asked the auxiliary to arrange for the pictures — and the proud parents wanted to buy the pictures too. Bill put the group on to a service which grew to a $20,000 a year business. The auxiliary opened a gift shop which was another money-maker and became, in effect, one of those foundations which help underwrite the objectives of the hospital. Most foundations have a special interest and the focus of the auxiliary was patients. They painted and redecorated lounges, contributed to social service, and I'm told that when the government ran short of money they bought equipment, but for patient care rather than teaching or research. When the auxiliary finally disbanded — and was replaced by a group called *Friends of the University Hospitals* — there was $200,000 to put into equipment for treating patients. But that was in May 1986, long after I'd become Professor Emeritus.

# Chapter 20

# 1962
*Professor Emeritus*

All good things, even long and useful associations with a hospital, must come to an end. Around the time the Clinical Services Wing was opening the university said good-bye to three men who had held the office of superintendent — Angus McGugan, Reg Adshead, and Ross Vant.

Mind you, the title of the job was changing. All within one year Angus retired as *superintendent*, Reg ran the hospital as *administrator* and Doug Wallace was named *executive director*. Doug's successor Bernie Snell was eventually elevated to *president*. "Titles devalue," Bernie says.

In October 1960 Angus left a rich legacy of crusty stories and launched a successful political career as alderman on the city council. From then until July 1961 Reg ran the hospital, a nice way to cap an association of 33 years. Then Reg departed for another career. He'd been advising the government on setting up the Foothills Hospital in Calgary and went south as administrator. Mind you, a number of our people followed Reg to the Foothills — including our director of nursing, head of radiology and supervisor of maintenance.

Doug Wallace had most of the qualifications the board was seeking in the first man to be known as executive director, though he acquired them more by fortune than design. To begin with he was a wartime graduate of the University of Alberta, and did his required military service with the RCAF. Back in his hometown of Wainwright he went into general practice with his father, organized an air force reserve unit, and was mayor of the town for six years. But he developed skin rash from medical practice and had to seek office work so he came to Edmonton with MSI, Medical Services Incorporated, the forerunner of Alberta Health Care. From that he went to the provincial government as Director of Hospital Services. With this varied background he was acceptable to all parties including the government, which claimed a large say in who should run the hospital. However, one party professed to be unimpressed. Doug liked to tell about his reception from Fanny Hooson, the first time he walked into the night cafeteria as top man. Doug had been one of the interns Fanny used to bully and pamper. She commented: "Well, they sure must have been scraping the bottom of the barrel."

Doug was a big, persuasive fellow — I don't think Angus or "Wash" Washburn ever felt a need to "persuade" anyone — but the times called for a conciliator, and Doug was certainly a natural. He was at ease with people and with mounds of detail and was to serve till December 1965 when he went on to the Toronto General in the same capacity and then on to be secretary-general of the Canadian Medical Association.

Bob Macbeth says: "It was a euphoric time, an easy time for someone like Doug to be Executive Director. He'd been President of the Chamber of Commerce in Wainwright, along with his other activities. We were all very young and full of enthusiasm. We had a gut feeling this was going to be the major medical centre of North America."

Mind you, in 1961 our board was thinking beyond the hiring of one man. Assessing the situation in which the hospital had been placed by burgeoning of expertise, public expectation and funds available, the board could see that a new structure was required at the top. The one-man rule of "Wash" Washburn's day wasn't the answer. Neither was "dual administration," imposed by the province in 1953, in which the board appointed a medical superintendent and the cabinet appointed a business administrator and defined his responsibilities. Two heads weren't better than one, but three might be better than two. Alberta had a new health minister by this time — Donovan Ross succeeded W. W. Cross — and the new man was agreeable to ending the arrangement. However, dual administration had been sanctified by legislation, and what the legislature had given only the legislature could take away. And this it did, by an amendment to our act (Statutes of Alberta 1962 Chapter 95). The board would appoint an executive director, a medical superintendent and business administrator, with the cabinet retaining a right of approval.

So the board, with cabinet approval, appointed Doug Wallace Executive Director, and reporting to him Bernie Snell, Medical Superintendent, and George Sherwood, Business Administrator. These three were formed into an executive committee, and then a fourth member was added, a wise move, long overdue — the Director of Nursing, Jeanie Clark.

I've noted the farewells of McGugan, Adshead and Vant, but there's another departure which must receive due prominence. In April 1961 Mark Marshall gave up the postgraduate program which he had run since the war. Mark had always maintained a firm grip on the program, and even in leaving he designated his successor. Dick Rossall, of cardiology, was the choice. Dick had caught Mark's eye while organizing work for residents in the department of medicine. Mark attended the meeting of the medical staff at which Dick gave his first report on the residency program. Afterwards Mark got up and said he had appreciated the support the staff had given him when he was running the program and was sure they'd accord the same consideration to Mark Two — a play on the designations given to later versions of rifles, tanks and airplanes. "Mark Two" was still in charge as this was written — the position of Chairman of the Committee on Graduate Training in the Faculty of Medicine being updated to Director of Graduate Medical Education. Mind you, Mark didn't give up till there was irrefutable evidence of success. When the program started after the war our graduates had to go away for training because there was no one to train them here. By 1961 they were back and eager to pass on their advanced knowledge. Going away might be desirable, but no longer necessary. In short order a half dozen took their entire training here and all passed the fellowship examination of the Royal College of Physicians and Surgeons.

There were three parties to postgraduate education: hospital, university, and Royal College. For 15 years it was a hospital program, and one of our proud successes. But by 1961 direction was shifting to the university — because of pressure from the Royal College. The College, trying to keep up with a burgeoning list of specialties, preferred to deal with universities.

In 1961 pressure from the Royal College brought a change in procedures in the hospital. Beds were assigned on the "ward system." As Don Wilson explains: "The all-powerful accreditation committee told us we had to improve teaching for residents. Staff doctors (doing a combination of clinical and teaching work) were assigned a teaching ward and had to limit their activities to it. They couldn't admit patients to other wards or more than a certain number each month. This concentrated patients geographically, so residents didn't have to chase them all over the hospital.

"Procedures were also changed to improve teaching by increasing responsibility. We made a rule that a patient could not be accompanied by documents from the doctor sending him in."

At the dawn of the '60s the University Hospital was caught up in all sorts of pressures from outside. It was no longer the totally self-contained institution, standing off in proud isolation, to which I came in 1929. But it was a safer place to be a patient, and if the teaching hospital was safer then it followed that all others would be.

It was difficult to leave a scene of such useful activity but I was resigned to the fact that the time had come for Ross Vant to retire. And it was arranged for September 1962.

In a way it was a good time to go. I was quite satisifed with the way my department was doing things, and supporting the work of obstetricians and gynaecologists all over the province. Not bad for a part-timer, of whom I was the last to head a department. My successor was geographic full-time. Bill Paul came from the University of Toronto and was very research-oriented, where I had no basic-research ability.

So in September 1962 I became *professor emeritus*. The term has been construed in a number of ways. When Stephen Leacock retired reluctantly from McGill he said it derived from the Latin é meaning out, and meritus, well-deserved. For me it meant "out to pasture," but the pastures were green and retirement from my profession was so gradual I feel privileged. I remained in practice with my partners till about 1980, and for a long time I was to enjoy an association with the hospital which I apparently wasn't supposed to have. I have to laugh at this. I used to go in and write summaries on patients for my partners Ron Horner and Dave Reid. When Ron retired he asked if he could do it and was told absolutely not — most improper. So Vant's Law is "Don't Ask!"

In my long association with the hospital I had to make many decisions. Some were better than others, as you can imagine, but I did manage to save one of the best for last. I was advised that as a retiring professor I was entitled to a banquet and did I want one? I said "hell, no," so they wondered if I'd accept a life membership in the Faculty Club. Mind you, this was long before they built the beautiful clubhouse overlooking the valley from Saskatchewan Drive — just a few rooms tucked away in Athabasca Hall. If they'd known how long I intended to stay around I'm sure they'd have insisted on the banquet.

I've never had cause to regret that decision. The new club is a three-block walk from my home, and the fellowship is stimulating. There's always good talk and inevitably there's talk of the hospital, the institution I saw first in 1920 when

*Reg Adshead 1960-61*

*Doug Wallace 1961-65*

*Chief executive officers*

it was half-a-building in open fields and was held by the army. Where I was clinician and teacher for 30 years and attended countless meetings of uncountable committees and for six hectic months in 1940 was superintendent.

The place I knew is unimaginable to most who work in the University Hospital of the present. But it really existed, and so did the people who made it succeed when logic said it should fail. Writing about them I can see their faces and hear their voices and laugh at the things they said. The Faculty Club is a fine spot to talk about them and their hospital and hear news of the continuation.

I like to hear about the continuation. When you think about it, it's their memorial.

# Book III
*Tony Cashman*

## 1962 — 1986

# Chapter 21

# 1962—1966
*Grasping the Future — Again*

*In the later history of the hospital there are few facts, only perceptions. — Bernard Snell, President 1966-1984*

When Geneva Purcell flew in from Montreal in 1962 to be interviewed for the position of Director of Nursing she formed a perception. The hospital was big and modern, but run like an institution of a hundred beds. The board made decisions on details, even the personal details of her employment. She liked to cook and had a pet Siamese cat named Symie. Her apartment in the nurses residence did not provide for cooking and rules did not provide for cats. So the board gave these matters due consideration and Don Avison the chairman came rumbling out of the meeting to advise Miss Purcell in his finest Scots-Uncle manner: "We'll build you a kitchen and you can keep your Siamese cat."

There was certainly a warm side to running a large hospital like one with a hundred beds. It was homey and Geneva Purcell was coming home. She had left Edmonton at eight when her family moved to a farm in Ontario, but retained bright memories of the city in the first war, with bands and soldiers marching. She brought more recent experience of 30 years in nursing, all but five centred on the Royal Victoria in Montreal, the teaching hospital of McGill. At the Royal Vic she had been student, staff nurse, administrator, surgical instructor, and supervisor of the maternity hospital. From McGill she had a diploma in nursing administration (1943) and a BSc (1955). She was away only from 1945 to 1949 as Director of Nursing at Brockville General and 1960-61 obtaining a master's degree at Boston University.

The board of the Royal Victoria would never have bothered itself with the nursing director's cat, and Symie became a great favourite of the student nurses, demonstrating the warm aspect of running a large hospital like one with a hundred beds. However, Geneva Purcell, starting 13 years in her new job, observed a debit side. She had a strong perception that efficiency was frustrated because minute details went to the board; every time a department wanted to move the matter had to be taken to the board; dollars were measured at board level. She longed for the flexibility of global budgeting, which enabled managers at other large hospitals of her experience to meet change and unexpected needs.

The avuncular style of board management disappeared — because it had to. It had served the institution well, but lagged behind practice elsewhere and progress in the University Hospital so its demise was inevitable. That is a perception of course. It is also a perception that the later history of the hospital has been an odyssey leading to the Walter C. Mackenzie Health Sciences Centre. But it's a fact that in this time Gordon K. Wynn was Chairman of the Board. He was appointed Vice-chairman in 1963 (by cabinet order 58/63), Chairman in January 1965 (by cabinet order 34/65), and served 14 years, fighting off the effects of a stroke towards the end to ensure that the Mackenzie Centre went ahead.

Gordon Wynn, obviously, rates a very long paragraph. He was the Wynn in Rule Wynn and Rule, a firm of architects founded in February 1938 when one of Edmonton's most eminent architects was riding out the depression teaching

*Geneva Purcell*
*Director of Nursing*
*1962-1975*
*Appointed to the Senate of the*
*University 1985*

*This is Simie, Miss Purcell's*
*Siamese cat — the only cat*
*ever to be voted on by the*
*hospital board*

art in his office over the Imperial Bank. The partners decided they wouldn't make any money, but would have fun. However they made some money after all. Foster and McGarvey gambled $10,000 expanding their funeral parlour and that was the start. By the time Gordon Wynn joined the air force in 1940 the firm had done Westglen High School, a $300,000 project on which Sid Parsons, future mayor of Edmonton, was inspector for the school board. After the war the city grew a skyline and Rule Wynn and Rule did the Milner Building, at 14 storeys the tallest office tower in sight. Gordon was busy in community activity — with the RCAF reserve, the Eskimo football club and the board of the Royal

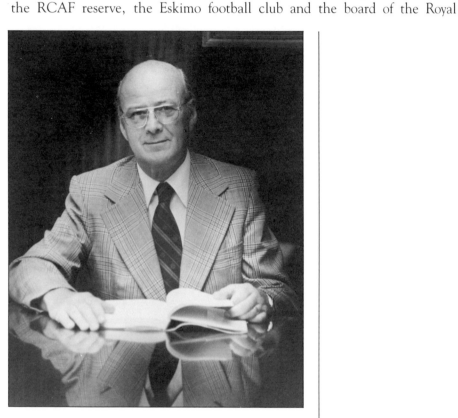

*Gordon Wynn*
*Chairman of the Board*
*1965-1978*

Alexandra Hospital. One day after he'd left the board there was a phone call from Sid Parsons, now mayor, who was ill in the Royal Alex. "Gordon, I want to see you." Mayor Parsons invited him out on the roof and pointed to a triangle of open bush bounded by 111th Avenue, Kingsway and 101st Street. "Do you think that would be a good place to reserve for the hospital?" Rule Wynn and Rule were architects for the Royal Alex's expansion into the triangle. These facts were duly noted by the man for whom the Walter C. Mackenzie Health Sciences Centre is named, then at the zenith of his remarkable influence. He added up the facts and formed a perception that Gordon Wynn would be an asset to the board of the University Hospital. He sounded out Gordon and then Donovan Ross the Minister of Health and the appointment was made. When Don Avison announced to unanimous regret that failing health would force him to relinquish the chairmanship after 10 years devoted service, Gordon was sounded out about being chairman. That appointment was made in January 1965 and he was chairman for the next 14 years, till Phase I of the Mackenzie Centre was safely in view.

Like three chairmen before him Gordon could claim relationship to the hospital by marriage. In the heyday of old Strathcona Major Marriott married a nurse from the rented house on 78th Avenue, H.H. Cooper married a popular superintendent of nurses, Ray Staples an assistant superintendent. In 1940 Agnes Corbett was a technician in the hospital lab when she resigned to marry Gordon and share his travels as an RCAF navigator — and received a dressing-down from Dr. Washburn because it cost *him* money to train lab assistants.

Agnes won her job on the strength of a BSc plus four months unpaid service in the University's biochemistry department. In the hospital lab she worked with two nurses and another young woman in a room on the first level south and was given amazing responsibility — matching blood for transfusions, being summoned by Dr. Hepburn or Dr. Pope to assist at patient examinations — duties for which she had little training. But she jumped if Dr. Washburn said to do something, or anyone in authority, or anyone who asserted authority.

The arrangement had obvious drawbacks, but it could be said that the superintendent did know every lab assistant in the hospital. That was no longer possible when Gordon Wynn became chairman, even with gregarious democrat Doug Wallace in Dr. Washburn's office. And 14 years later, as Gordon was leaving, even doctors wore identification pictures so imposters could not infiltrate the operating room and at meetings of the medical staff the presiding officer would lean to a neighbour and whisper "Who's that fellah next to Dr. So-and-So?" As to individual dollars they were no longer weighed at board level — just too many of them. An operating budget of $9,774,000 in 1965 grew to $80,000,000 in 1979. And 5,000 employees walked the corridors. Those are all facts, but the most surprising is this: construction was underway on the ultimate hospital — which would reduce the number of patient beds by 156!

Facts are stubborn. Tobias Smollett said it two centuries ago, but perceptions have been stubborn too in the later history of the University Hospital. It is arguable that perceptions shaped the destiny of the hospital in the '60s and '70s and into the '80s and that many were forced on the institution from the outside. The later history may be perceived as a journey on a long long trail leading to the Mackenzie Centre. From this perception flows Book Three.

275

1962—1966

# Chapter 22

# 1962
*Wallace's Warriors*

The chief stewardship of Doug Wallace — October 1 1961 – December 31 1965 — is commemorated every day by a unique professional association known as Wallace's Warriors. The Nursing Reserve of the University Hospital, the only one of its kind, is a textbook illustration of the Wallace philosophy, style and method.

His successor Bernard Snell has noted: "Doug was the most articulate man on paper I've ever seen. He could dictate straight on to a machine or on to paper his thoughts on something and it would never have to be changed."

Ruth Wallace Johns — Doug's widow, he died in 1976 — tells how he developed his most detailed thoughts. He liked to retreat into the den on Sunday afternoons and think them out on paper. One Sunday he emerged from a long session in the den with a plan for a nursing reserve based on his experience with the air force. As executive director of the hospital he contended with a chronic shortage of graduate nurses for day-to-day operation. The University Hospital was 20 percent below establishment with an annual turnover near 100 percent. Then there was the Cuban Missile Crisis, still a recent event with a high profile in the minds of hospital administrators who were all working on disaster plans. His research indicated that 1,200 registered nurses were out there, not very far away, who had given up nursing to raise families. He thought a significant number might now be willing and able to come back. Did Ruth think it would be feasible to invite them to a retraining-and-work program which would let them work in the profession again and still observe their first responsibilities to their families?

Ruth was a graduate of the Royal Alex. She said it sounded like a great idea and she wanted to be in on it. Geneva Purcell, the Director of Nursing, thought it was a good idea but she had been in the city only a month and laughed: "Dr. Wallace, you're ready to run and I'm about ready to creep." On October 2 1962 he sent a letter to alumnae of the University Hospital with the thoughts he had put together that Sunday in the den. He proposed a pilot project involving 30 nurses, but response was so positive that when the program started no less than 72 answered the call, including graduates of other hospitals.

They volunteered for a program of lectures one evening a week — planned by the nursing advisory board and a special advisory committee appointed by the hospital board — to be followed by one or two weeks in the wards — mornings only — depending on how long they'd been away and for some the absence had been 20 years.

The pilot program was financed from the research fund which Angus McGugan had salted away during his canny chief stewardship. The fund provided honorariums for the instructors, half-day office help and a salary for Eva Macklam, the coordinator. Mrs. Macklam's grant covered only six months, but she stayed 11 years, interviewing applicants, coordinating the training and scheduling work.

When the program was offered a second year 63 nurses reappeared and 52 surfaced for the third. Biggest of all was the class of '67, when some boosters urged the recruiting of an even hundred to mark the Canadian centennial. The drive came within nine of that patriotic objective. The program continued and to 1986 some 700 former nurses had come back in the refresher course.

Obviously a lasting success, it is the only known success, though reserve schemes were tried elsewhere in Canada, including another Edmonton hospital.

Flexibility was the key to success. Right out of the military reserve manual which Doug Wallace used as a model, the hospital recognized family responsibilities as first call and did not demand a more rigid commitment than a nurse with a family could give. Reservists were asked to work one or two shifts a week, at their convenience, and give a block of time in summer when the shortage was most pressing.

The Wallace philosophy was a large contributor to enduring success. He thought the returning nurses should have their own association, otherwise they would be absorbed into the hospital operation and the reserve would lose its identity. This was at a time when the lives of hospital administrators were being complicated by a host of outside entities created by the province — through labour legislation and expansion of the bureaucracy — so it is surely remarkable that he would be eager to deal with one more outside entity, even if it was named in his honour.

The association was formed during the second winter. Incorporated under the Societies Act as The Nursing Reserve of the University of Alberta Hospital, it was already known far and wide as Wallace's Warriors.

The program enjoyed the benefit of a good start, an aid to success in any enterprise. While the first group was retraining Geneva Purcell spread word throughout the hospital on what was happening and what to expect when they came into the wards. And there was another line of communication. Four of the pilot group were wives of doctors on the medical staff. Ruth Wallace was joined by Monique (Bob) Macbeth, Eva (Les) Willox and Betty (Frank) Elliott, who became founding president of the reserve association.

Some returnees had to explain to friends that their families were not in financial distress. Though attitudes were changing it was not yet totally accepted that a married woman would work for interest rather than necessity. The very existence of the retraining program recognized that the old axiom "once a nurse always a nurse" no longer applied. There had been too many changes, with more coming, but the changes added interest to returning. A highlight of the first course was "new equipment night" with tremendous interest in an electric thermometer shaker.

When Wallace's Warriors reached the trenches they found more changes. Bed rest was gone. Once an article of faith, bed rest was no longer considered good for the patient or the hospital, and complicated surgery cases were quickly up and doing. Drugs were used more freely. In fact everything was used more freely.

However there was no change in basic bedside nursing — understanding the needs and fears of the patient — and the people in the beds appreciated the maturity of Wallace's Warriors. So did the student nurses, who recognized their

*278*

*1962*

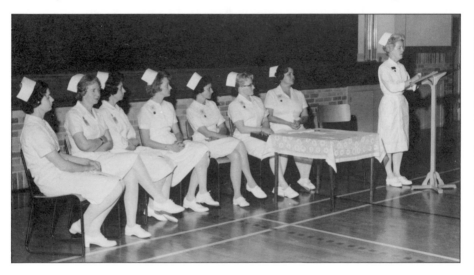

*Eva Macklam at the lectern,
with a company of Wallace's
Warriors — 1965*

life experience and accepted them as role models. With the reservists on call students were no longer plucked out of their training rotations to meet short-term needs of the hospital, and everybody appreciated that. The students helped the returnees with the new techniques and told surprising stories about changes in student lifestyle. They were going on a five-day week. The board was putting a shampoo room and a games room in the nurses residence, and some seniors were being allowed to live out in Garneau Towers, though there was some caution about this because of the Canada Pension Plan. It was to come into force in 1966. The board was careful to designate the rent as an honorarium "to avoid the possibility of a precedent which might conceivably bring all student nurses under the Plan."

In the fourth quarter of 1963 the hospital received from the reserve the equivalent service of 12 staff nurses. By 1973 the contribution had tripled, and through those 10 years the reserve worked 81,859 shifts, all in spots where otherwise service would have been stretched thin.

Another contribution, intangible but invaluable, was continuity. With a theoretically "permanent staff" on the move, family obligations committed the reservists to staying within call. Cathy Sterrenberg, a member of the pilot group, gave the most continuity, remaining on call for 22 years.

The reserve had opportunities to work in leading-edge developments in medicine and surgery. Special nursing, and constant or intensive care, have been essential to most of the new procedures. So has high technology, in diagnosis and treatment, and new equipment night in the refresher course has become "scary." That description was chosen by Wenda Kurany, who trained originally in Leeds, England, and pointed out that the reserve has become an international organization with members from Britain, Europe, the United States and the Philippines.

In 1986 the association listed some 220 members with 100 on the active roster.

Each April there is a banquet, commemorating the potluck supper which marked completion of the second program, and members come long distances to participate. Among other activities they present a scholarship to a graduate nurse in memory of the instigator of Wallace's Warriors — of all the personalities in the long history of the University Hospital one of the most engaging.

# Chapter 23

# 1962—1965
*State of the Art*

In Doug Wallace's time the cost of running the hospital increased by half — despite the best efforts of Ken Hawkins. He was appointed to the board in 1963, along with other members who will be introduced later. The province had ceased the practice of appointing active civil servants to the board but Mr. Hawkins had recently retired as deputy provincial treasurer, and performed a ritual which became a tradition at board meetings. He carried a slip of paper which he took out and read when a spending appropriation was on the table. Sometimes he read it aloud: "In 1906 the entire budget of the province of Alberta was $500,000." He would fold it away carefully for future reference and vote "no."

Mr. Hawkins had served the province in heroic days of dust bowl and debt, and felt that spending was a temptation to be resisted. However, there was no holding the rising tide.

Expense rose from $6.65 million in 1961 to $9.75 million in 1965. The components of expense remained constant, within a percentage point, so that in 1965 salaries took 73.2 cents of the outgoing dollar, medical supplies 14.38 cents, food 5.74, maintenance 3.6 and miscellaneous items 3.08 cents. However, within the revenue dollar there was a significant shift. Revenue from the Alberta Hospitalization Benefits Plan rose from 64.47 cents to 75.4. On the other hand revenue from Blue Cross, the Workmens' Compensation Board and insurance schemes dropped from 18.82 cents to 15.94, the DVA contribution from 9.47 cents to 4.51, income from direct provincial grants and private rooms from 6.92 cents to 4.15.

Mr. Hawkins couldn't see why the cost should keep rising when the number of beds remained the same. He could point to 1961, when on an average day there were 958 patients in bed, and to 1965 when the average actually declined to 921. The number of operations remained exactly the same — 46 per day. One reason was the increase in staff. Non-medical staff went from 1,435 to 1,758, as at this stage anyway technological change was very much increasing the number of jobs. The medical staff increased — from 169 to 198. The establishment of certified nursing aides, ward aides, nursing orderlies and ward clerks increased from 335 to 438. The number of graduate nurses went from 342 to 446 and the increase included a newcomer from Ireland, who offers an Irish view of the medical staff of the time. Mrs. Judy Rogers landed in 1963 and spent 20 years on night duty in the maternity case room. "Nurses were bowing to the doctors an awful lot," she recalls. "I had some fighting back with the doctors. Doctors thought they were king of the castle. I changed that a wee bit."

All aspects of hospital care were changing a wee bit — and more — every day and the board could not turn a blind eye to progress when patients might benefit. The term *state of the art* had not yet invaded the language, but the board was dealing with it in fact, and it was forcing a relentless upwards thrust to the cost. Applied to hospital care state of the art has come to mean the most recent proven technology no longer experimental, but accepted as reliable. State of the art involves equipment (though it may also be drugs or medical supplies) and the skills to use it. State of the art raises esprit de corps within the hospital staff, draws valuable attention to the work of the hospital and can make celebrities of doctors and patients. State of the art is expensive. State of the art is new — it is "leading edge" to employ another term which had not yet enriched the language of Shakespeare and Churchill — and therefore won't be on the current budget. In which case most hospital boards will take the view that the extra level of patient care transcends budgets and face the financing later.

State of the art was not a budgetary consideration in the '30s and '40s when Dr. Hepburn was developing his own skills and tools for brain surgery. By the '50s this had changed totally. State of the art developments for polio patients — helping them to breathe and recover use of limbs — were an ungrudged expense. The heart-lung pump was state of the art for open-heart surgery. In Doug Wallace's time the Kiil artificial kidney was state of the art. In December 1962 the University Hospital put in service the second in the world.

The Kiil machine could treat cases of chronic renal failure, unlike two earlier machines which were on the premises — a Skaggs-Leonard model acquired in the mid-50s by the surgical division of urology, and a Kaulpf model brought in by the medical division of endocrinology and metabolism. These machines could save healthy people who needed to be kept alive through a period of trauma till their healthy bodies resumed normal function. The physical application was pretty severe, the concentration of salts strong and tricky, suitable for giving a last chance to an accident victim whose kidneys had shut down or someone who had overdosed on drugs, but not for use two or three times a week on a patient suffering chronic renal failure and the associated complications.

Drastic though the procedure was the hospital used the Kaulpf machine to try to give two dying patients a last wish. One was a man who wanted to hang on for a last visit from his son, working in Africa. He got his wish but an East Indian student did not. He'd hoped to make a journey home and die in his native land.

The Kiil artifical kidney, known as the Seattle kidney because it was developed at the University of Washington, gave promise of being able to relieve chronic renal failure. Installed at the University of Alberta Hospital in the fall of 1962 it was very definitely state of the art.

State of the art requires not only equipment, but the skills to use it, and skills in dialysis came from both medicine and surgery. On the medical side Lionel McLeod (head of endocrinology) established a helpful companionship with Dr. Belding Scribner, who was pioneering the use of the Kiil machine at the University of Washington. (Dr. Scribner was head of nephrology, the medical specialty of the kidney. In 1968 the University of Alberta Hospital would separate nephrology from endocrinology as a division of its own.) Lionel made several visits to Seattle, and returned from one trip with a Kiil machine.

On the surgical side, Bill Lakey of the division of urology had specialized in dialysis in his postgraduate program. Bill's career was fine-tuned by Walter Mackenzie. Among the wide circle of Mackenzie friends in high places was Dr. R.M. Nesbit of the University of Michigan, who was pioneering a new method

*Mutual congratulations are in order. Doug Wallace (Executive Director) and Bernard Snell (Medical Superintendent) display a certificate from the Canadian Council on Hospital Accreditation. Other accreditation teams come in to rate teaching, but this concerns patient care — physical plant, admission, diagnosis and treatment facilities, clinical procedures, competence and ethical standards of the staff. The Council is composed of five interested bodies: Canadian Hospital Association, Canadian Medical Association, Royal College of Physicians and Surgeons of Canada, Canadian Nurses Association and the Canadian Long Term Care Association. The accreditation teams come every three years — this certificate is dated October 31 1962.*

of prostate surgery and operating a dialysis program. Bill returned to the University Hospital in 1960, joined Jim Metcalfe in urology and eventually became head of the division.

The term kidney "machine" was misleading, as it was an uneasy alliance of unlikely components. Two bulky components were stainless-steel holding tanks, measuring four feet in all directions, bearing the crest of *Freezer Sweden*, an insignia usually seen on equipment in ice cream parlours. The artificial kidney required tanks which could be temperature-controlled and easily sterilized. Dr. Scribner persuaded Freezer Sweden to build two adaptations of their ice cream holders for the Seattle kidney and another two for Edmonton, which came as a gift. There were also three plastic "boards" with long grooves along which the blood of the patient passed while being dialysed. Resistance on plastic is light and the heart of the patient could pump it along, eliminating the awkward high-pressure pumps of earlier models.

The first patient selected for the machine was a 39-year-old engineer named Keith Taylor. It was arranged with Dr. Scribner that he would be started in Seattle and be accompanied by a resident and a technician who would continue the program in Edmonton. The resident was Ray Ulan, who graduated from the U of A at precisely the right moment to be in on the start of something big and was still involved a quarter-century later. The technician was Eunice Chesney, whose special contribution is noteworthy. A graduate biochemist, she took what appeared to some a lesser job because of its importance in saving life.

In December the machine arrived in Edmonton and made page one news on two consecutive days.

---

*December 21:* **Doctors Race with Time to Save City Girl's Life**
*December 22:* **Machine Gives Girl New Lease on Life**

---

Dianne Sutton was 17. Her kidneys had failed. Her parents had read about Keith Taylor and appealed to the University Hospital. The team was willing, but the machine was still in parts. At 9 am they began the assembly. A vital tube was missing. A call went to Seattle for the part and at 2 pm it arrived by air express. By 4 pm the fluids were rolling into the tank. At 6 pm Dianne was wheeled in. At 7:15 the fluid was flowing into her arm, and 12 hours later she was out of danger. As the *Journal* said, what the machine gave her was only a lease on life, but it was of fair duration. It was the same for Keith Taylor who appreciated the extra time and was a vigorous booster. A Kiwanian, he spread the word to the clubs and the first outside financial help came from Keith's South Side Kiwanis Club.

Other hospital departments joined in. Pharmacy provided salts for the solutions. Dr. Ted Bell offered a room in his clinical services laboratory but from dusk to dawn only — during the day the room was needed for lab work. So the apparatus had to be trundled from storage each evening and dismantled in the morning when the patient went home or to work. A second nurse was needed to supervise from 11 pm on, and a mature nurse who could work on her own. The director of nursing found Alma Foster, a mother of three children whose husband had gone back to university. The kidney program functioned through one-night stands for a whole year.

Each patient was a human interest story. Then came Robin Eady, whose story commanded international interest. Robin was English. His father lived in Egypt and sold medical equipment. In 1953 the father had to be informed that his only daughter, flying out from England for a visit, had gone down in the

*1964 — the designation "state of the art" applies to helicopter flights direct to the door of the University Hospital's emergency department*

Mediterranean with that pioneering Comet jet liner. Robin entered medical school, at Guy's Hospital in London, and the father had to be informed that his only son was dying of kidney failure. This was a tragedy with a rare reverse twist. In Life magazine the father read about the artificial kidney at the University of Washington. With his knowledge of the business he set out for Seattle to give Robin a last chance. Dr. Scribner put Robin on the machine and results were encouraging, but he knew he couldn't keep a foreign national on the program when Americans were in need. So he thought about the second machine in the world — "in a part of the Empire" as he said — and phoned Lionel McLeod. He described the dilemma and suggested that since the program was just starting in Edmonton a patient who was also a medical student might expedite the progress. Robin survived in Edmonton. He was able to work as a lab technician and eventually to return to his medical studies in London. He became a well-known dermatologist, married a nurse, and some 20 years later was back in Edmonton on a visit.

With dialysis an accomplished fact the surgical side of the house carried on to the next step. In 1965 Bill Lakey began experiments leading to kidney transplants.

———————

In the early '60s "the pill" was state of the art. The word pill had been in the language for centuries, but in the tenure of Doug Wallace it was reserved for a product which Ron Horner, the obstetrician, heard about first from a "detail man" (or salesman) for a drug company. Detail men often brought news before the medical journals. This one confided: "What would you say if I told you that in a few months you can order a drug that will keep your patients from getting pregnant?" Ron answered: "I'd say you were kidding." But it was true. On August 18 1960 a contraceptive pill was put on the market by the G.D. Searle Company of Skokie, Illinois. The pharmacy of the University Hospital ground out a mountain of pills in this time — among 815 daily "pharmacy services" in 1961 building to 1,062 in 1965 — but "the pill" which captured the title was the one created by Dr. John Rock of Boston. It was introduced at the teaching clinics, held weekly in the outpatient department for medical students and residents in the obstetrical-gynaecological phase of training. These clinics, and others worldwide, showed something about Enovid 10, 10 representing milligrams. The dose was 20 times more powerful than necessary.

———————

The pill was contentious, raising an ethical controversy over whether it was a natural or artificial form of birth control. However there was nothing contentious about pacemakers.

In 1963 they were state of the art and a pacemaker program at the University Hospital came about through interaction of cardiology and its operating cousin, cardiovascular surgery. The cousins met twice a week, one meeting to discuss patients, the other to talk problems and possibilities. From the other discussions the pacemaker program was born. The medical side selected the first recipient. Surgery sewed in the device, about the size of a pocket-watch, patient and pacemaker adjusted well to each other and before the year was out seven more were installed.

---

Meanwhile, advances in cardiovascular surgical art were drawing national attention to the University Hospital, with a number of Canadian firsts to report.

*June 1962 — First mitral valve replacement
with an artificial mechanical valve
1963 — First aortic valve replacement
with a mechanical valve
First multiple valve replacement
First replacement of the ascending aorta*

These milestones were well-covered by the press and also by the electronic media. This was the heyday of "the young doctor" on television and the CBC was delighted to find a live Canadian counterpart of that other young Irish doctor, the fictional Ben Casey. On July 18 1963 Dr. Callaghan brought TV cameras into the operating room. A closed circuit network was run from the hospital to the Macdonald Hotel for a convention of the Royal College of Physicians and Surgeons. In 1965, the CBC carried part of an operation live on the network.

---

In 1965 cornea transplants exhibited all the attributes of state of the art with the important exception of stress on hospital budgets. Replacement of "the window of the eye" was feasible before kidneys and hearts because corneal tissue is avascular, with no blood vessels to provoke autoimmune rejection. All that was required was surgical expertise and that was brought back from Washington D.C. by Dr. Don Hassard. A Grande Prairie product and U of A graduate he had been a resident when Dr. Don Rees performed the first full implant with the consent of a donor whose eye had to be removed for other medical reasons. (That cornea was still in service as this this was written.) Dr. Hassard's expertise was acquired thanks to one of those public service organizations which have done much to advance specialized medicine. The Lions Clubs offered a fellowship at the Eye Bank Institute in Washington and he came back two years later with the technique.

The program he established at the University Hospital was prairie regional because he was the only one doing it, a condition which prevailed a long time. The Canadian National Institute for the Blind brought in donors, enough for 30 implants the first year. Through 20 years Don Hassard has performed the operation 1,500 times. What this figure means in economic terms to the community, and human terms of people being able to resume or continue normal lives, is beyond calculation.

*July 18 1963 — open-heart surgery and both state of the art. Dr. Callaghan uses one to demonstrate the other to the Royal College of Physicians and Surgeons of Canada meeting at the Macdonald Hotel*

Each implant is a personal drama. Several have involved a prominent beneficiary and benefactor of the program, John Dahl of Whitecourt. A former mayor of the town, he has been able to carry on a contracting business despite a disease which breaks down his corneas after six to eight years. The program has alos provided normal lives for three sons with the same affliction.

With help from many quarters, including free transportation for corneas from bus and airlines, the CNIB carried on the donor and collection process until success made it too much to handle. Then the Lions Club, which made it possible in the first place, came back and financed an eye bank in the CNIB office. The procedure which the CNIB sees as "the simplest, least expensive and most successful" transplant program causes little strain on the budget of the University Hospital and little strain on the operating room. Most are done at night as emergencies. Somebody on the waiting list of 250 may be phoned at 10 pm and told to be at the hospital at midnight, to become another beneficiary of a program proclaimed state of the art in 1965.

---

In 1965 computers were state of the art and Bob Fraser relinquished clinical practice for a year to convert the records of the division of cardiology to computer symbols.

The term "networking" had not yet graced the language, but the project was a fine example of it. Bob's friend Dr. Harold Smith, cardiologist at Mayos, had developed a system in conjunction with software experts from IBM. He persuaded IBM to lend the program to Edmonton without charge. It was designed to work with an IBM 1800 model, of which there was one on campus. Bob set to work on the hospital's first computer program, coding information on all cardiology patients from 1953 on, for storage in the computer and instant retrieval when needed.

Since then computer programs have developed along divisional lines. General hospital records adhered to an internationally-recognized protocol, too broad for specialized work. In addition hospital records were not yet combined with emergency and outpatient services and a patient might have a record in all three, important in diagnosis.

As this was written the latest state of the art computer program could yield instant profiles on 30,000 heart patients.

---

In 1965 cardio-pulmonary resuscitation was state of the art. Staff were trained in the procedure known by the initials CPR, a coronary care unit was established, mobile equipment bays known as "crash wagons" were stationed around the hospital, and a hundred patients were treated.

CPR came on very quickly. In the early '60s researchers at Johns Hopkins published some interesting findings about ventricular fibrillation, a condition which had been dealt with in the operating room where the healthy heart of a patient under anaesthetic would suddenly stop beating. Surgeons found they could expose the heart and manipulate it back into action. New research showed that the same effect could be achieved by rhythmic compression of the heart from the outside. No longer was a surgeon the only person who could save a victim of cardiac arrest.

The news in the medical journals was read with interest everywhere, and with particular interest by two senior residents in cardiology at the Royal Victoria Hospital of Montreal, who stayed on after their regular terms to train staff in CPR and see how a program would work in a large hospital. At the University of Alberta Hospital Russ Taylor, of cardiology, heard about the project and went down to Montreal to live in the Royal Vic and observe it at close range. Such visits were easy to arrange then at a time "when everybody knew each other."

Russ returned convinced and set up an in-service training program, for residents and the nursing team in cardiology initially and extending to other divisions. It was a new program and a new program must compete for attention, money and space. CPR attracted a great deal of attention from an incident considered to be the first use of cardio-pulmonary resuscitation in the hospital. The near-victim happened to be a prominent member of the medical staff.

Dr. E.F. (Ted) Donald had been well-known around the hospital since his student days of the early '30s when he was an outstanding football player and swimmer. Since then he had become known far afield and was due to be next president of the Canadian Medical Association. The rescue of Ted Donald was a boon to him of course and to the program, and was achieved against improbable odds.

It happened on a winter afternoon of bitter cold. In the hospital Dr. Ken Thomson received a call from overtown that Ted had suffered an attack in the office of the Alberta Medical Association and was being brought to the emergency. Ted's car wouldn't start in the intense cold and precious moments slipped away while another was borrowed. But incalculable odds were working in favour of Ted Donald.

As Ken Thomson received the call there happened to be sitting nearby in the doctors' lounge, engaged in light conversation, the only men in the hospital who had used CPR on an actual case of cardiac arrest — Dick Rossall of cardiology and Don Wilson, Chairman of the Department of Medicine. The previous summer they had restored the heartbeat of a little girl who had fallen from a dock at Pigeon Lake, though brain damage was so advanced that she died next day. Ken said: "Boys, I may need your help."

Ken and Don moved towards the emergency while Dick Rossall made a quick detour, up two flights of steps to his office to grab the de-fibrillator, a device kept on standby during catheterizing of heart valves. It had never been used for resuscitation. He shouted at an orderly for help and they ran for the elevator to take them and the machine down two floors to emergency. The elevator doors happened to be standing open at their floor — anyone familiar with the older hospital will appreciate the odds against that — and no precious time was lost.

Meanwhile Don Wilson found Ted already in cardiac arrest. An alert young nurse supplied some critical information. "Dr. Donald arrested three minutes ago." CPR had to start within four minutes. The heart was squeezed back to life and late that night Ted Donald was again conscious.

He didn't recover sufficiently to be president of the Canadian Medical Association, but was able to resume work eventually and when he did CPR was firmly established with a coronary care unit in dedicated space. Russ Taylor was given a two-bed semi-private room on Station 41, with a machine for monitoring heart action and a TV camera. He was able to buy the monitor, the TV equipment was borrowed from cardiovascular surgery which had acquired it for a film project which never quite got off the ground. The camera was placed in a corner with a closed circuit to a TV screen in the nursing station. Once established the coronary care unit was so heavily-used it expanded to a four-bed ward across the hall and then to two six-bed wards, and knowledge of the procedure known as CPR extended through the staff of the hospital and then beyond. Taken up by the Alberta Heart Foundation the principles have been taught to thousands.

In the University Hospital today people qualified in the procedure wear a red-and-white badge reading Cardiac Arrest Team. Teams are not formally organized. They just coalesce when CPR is needed. The person nearest the victim initiates the action. A "code" call goes out on the hospital intercom, and others take up places in the team in the order in which they arrive.

CPR was state of the art in December 1965 when Doug Wallace relinquished his stewardship to move to the Toronto General.

# Chapter 24

# 1966——1971
*The Centennial Hospital that Wasn't*

*No organization on earth is set up quite as illogically as a teaching hospital . . . motivated like a charity, operated like a business, regulated like a profession and governed like nothing else in our society.*
*Bernard Snell, Executive Director from January 1 1966*

As the author of the above observation commenced 18 years as chief executive, the administration, the board, the committees which laboured to harmonize the paradoxes in a teaching hospital, were studying a concept which was more than a hospital. They were talking health sciences centre.

The concept seemed new and yet it was implicit in the earliest visions of the hospital. In 1909 Henry Marshall Tory wrote: "I venture to say that in five years we should be in possession of the centre of medical science for western Canada."

In 1930, Lieutenant Governor Egbert, in declaring open the first extension of the hospital Dr. Tory brought to the campus, predicted that it would become a health centre for all Alberta, which, in the field of research and medical service to the people of Alberta, would one day be comparable to the clinic of the Mayo Brothers.

By 1966 it seemed the time had come to honour the prophecies. Trained medical specialists were in hand, thanks in large part to the hospital's own postgraduate program. Financial resources were in the hands of the provincial government.

On January 20 the board engaged a planning coordinator for a health sciences centre. In the negotiations are two signs of the times. A salary of $18,000 was required to lure Dr. John Read from Washington D.C. and his letter of acceptance took two days to reach Edmonton.

Hundreds were caught up in the urge to help conceive, design and execute a health sciences centre. They formed a huge ad hoc committee, by spontaneous combustion of an idea, and their efforts deserved kinder than a "stop work" order from a new provincial government when earth movers were on the site in the fall of 1971.

A strong factor in the campaign, which was not wasted but paid off eventually in a centre of a different concept, was the board — fresh, enthusiastic and new to the job. The senior members, in point of service, held seats by virtue of their positions at the university, and shared the enthusiasm. Included was the president, Walter Johns, classical scholar who rarely missed a meeting and characteristically greeted every idea as though it were the most interesting he had ever heard. And Walter Mackenzie, Dean of Medicine, whose office was a sort of secretariat for an international network of personal influence and intelligence-gathering on talented people and advances in medicine likely to become state of the art.

Four new brooms were appointed to the board in January 1963 (by Order-in-Council 58/63) — Gordon Wynn and Ken Hawkins, who have been introduced earlier, along with a chartered accountant and a lawyer. Elvin Christenson, served a dozen years, took a sort of sabbatical to be national president of the Canadian Association of Chartered Accountants, and then signed on again to be chairman of the University Hospital Foundation. He was recruited by Don Avison, looking to the end of his time as chairman, and seeking out people with special skills.

Eric McCuaig was the lawyer. One day he was invited to lunch by Donovan Ross. He and the Minister of Health had grown up as neighbours in Garneau and served together in the navy. The minister wanted to offer Eric the chairmanship of a new board being set up to administer the old Royal Alex — which the province had bought from the city to convert to the Glenrose Auxiliary Hospital. But between the invitation and the lunch Don Avison called with another proposal. He asked Eric to think about the board of the University Hospital. There were a number of attractions to the Avison offer. Being a member would likely take less time away from law practice than being a chairman. He had grown up practically in the shadow of the University Hospital. And then there was the family connection. His grandfather was A.C. Rutherford, first premier and godfather of the university and its affiliated teaching hospital. The minister, who made all appointments, went along.

In 1965 Order-in-Council 34/65 increased the board to nine members, named Gordon Wynn Chairman and appointed three more new brooms — a dentist, a farmer and a social welfare advocate.

Dr. Jack Young attributes his appointment to a long discussion with the minister at a social occasion in which he had argued that health care was costing too much. Roger Parker farmed at Ardrossan, was reeve of the County of Strathcona, and a board member of the Edmonton Hospital District No. 24. Marjorie Bowker told the minister she knew nothing about hospitals and was assured: "That's why we want you." However the first woman appointed to the board understood the subtleties of getting things done on campus — with husband Wilbur the dean of law — and she too was a lawyer. The next year she was named judge of the juvenile and family court, a court very much oriented towards social work, and as a member of the hospital board pressed for revival of the hospital's social service department, which had lapsed in the early '60s.

The board was small, only nine compared to 38 civic appointees at the Royal Alex. Every member had to chair a committee. They worked in harmony, and Mrs. Bowker says: "Much of the time we talked about the difficulties of carrying on sophisticated medical procedures in an outdated facility."

This is the board which caught the idea of a health sciences centre and pushed it to the plateau, which, in the disappointing fall of 1971, had all the appearance of an abyss. Towards the end some new faces appeared. Walter Johns retired and the president's seat was taken by Max Wyman. Stan Milner and Ken

Campbell replaced people who had to drop out and in 1970 the board was increased to 10 when the medical staff of the hospital was given the right to nominate a representative, the first of whom was Dr. Ron Wensel.

To a layman it might seem that the centre concept grew from a very little acorn, emerging as it did, from discussions about an auditorium. But an auditorium is an integral part of a teaching hospital, a hub for drawing people together in staff, educational and scientific meetings. The University Hospital was trying to use the auditorium in the Mewburn pavilion, which was actually a recreation hall and would seat 150 at a pinch. It was inadequate in the early '50s when an auditorium was the final item in a series of developments approved by the provincial government. The polio-paediatric wing was up; so were the extension of the nurses residence, the house staff residence and clinical services wing. But when time came to build the 250-seat theatre the government seemed to lose interest. So the board decided to go it alone.

A committee was appointed to see what should be expected of a modern auditorium: the medical superintendent, heads of medicine and surgery, and Dr. D.F. (Tim) Cameron, representing the university. They arrived quickly at the requirements, but then began to see the auditorium in a different setting — not as the final item in an old plan but an item in a series of new developments which would create a health sciences centre.

Among university faculties, medicine was not the only one concerned with health. They perceived a grouping of buildings, some hospital, some university, all health-related. The board approved the enlarged concept on December 16 1965 and five weeks later a planning coordinator was engaged.

There were several thoughts about the qualifications of the planner. Some said he should be a medical doctor, others an architect, some a hospital administrator, some a hospital consultant with experience. Walter Mackenzie, through his international grapevine, heard of a young Canadian in Washington D.C. who possessed something of all the suggested qualifications. John Read was 27. He had an MD from Toronto. In student days he'd worked as a draftsman and understood architectural terms and drawings. He'd interned at Sick Children's Hospital in Toronto during a period of expansion. And he was employed by Gordon Friesen, a Canadian with a large hospital consulting business, involving some 70 projects in the United States and Europe. Although John had grown up in London, Ontario, where his father was a doctor, he had a sense of the University of Alberta through his father's cousin, Robert Newton, President of the University 1941 to 1950. The Newtons used to visit in Ontario and his father and the president would load the boat with strong drink and pipe tobacco, two things Mrs. Newton abhorred, and go fishing peacefully out of sight down the lake. The president's lady often dined in the student cafeteria in Edmonton and the rule was that students mightn't smoke until she had departed. John Read spent 19 years with the University Hospital, the last 18 as Medical Superintendent (or Vice-president, Medical) and at the age of 33 won a Vanier award as an outstanding young Canadian.

Arriving in Edmonton in 1966 he found a pleasing smallness, a helpful ambience in which to plan a project involving many parties. Each morning began with a relaxing eight minute drive to work, rather than three-quarters of an hour of tension. The house staff of the hospital was still small enough for TGIFs, the medical staff small enough for an annual banquet and dance. The medical profession was free of the politics which plagued Ontario. The site of the proposed centre was a checkerboard with parcels held by the university, the hospital, the provincial departments of health and public works. But important compromises were made by gentlemen's agreement — handshakes followed by letters of understanding, and lawyers, if any, came in only to tidy up.

*The new young man on the block, Dr. John Read, 27*

The University was to set two important pieces on the site — two detached buildings in symbolic relationship to the hospital.

On the southwest was to be a Clinical Sciences Building to provide offices and clinical facilities for medical staff treating patients of the hospital. These were all medical doctors, holding joint appointments in the hospital and faculty of medicine, in the disciplines of medicine, surgery, obstetrics and sub-specialties which had emerged since the war. The space was needed. There were more doctors and more and more had full-time geographic appointments with no offices overtown.

On the northwest was to be a Medical Sciences Building, housing those branches of medicine not concerned directly with treatment of patients — physiology, biochemistry, anatomy, pharmacology, pathology, microbiology. Very few of the university staff in this area are medical doctors, but their work is basic to health care, and used to be known as the pre-clinical sciences.

There was also talk of separate buildings in the complex for rehabilitation medicine and the faculties of nursing, dentistry, and pharmacy.

The buildings signifying Clinical and Medical Sciences went up — 12 and six storeys respectively — and may be seen today flanking the Mackenzie Centre. The buildings to identify nursing, rehabilitation, dentistry and pharmacy did not. Nor did the Centennial Hospital, the consuming interest of the hospital board and staff, and thereby hangs a tale — of frustration.

The entire hospital community got caught up in the excitement of planning and designing a state of the art facility for treating patients. The proposed name *Centennial* was a natural, coinciding with that exuberant time when people were thinking in a broad historic dimension. All departments came into the planning office to tell how they saw the futures of their special areas and what facilities were needed. However, as John Read saw it: "There was still an all-pervasive idea that we should keep everything that was there. The notion that old buildings were not economic and were better knocked down didn't come till later." That meant planners of the Centennial Hospital had to step carefully around the past, being careful not to tramp on any of the hodgepodge already on the site. It meant there was no way to go but up. The only way was a high-rise.

In the old quarters would continue to be business as usual. The *un*-usual, the innovative, the leading edge, the state of the art, the quest for new frontiers, would be concentrated in the high-rise.

Architect Ron Clarke described it as "a pencil on a matchbox." Beds were in the pencil, services in the matchbox and a major service was the auditorium which sparked the campaign for a health sciences centre in the first place. An 11-storey hospital was an idea new and startling to Edmontonians, but several existed in the United States and John Read was personally acquainted with a notable example at Bethesda, Maryland, planned by Gordon Friesen Associates. A welcome appeal of the high-rise hospital was escape from ever-lengthening horizontal corridors which had to be travelled incessantly by patient, workers and wheeled carriers. Since 1914 the University Hospital had been locked into a system of central corridors with rigid widths and ceiling heights designed into the original unit by Meyer Sturm. All expansion wings had been forced to match up to the corridor specifications of the famed Chicago architect and since he designed many hospitals there must have been miles of Sturm corridors across North America. A likely recurring nightmare of people engaged in care of the sick was being trapped in an endless corridor, extending relentlessly fore and aft. Advanced technologies made the high-rise feasible, not least of which was in the matter of elevators — quantum leaps ahead of the technology which had driven Colonel Mewburn to multi-hued profanity.

Progress on the Centennial Hospital was markedly slower than on its

1967-1969 — the first new unit of the health sciences centre takes its place on the grounds and on the skyline, rising above the Polio and 1951 wings. The Clinical Sciences Building belongs to the university and houses medical departments with dual responsibility to hospital and Faculty of Medicine. The crane in the background is probably at work on the companion piece, number two in the plan, the university's Medical Sciences Building, which will be occupied in 1972

ancestor, the Strathcona Hospital of 1906, which took shape in exactly 17 days. Many factors intervened. Size was a factor — about 70 times the size in beds alone. Cost was a factor — about 26,000 times the cost. Complexity was a factor, too complex to quantify. And uncertainty was a factor, a very large one. In 1906 there was nothing to be uncertain about, but the Centennial Hospital had to include the latest in technologies which were in a state of ferment, with anybody's guess as to how they would harden into accepted formats. They were difficult to price or work into an architectural design. The prime example was computer technology.

*Watch this space — in 1971 the board puts a fence around it to mark the site of the Centennial Hospital. A corner of the present hostel is visible on the right, of the provincial lab on the left, with the Polio Wing in the background. But the project never gets past the fence*

In April 1966 the cabinet approved a planning process for the health sciences centre.

In May 1968 the completed plan was sent to cabinet, where favourable reaction was tempered by concern about cost. As a result the hospital portion was reduced by 106 beds and in December the government approved the revised plan, with funding to be phased in over eight years.

In the spring of 1969 the Clinical Sciences Building opened — the first phase of the centre — and excitement was genuine as the medical staff moved into spacious new offices with a view. But when the glow of achievement passed a loss was recognized. The hospital had been a rabbit warren, but in a warren there is constant communication and with it continuous fine-tuning of understanding. The chairman of medicine had always been next door to the executive director. Now he was a long way off, a hidden cost of the Clinical Sciences Building.

Meantime architect Ron Clarke plugged ahead, designing and redesigning as medical and technical staff kept coming in with state of the art ideas for their corners of pencil and matchbox. Finally, on October 24 1970 the board decided it was time to get on with it and regretfully ordered the architect to accept no more bright ideas.

1971 was marked by continuing concerns of the cabinet about costs. But these were resolved finally at a meeting of minds in which $42 million in "terminal" dollars was pledged. Anticipation ran high. Fencing went up around the site — between the polio wing and 114th Street. Signs went up. Earth movers lumbered in. But there was a flaw. The agreement with the government was dated August 21 1971. Nine days later that government was defeated at the polls. One of the first acts of the new regime was an order to stop work on the Centennial Hospital.

The effect was described with poignancy in the board's annual report: "By September 1971, after six years of work by hundreds of people, planning for the project and site preparation were completed. Construction was about to begin when a "hold" was ordered because of the exigencies of the provincial economy and to allow our new government an opportunity to evaluate its priorities. As of year-end the freeze on construction was still in force, resulting in major concern, to the board and medical staff of the hospital and to the faculty of medicine, as the pressures on our inadequate facilities grow."

# Chapter 25

# 1966—1971
*The Hospital that Was*

There is rich statistical evidence of the growth which was putting pressure on facilities and on staff as well.

From early 1966 when planning began on the health sciences centre, to the demise of the Centennial Hospital in late 1971, the cost of running the institution doubled almost exactly — growing from $11.26 million to $22.6 million.

Non-medical staff (regular and part-time) grew from 1,758 to 2,910.

The nursing team grew from 924 to 1,605.

Administrative and clerical staff grew from 91 to 276.

Professional and technical staff stood at 246, general service staff at 783.

Medical staff declined slightly to 189 with more full-time geographic appointments. The makeup of the house staff of 176 was clear indication of a teaching hospital. Fewer than 20 percent were old-style interns — the rest were residents on specialist postgraduate programs.

In 1971 the number of beds grew by 204 to a total of 1,253 — plus 117 infant bassinets. This was accomplished by a stroke of the pen effective January 1 when the University Hospital took over operation of the Aberhart Memorial Hospital, west across 114th Street. The Aberhart, opened in 1952, had been built by the province specifically for tuberculosis, but with control of the disease the TB wards stood half-empty. Plans were made to convert the unused wards for long-term polio and respiratory disease patients, mental health and extended care.

At takeover all beds in the Aberhart were listed as assigned to TB. In the main hospital a constant adjustment of priorities had produced the following allocation of beds: surgical 374, medical 291, obstetrical and gynaecological 256, paediatric 108, psychiatric 64, rehabilitation and polio 51, ophthalmology 27, and intensive care 8. Intensive care was a product of the 1966-71 period, to which we'll return.

A complex institution needs a philosophy to keep it on even keel and straight course — especially when planning a Centennial Hospital, more especially when the project is abruptly cancelled. In this period the University Hospital became perhaps the first anywhere to define and declare a philosophy.

The institution had travelled far along many roads since 1906 when Strathcona created a hospital in 17 days. A retroactive philosophy for that pioneer health centre has been proposed by Bernard Snell: "To care for patients in the immediate vicinity with resources immediately available." It was a worthy ideal for a frontier community of 3,300 souls and the rented house was suited to the ideal.

Sixty years later the people involved "understood" what the hospital had become, but it was a wordless understanding — like the meaning of being a Canadian. The board felt it should be converted somehow to explicit words. Marjorie Bowker was named chairman of an ad hoc committee to work with senior staff, bring out the motivating intangibles, relate every tangible to one of them, and express the results in a logical structure in plain English. The process consumed a frustrating year, in which the English language seemed far less rich

April 1966 — smiling board chairman Gordon Wynn cuts a ribbon, obviously pleased to be opening a facility which will make money for the hospital instead of costing. It's the Gift Shop by the main entrance. It will be operated for the next 20 years by the Auxiliary, whose president, Mrs. Bob Fraser, waits patiently

than it was reputed to be. On one plane they sought a document which would set out what patients and staff should expect of the hospital, and what the hospital should expect of them. On another plane it would define an ideal towards which all facets of the hospital could aspire.

The document was structured and worded by Mrs. Bowker, with the aid of her legal training. It has stood the test of time, and as this was written hospitals everywhere were hammering out "mission statements" to explain their existence. The University Hospital's philosophy is reproduced here, exactly as adopted on March 28 1968 — with the deletion of one word from Section IV (c)

Marjorie Bowker

which Walter Mackenzie suggested was superfluous.

### Philosophy of The University of Alberta Hospital

**The University of Alberta Hospital**, acting through its **board, accepts the responsibility** entrusted to it of providing to the citizens of Edmonton and of Alberta the highest quality of health services, and of acting as the major referral, teaching, and research hospital of the Faculty of Medicine of the University of Alberta, and **to this end** it subscribes to the following philosophy.

I    **Establishment**, maintenance, development, and expansion of a physical plant and facilities appropriate to the proper functioning of the Hospital and the fulfillment of its objectives.

II   **Acquisition** of public and private funds to insure the efficient operation of the Hospital on a sound financial basis.

III  **Provision** for optimum quality of **health care to the patient** through adherence to the following principles:

    a    Hospital activities directed primarily to patient care on the basis that the health needs of the patient take precedence over all other functions and considerations

    b    Administering to the physical, psychological, social, and spiritual needs of patients with the aim of restoring them to health as soon as possible in order that they may resume their places in home and community

    c    All patients accorded equal quality of care, consideration, and respect regardless of race, colour, religion, social or economic status

    d    Availability of the widest possible range of diagnostic and therapeutic services, based on most recent developments in the prevention and treatment of illness and disease, such services to be provided where necessary in cooperation with other medical services and institutions

    e    The highest ethical standards in respect to all services and activities connected with the Hospital

    f    Liaison with health and social agencies throughout the Province for referral of patients for after-care treatment and supervision

g    Standards of patient care to be such as to provide stimulus and leadership to persons engaged in health services throughout the Province and to persons receiving training and experience within the Hospital

h    Acceptance and recognition of the Hospital's dual role as an active general hospital for the Edmonton area and a referral centre for the Province of Alberta

IV   **Provision for** and **participation in** the **education and training of personnel in all fields of health services**, in particular by means of the following:

a    Training of graduate and undergraduate medical and dental students, nurses, pharmacists, dietitians, social workers, certified nursing aides, nursing orderlies, radiological technicians, laboratory scientists, laboratory technicians, physiotherapists, occupational therapists, and other health personnel

b    Close liaison and cooperation in education matters with the Faculty of Medicine and other faculties and departments of the University of Alberta, and with other educational institutions, schools of nursing, and health agencies

c    Joint responsibility with the Board of Governors and the Faculties of Medicine and Dentistry of the University of Alberta in respect to appointments of professional personnel to the clinical teaching staff of the Hospital

d    Orientation and in-service programs for the training of new staff to assist in their understanding of hospital policies, procedures, and practices

e    Provision for continuing education of staff, especially with respect to new policies and procedures

f    Periodic evaluation of the effectiveness of such educational and training programs

g    Encouragement to staff to express opinions and offer recommendations through appropriate channels of communication with a view to furtherance of the educational and other objectives of the Hospital

h    Education of patients in prevention of illness and disease and in self-care, particularly in respect to procedures and treatment to be followed on discharge from Hospital

i     Encouragement to young persons to undertake vocations in health and hospital fields in order to achieve and maintain adequate numbers of qualified persons in all branches of health services

V   **Provision for** and **encouragement of research** in all fields related to health care, in cooperation with the University of Alberta and other research agencies and institutions, and in accordance with accepted medical practice and ethical standards, in respect of the following:

a     Prevention and treatment of illness and disease

b     Rehabilitation for physical, mental, or emotional disorders

c     Development of improved methods for providing health care

d     Investigation and experimentation with new techniques, procedures, and drugs

e     Educational developments in all fields of health training, both in respect to content of instruction and teaching methods

VI  **Promotion** of **good public and employee relations** through an administrative policy designed to insure the following:

a     Fair compensation to employees for services in the form of financial returns and personal satisfaction, and to this end the University Hospital Board will negotiate in good faith with representatives of both professional and non-professional employees with a view to effecting mutually-satisfactory terms and conditions of service

b     Cooperation with the Alberta Hospital Association and with major professional organizations in the Province within the limits prescribed by legislation governing the University Hospital, and consistent with the Hospital's standards and policies

---

This lean wiry document emerged against a backdrop of the most massive and massively-publicized document on health ever produced in Canada — the Hall report. Chaired by Mr. Justice Emmett Hall, the Royal Commission on Health Services was convened by the federal authority to show how to make "the best possible health care available to all Canadians." The commission recommended "universal programmes," which cleared the way for Medicare.

The commission reported in two volumes, in 1964 and '65. On July 19 1965 Prime Minister Pearson informed a federal-provincial conference that legislation was coming — enabling legislation — similar to the 1958 plan for cost-sharing on hospitalization — from which provincial governments could opt out at their political peril. The National Medical Services Act was introduced on July 12 1966 and passed December 8, but was slow coming into effect because of the high-voltage debate it sparked. The medical profession, which had to deliver the services, was upset at being largely ignored and provincial governments perceived "universality" as a Trojan horse by which Ottawa winkled its way into provincial jurisdictions. Ottawa proclaimed the plan in effect on July 1 1968 when only two provinces had signed agreements. Alberta joined a year later to the day.

The federal-provincial agreement on hospitalization, which took effect April 1 1958, made a profound difference to the University Hospital and its patients, but Medicare, which gave every citizen the right to consult a doctor of his choice and have the service paid for, made an interesting, but minor impact on the hospital and patients were affected less in Alberta than elsewhere in Canada.

As for patients, Alberta had been well-served, initially by MSI — Medical Services Incorporated — an insurance plan run jointly by the Alberta Medical Association and the College of Physicians and Surgeons of Alberta, in which participating doctors pledged to not extra bill. In 1969 MSI was rolled into a provincial scheme, which achieved 90 percent coverage before being rolled in turn into Medicare.

As for the University Hospital, the Hall commission estimated that half of all Canadians were deprived of proper doctor's care by poverty, and Medicare swept away the "indigent patient" on whom many teaching hospitals had depended for clinical cases for the students. But in Alberta, comparatively few people had ever been "medically indigent" and Bernard Snell estimates that the University Hospital's portion of charity cases was only 10 percent of comparable Eastern institutions.

To make up for this all patients of the University Hospital had long been regarded as "teaching material." Ken Thomson says: "The proposition was put diplomatically of course. The attending physician would probably say: 'I've got a bunch of students I'd like you to see — if you approve.' " The patient had to approve. He could opt out like a province, but few ever did. Bob Macbeth says: "In my career at the University Hospital I never knew a patient who wasn't a private patient," meaning that all, paying or otherwise, were treated with equal courtesy. The point could have been put the other way — "all were public patients" — meaning they were available as clinical cases for students.

The major impact of Medicare was felt away from the bed area, in the Department of Ambulatory Care, an umbrella setup created to combine emergency and outpatient services with a new family clinic. Ambulatory care was one of these hospital/faculty hybrids, with the impetus in this case coming from the university side of the house. It reflected a trend in medical schools nationwide to recognize family medicine as a specialty and develop a teaching program oriented towards office rather than hospital practice. The department came into existence under Lloyd Grisdale, an exceedingly versatile chap who handled many assignments for the linked institutions. In January 1966 he was named Assistant Dean in the Faculty of Medicine with a joint appointment as Director of Ambulatory Care. The family teaching clinics were housed in the hospital in the Outpatient-Emergency area and there the Medicare chickens came home to roost. When every citizen could have a doctor waiting rooms filled up and emergency became the second line of defense for people needing medical attention. So emergency exploded.

*Two smiles that win friends and influence people. Walter Mackenzie's and Lloyd Grisdale's*

The word "exploded" has been chosen by Dr. Harold Kuckertz, who took over the emergency in March 1968. Dr. Kuckertz holds several distinctions. He is the only general practitioner to head a division of the hospital. He and his wife Bertha, also a doctor, are the last residents of Edmonton to enter the great northwest via Hudson Bay, traditional gateway of the fur traders. Thanks to an English friend with shipping connections they were able to travel by freighter in 1953. He left a rural practice in Saskatchewan when kidney failure put him in need of the renal dialysis program of the University Hospital, so he was both patient and member of the medical staff.

In 1968 he was the only MD in full-time attendance abetted by residents who were conscripted away from their regular rotations to the intense displeasure of the house-men and their chiefs. When he left six years later the service had six full-time physicians and employed many residents part-time — and he notes with a characteristic smile that when residents could augment their meager incomes, "the change of heart was stunning. Before that emergency duty was an imposition and no learning experience at all. All of a sudden it was a great learning experience and they were queueing up." The patients were queueing up too. Ten percent of hospital admissions were coming through the emergency.

Established policies were blown away. First to go was the rule that emergency patients could not return for a followup visit. When the client's problem was ultimately resolved he was given a card with the record of treatment and a referral to a doctor in family practice — preferably one just starting out.

The staff noted a sizeable clientele who didn't see the need of a regular doctor. "These people weren't stupid. They just weren't sick very much and when they were they knew where they could get good treatment." Some patients were difficult. They might arrive in a rage, having been turned down by a doctor, and delays caused by overcrowding gave their dispositions no transfusion of sunshine. Some of the delays were eased by improving organization, others by having x-ray, pharmacy and clinical laboratory facilities right in the area.

There was an interesting financial twist to the emergency explosion. Medicare, which triggered it, started picking up the bills. MDs were seeing patients, residents were licensed to practice. The beauty of it was that each episode was a "visit" — for which the hospital could bill the author of the explosion, Medicare.

That was one side of the Medicare coin, but there was another — which caught the hospital by surprise. It was expected that when everyone had a doctor the outpatient service would disappear. The board was so confident of this that early in 1968 the imminent demise was made official policy. However, it didn't happen, and in 1971 when the outpatients hadn't disappeared or much diminished the board did the best it could in the circumstances and changed the name of the service. The new name was health science clinics, clinics being plural and very much so. As this was written no less than 47 were functioning, all specialties in the postgraduate teaching program. The new name reflected this important shift in direction. Patients were referred to clinics by a personal physician, in marked contrast to the walk-in clinic on Jasper Avenue where some clients had to be referred to the police.

In this period when events were at a hard boil, a decision was made on which route to go with an imperative new concept — the Intensive Care Unit.

A number of things had come together by June 20 1968 when the hospital board confirmed a recommendation of the medical staff favouring a particular style of ICU.

For many years there had been a concept known as *"constant* care," in which very sick patients were brought together for 24-hour monitoring. But *constant* care did not imply high-technology life-support systems, which intensive care did, and urgently. Mixed in was another concept known as *special* care. Traditionally hospitals had done the best they could for the sickest patients by putting them adjacent to a nursing station, as close as possible to whatever life-extending skills might be available.

As a teaching and referral centre for northern Alberta the University Hospital had many tertiary, or very sick, patients with specialized afflictions. Advances of the '50s and '60s built a need for a complex kind of special care, especially the advances in surgery, where lengthy complicated operations were followed by a critical post-operative period of hours or days.

There was talk of each specialty with its own ICU, but some gallows humour disposed of that idea. The saying went: "If a patient has nine tubes and five consultants he's dead" — meaning that he had no one to coordinate his care. Two factors seemed obvious. Not all patients would fit easily into categories and for 75 percent the urgent need would be respiratory support. Brian Sproule, head of the division of pulmonary medicine, was chairman of a committee set up to recommend a direction for intensive care. Another pulmonary specialist was chosen to run the unit and sent away for advanced work in what has come to be recognized as *Critical Care Medicine*. Garner King, a U of A graduate, went to Colorado Medical Centre in Denver, one of the few teaching hospitals anywhere with a mixed medical-surgical ICU. He returned in November 1970 and was still in charge as this was written.

The first unit was set up in a sunroom on Station 67 of the polio wing. A welcome improvement in respirators — the *volume* type — was moved in, along with cardiac monitors and intravenous equipment. The sunroom held four beds comfortably, but could be pushed to five.

The ICU solved urgent practical problems but bred philosophical ones, concerning transfer of functions. It was still accepted that final responsibility for a patient must reside with his attending physician. However the system demanded some transfer of functions, first of all between the physician and the staff of the ICU. Who decided whether a patient should be admitted to intensive care? Who decided on treatment while the patient was in the unit? Who decided when he could be released? The verdict was that these functions must be transferred to the staff of the unit — which had happened in the '50s when the isolation ward of the Royal Alex was a de facto ICU for polio victims. The ICU is a hospital in microcosm.

Then there was transfer of functions from physician to nurse. This had been going on since 1906 at the Strathcona frontier hospital, when the nurse took over at some point though no one could define exactly where. The problem was magnified in the ICU where nurses possessed highly-developed skills, formerly the exclusive property of the doctors. For example they could, and had to, interpret electrocardiograms and decide on immediate response.

The hospital, alas, did not possess a Solomon to harmonize these philosophical discords and had to institute a training program to impart MD skills to more nurses.

Garner King was a live-in head of intensive care in 1971 as the unit handled 150 patients without benefit of residents, only junior interns. However there were three important people still active as this was written — nurse Bonita Price, technician Alan Wells and respiratory therapist Linda Bradley — all of whom draw intensive praise from their chief. Over the years separate ICUs have developed for coronary care, neonatal care and neurological observation, but the principle of the general unit has developed smoothly along a route charted in 1968.

Intensive care was a product of specialization. Other products were six new divisions in the Department of Medicine. Each went through the usual channels. Some years earlier people got interested in a smaller field of knowledge seeking finer diagnosis and treatment. They came to favour a separate division and eventually said: "Let's do it." Having said that, the university found specialists qualified to teach and the hospitals allocated beds for clinical experience. The proposal, with supporting documentation, was submitted to the Royal College of Physicians and Surgeons of Canada. When the Royal College gave its stamp postgraduates were enrolled in the College's approved residency program, with money for their salaries available from a federal-provincial fund, and Alberta's sick had another special service available to them in the University Hospital.

The Department of Medicine went through channels six times, hatching the divisions of gastroenterology, clinical haematology and immunology-nephrology in 1968, infectious diseases and rheumatology in 1969, medical oncology in 1970. Thus was the medical side of the house brought up to the full list of specialties offered to patients, a condition reached by the surgical side of the house in the 1950s.

*Immunology and Nephrology*

The informed layman knows that immunology is the study of the immune system of the body and that nephrology is the study of the kidney. Why they should be combined in one division is sure to be a mystery, but the rationale is one of historical timing. Immunology seeks the reasons for the body rejecting implants and in the late '60s the only organs being transferred in Alberta were kidneys. The immune system is the body's defense against invaders. If invaded by smallpox, the system sets up agents to fight back, and these can be transmitted through serum to help other bodies fight off smallpox. The problem for the immunologist is that the body will fight just as hard to reject a foreign object which is beneficial as one which is damaging. The body will try to reject a desperately-needed new kidney or heart or liver.

Nephrology worked hand-in-surgical glove with its operating cousin, urology, to develop a kidney transplant program. In his 1965 annual report the head of surgery noted: "It is planned to bring kidney transplantation out of the laboratory and into the hospital in the near future."

In the lab, two urologists were experimenting with animals. Bill Lakey was one, the other was Rex Boake. Rex was a recent graduate who had done advanced study at UCLA, but became best known to the wider community 20 years later as president of the Eskimo football club when the general manager departed abruptly for Montreal.

In 1966 a dialysis program was established with six beds in a sunporch known as Station 67. There the medical side was treating patients with failing kidneys and identifying candidates for transplant. By 1967 both medicine and surgery felt it was reasonable to proceed to transplants in humans. Five operations were attempted, with the most promising candidate a teen-age lad from the Saddle Lake Indian reserve whose donor was his twin brother.

Results were discouraging, but five more were attempted the next year and one recipient was a boy who was able to live 15 extra years. The dialysis unit moved to larger space, with 13 beds in the Mewburn pavilion, and the first intensive care unit occupied Station 67. There is a now-it-can-be-told story of 1968, in which immunology played a decisive, and negative role. The previous December Dr. Christiaan Barnard of South Africa burst into the news with the world's first heart transplant. The event created huge interest everywhere. In Edmonton the Special Services and Research Committee of the University Hospital was so impressed that prolonged study was given to a transplant program which came very close to happening.

Because of the sensational nature of the subject it was kept hush-hush from press and public. The committee discussed it at special meetings, decisions were recorded in longhand and not included with the regular minutes. Two men who had worked in open-heart surgery were sent to Houston and Montreal to observe the procedure; Cecil Couves of the surgical side and Joe Dvorkin of the medical. There were meetings of the medical disciplines at which legal advisers were in attendance. Medicine was into areas where legal responsibility had to be defined. Clergy were in attendance too. As the saying went, medicine was into areas where doctors had to "play God," deciding who should benefit and who put at risk.

Nothing happened — eventually. As Cecil Couves recalls: "In the beginning I was very much in favour, it seemed to promise an exciting episode. But by the time we worked out the program — it ran to 20 pages with charts and diagrams — the procedure itself had come into disrepute. Major rejection factors had not been solved. This came to the fore. John Callaghan had said it all along. The program was never formally cancelled. It just petered out."

And there is another now-it-can-be-told story of that summer of 1968. By arrangement with Dr. Couves a young university student was practicing heart-lung transplants in the animal lab. He was 19 and had not yet been admitted to medical school but was keen to pursue that specialty. The arrangement tells something of his determination. He'd been told that Dr. Couves had lab space, but didn't know how to approach him. So he hit on the idea of contriving an appointment as a patient, and once in the door confessed: "Honestly there's nothing wrong with me, I want to work in your lab." Ingenuity was rewarded and the young man was authorized to investigate transplant surgery in the animal lab. He worked diligently that summer without drawing any remuneration, or

*Here's history in the making. It's the summer of 1968. The young man on the left looks familiar. He's 19, practicing heart transplants in the animal lab of the U of A, and hoping to be admitted to medical school. The name is Modry, first name Dennis*

any attention either. In 1968 no bells were rung by the name *Dennis Modry*.

But interest in transplants remained strong, so strong that the next year there was a transplantation laboratory, to study the factors in rejection, the research component in the new medical divison of immunology and nephrology.

Nephrology was represented by Rae Ulan, whose postgraduate career had coincided with the emergence of nephrology as an ad hoc medical specialty in 1962. He was in charge of a dialysis program, which by 1969 had some 25

*Don Buchanan*

chronic patients, all coming to the hospital for treatment.

Immunology was represented by John Dossetor, MD from Oxford, who for eight years had been director of the renal and urological research unit at Royal Victoria, teaching hospital of McGill. Dr. Dossetor came to add the research dimension, the transplantation laboratory. The province offered $300,000 to equip space in the Clinical Services Wing and the Medical Research Council provided support for two major researchers. Known in-house as the tissue-typing (or tissue-matching) lab it extended the work Dr. Buchanan and the Red Cross had begun in matching blood groups. Blood typing involves the red cells. Tissue matching extends to the white cells, which have antigens, protein substances which allow antibodies to develop. It identifies more fully organs compatible with the body of the recipient.

The lab added the research component to patient care and teaching.

In 1969 the surgical team did 11 transplants followed by 16 in 1970, and with more knowledge of rejection it became a routine operation, with some 400 through 1985. Immunology began in tandem with nephrology because kidneys were the only complete organs being transplanted, but as time went on immunology opened the way to transplants of liver, pancreas and heart.

And the dialysis program was on the verge of something very big. In the next decade it was to become one of the biggest programs of the hospital, in-house and beyond.

## Infectious Diseases

When George Goldsand returned from postgraduate specialization at the University of Pittsburgh to head this new division, the second in Canada, his friends said: "Nice to see you back, George, but what are you going to do? All the infectious diseases have been conquered." That was true, in the sense of the old "fever" hospitals which treated typhoid, smallpox, diphtheria, scarlet fever and polio. In fact George had been an intern in 1960 when the University Hospital received the last acute polio cases and he says: "It's difficult now to make my residents understand the anguish associated with that disease."

But there was a subtle new order in which an infectious disease specialty grew out of internal medicine. In the old order, particularly in Britain, doctors who treated fevers were medical biologists whose work was lab-centred. They weren't members of clinical staffs.

George explains why he found plenty to do, why in 1986 he headed a division of infectious diseases with seven full-time doctors: "We're busily involved in the diseases of medical progress. People are living longer. We have intensive care units. There have been advances in treatment of cancers. Organ transplants have become common. The drugs patients are given increase their susceptibility to infection and the infections are more resistant to commonly available treatments."

George was recently a patient in the hospital and jolted a young resident who came around to take his medical history and that of his family as George had taught him. The resident was dismayed by the history of George's grandparents. What sort of health had they experienced? George couldn't really say about that, he knew only how they had died — his father's parents in a Nazi gas chamber and his mother's shot on a country road in Austria. George and his parents escaped to Alberta just before the war when he was three years old and he still has his father's Austrian passport, stamped with Swastikas and big red J's. The Goldsand family were victims of an infectious disease of the spirit, which, it's to be hoped, is under control too.

## Rheumatology

John Percy brought a research component to the admirable clinical pioneering of E.G. "Cappy" Kidd. With a research dimension hospital-and-faculty moved to create the eighth division of rheumatology in Canada. A product of "Geordie" country in the north of England, Dr. Percy was completing a two-year Fulbright scholarship at Colorado Medical Centre when he was scouted by a member of the University Hospital staff. He came for a look, was impressed by the activity on campus, better than UCLA, and chose Edmonton as a place to raise a family.

On the strength of primary pilot training in the RAF he became a "flying doctor," commuting to monthly outreach clinics established by the division in Fort McMurray, Peace River, Grande Prairie, High Prairie, Mannville and Red Deer. The outreach program had two objectives — to have patients treated by their own doctors and to protect the position of the University Hospital as a tertiary referral centre for people needing the full resources of a teaching and research centre. A paediatric clinic at the Glenrose Hospital School was another outreach project.

Financial support for research came from several outside sources. The Canadian Arthritis and Rheumatic Society continued its contribution. Funding also came from the Medical Research Council of Canada, the kidney foundation, the lupus foundation and the MSI foundation. When governments took over medical insurance the reserve of Medical Services Incorporated became another foundation funding research.

Since 1968 two new treatments have been developed to go with the gold salt pioneered by Dr. Kidd — penicillamine, and methotrexate, a drug used to treat cancer. Eighteen years later Dr. Percy was still head of the division and able to say: "In 1986 no one should get crippled from arthritis. There is no cure, but it can be put into remission. In 1968 everybody knew someone who had arthritis, now they know someone who has arthritis and is doing well, so patients are optimistic. The problem in the hospital is that the arthritic patient can't compete with a cardiac patient. It's important to keep a man from dying, but it's just as important to keep him from being crippled."

## Gastroenterology

The medical specialty and study of stomach and intestines was formalized as a division when two Alberta graduates came home with postgraduate skills. Dick Sherbaniuk was in Detroit. Ron Wensel had two years at the University of

Washington and had a "homer's" interest in returning. His father was an old-time south side merchant and his wife's great-grandfather John Gainer had signed the original petition in favour of a Strathcona cottage hospital. Though gastroenterology was recognized medically it was scarcely a household word. In his first year of practice Ron made $6,000 and only because Joe Dvorkin, ever a kindly leading light in the lives of younger colleagues, let him share an office.

Fibre optics was just coming to the aid of medicine. Financed by the Special Services and Research Committee, the division was able to order two gastroscopes, which transmitted an internal image along a single strand of light, an image which could be shown on a screen and viewed by a group. The gastroscope, even in its simple 1967 form, was a huge advance over the endo-scope, in which the picture of an ulcer was relayed mechanically through 50 tiny mirrors. A later advance was the colonoscope, which can show and remove polyps. It made news with the operation on President Reagan.

The division began with an examining room in the emergency and no beds. In 1970 a few beds were obtained (en route to 26).

This provided a clinical base. In 1971 the essential research component was added with the arrival of Dr. Fred Weinstein from Saskatchewan. However, a doctor can't pursue research and academic trains of thought if his phone is ringing — or worse, as nowadays, his beeper is howling. At special times Wensel and Sherbaniuk created an "ivory tower" for their research-minded colleague by intercepting his clinical calls, a scheme which has been adopted by other divisions. Fred Weinstein's work ultimately took him to UCLA's Centre for Ulcer Research which has a huge referral base, all of North America. The postgraduate teaching component has also shown commendable results. Four-teen residents have qualified for the Royal College fellowship without a single failure.

*Clinical Haematology and Medical Oncology*

CH is defined as the science encompassing the generation, anatomy, physiology, pathology and therapeutics of the blood; MO as the scientific study of tumors (cancers).

They were linked because at this early stage chemotherapy was being used only against blood cancers and because Adam Little was qualified in both areas.

Though later separated, neither developed as they have in other medical centres. "Oncology didn't develop because of the close proximity of the W. W. Cross Institute," Dr. Little says. The Cross opened in 1969 — he was head of cancer services for the province when it was being planned. "We clinicians saw haematology as a bridge between bedside medicine and the lab," he says, "but we had opposition." As Don Wilson, who as Chairman of Medicine set up the division, explains: "Oncology was acknowledged to be a medical thing, but with CH three groups thought they should run it — the clinicians of internal medicine, the pathologists and the people in the clinical services lab." A visiting committee headed by Dr. Ronald Christie, Dean of Medicine at McGill tried to resolve the impasse, but no compromise was achieved. Victor Jackson, the humourous Scot who arrived a little later to plan the Mackenzie Centre, has a term for the condition: "Ah, the intertribal warfare."

With the latest specialties in place the third head of the Department of Medicine moved on to greener pastures. After 14 years, in which he oversaw the creation of nine new divisions and the splitoff of three others to autonomous departments, Don Wilson resigned in August 1969. The hospital's first geographic full-time medical man, he had come as a scholar of the Markle Foundation and left to start a project for the McLaughlin Foundation, financed by Canadian automobile magnate Colonel Robert McLaughlin, who was then 98 years old and not slowing down for the curves. A computer centre was established in Edmonton with the aim of creating a national information bank for Canadian medical schools. Bob Fraser, of cardiology, succeeded Don Wilson for a five year term. In the other traditional clinical professorships, Bob Macbeth continued head of surgery. Head of obstetrics and gynaecology (they all became chairmen the next year) was Peter Beck, 1965-1981. Dr. Beck had come from Queen's and cites two reasons: "Walter Mackenzie told me what a great place this was going to be and I had a lot of respect for Ross Vant. I'd served on a committee with him and some people from Britain. He's really an outstanding person."

New medical procedures were a feature of the age. Bypass surgery, pacemakers, renal dialysis, kidney transplants, were instigated by medical research and brought nothing but satisfaction.

However, it would be expected that if the parliament of Canada ever got into the business of instituting medical procedures controversy would erupt, and expectations were realized in 1968 with a massive set of amendments to the Criminal Code. Section 237 was the cause. It concerned abortions. They had always been illegal but "therapeutic" abortions would be allowed under certain conditions if the health of the mother was at risk.

Hospitals were reluctant to touch the enabling legislation, some on moral grounds, others on the ground that hassles were inevitable and they had enough already. In Edmonton the Misericordia and General abstained. The Royal Alex agreed, which put the board of the University Hospital under severe pressure — from the Royal Alex and some of its own doctors.

On January 20 1970 the decision was made. In precise conformity with the law a "therapeutic abortions committee" of five members of the medical staff was established. This panel was to review each case. There had to be a medical basis for an application — heart or psychiatric problems were often cited — though a member of the original committee says: "I suspect that social considerations crept in. Anyway the recommendations all came from fellow members of the medical staff and it would have put us in a very difficult position to go against one of our own colleagues."

The moral considerations which divided the community also affected medical and nursing staffs of the University Hospital. Those unable to participate because of their convictions were not required to, though some were disturbed that the procedure was going on at all. A fear that facilities would be overwhelmed by demands for abortions was not realized, and parliament, which has since decided to stay out of the bedrooms of the nation has mercifully stayed out of the operating rooms.

In the late '60s the initials KPM took on significance in the progress of the hospital — KPM for Kates, Peat, Marwick & Co., management consultants. The board hired KPM to survey the administrative structure. KPM made its report in 1968 and the major recommendation was to divide three ways the responsibilities of the business administrator. George Sherwood would retain buildings and grounds (though the grounds were fast disappearing under new

*Joe Newhouse*

buildings) and the support services — laundry, dietary, housekeeping, pharmacy, purchasing, supply, mail, security. There would be two new jobs of rank equal to the business administrator — Director of Finance and Director of Manpower.

With the recommendation approved KPM was given a mandate to recruit. Manpower director Rod Larsen came from Eaton's department store chain. Joe Newhouse was a chartered accountant with Husky Oil. Joe was to stay 13 years and would for one long stretch be acting executive director of the hospital.

"I knew nothing about health care or hospitals," Joe recalls with amusement. "I was in the cafeteria having coffee with Bernie Snell and I told him my first great idea: 'Why don't we charge the doctors for the operating room?' Bernie had a good laugh. He said charging the surgeons made good economic sense, but he went on to explain that no organization on earth is set up quite so illogically as a teaching hospital. He said a teaching hospital is organized like nothing else in our society.

"I had a lot to get used to. The biggest difference between the oil business and the hospital was the darn meetings. In the oil business we'd have one meeting. A senior guy would come in and say 'This is what we're going to do,' and you went out with authority and money to do it. In the hospital so many people and professions had to be involved — the doctors, the nurses, the government — we had to go through a hell of a lot of meetings to get a consensus and when we agreed what should be done we really didn't know if anyone had authority and if he did he likely didn't have the money.

"When you have to run an operation illogically and make it go, your business methods have to be better than average. But this wasn't the case. What was happening was that people with training only in their professions were being asked to run a multi-million dollar business and they weren't trained for that. When I came there was an American outfit called TRW around, advising the board how to install computers in the Centennial Hospital. TRW is a big player in the US space program but the hospital's accounting was like a corner grocery store.

"Department heads weren't involved in the budget process. A budget was sent to the government each year, but it was made up in the accounting office where they added percentages here and there. That satisfied the government. Accounting made up a monthly report, but that just went to the government too. The process satisfied the government but defeated the primary purpose of budgeting.

"I went to the board with a proposal to set up a budgeting system by area of responsibility. This was neither new nor revolutionary I can tell you. Department heads participated and got monthly feedback to see where they stood. I found that in a hospital it's not easy to budget by areas of responsibility. In the operating room the surgeon is in charge, but he's in business for himself. In the Intensive Care Unit a nurse is responsible, but a doctor is in charge. The process helped people get a handle on costs.

"In my first annual report (for 1968) I wrote that 'if a physician examined our financial state of health he would prescribe a transfusion of money.' We had a perpetual overdraft, one-and-a-half million and going higher. Most of it was money the provincial government owed us. That's how we saw it anyway. We had issues that went back for years — we claimed they were covered by hospitalization grants and provincial accountants said they weren't. Bernie and I sat down with the head man on all the outstanding issues with a sheaf of documents that thick on everything. Eventually we got it all.

"It's hard to say what causes things. I got a lot of credit I'm not sure I deserved — but we started 1969 with a deficit of $1,420,000 and wound up with a surplus of $669,000."

That was Joe Newhouse's experience. Rod Larsen was in his office in Eaton's Calgary store when KPM came headhunting a director of manpower for the University Hospital. Rod stepped into a situation of daunting complexity. Among the non-medical staff specialization had woven a tangled web. In the '30s Dr. Washburn could call every worker in the hospital by name. By 1968 Dr. Snell would have done well to recite from memory the name of every job category.

Rod found that about a fifth of the employees were successors of the so-called "sub" staff of Dr. Washburn's day. Working in the laundry, the kitchens, the housekeeping services, they belonged to Branch 23 of the Civil Service Association. But the hospital was also dealing with registered nurses, certified nursing aides, combined lab-x-ray technicians, dietary technicians, pharmacists, physiotherapists, inhalation therapists, radiographers, medical laboratory technologists, dietitians, remedial gymnasts, psychiatric nurses, orthoptists, glaucoma technologists, medical social workers, laboratory scientists, psychologists, speech therapists, and computer programmer analysts. The first director of computing services, Donald Fenna, was engaged in 1968, the result of another KPM recommendation. It was a joint appointment with the Faculty of Medicine. Dr. Fenna came from Australia, where he had been Deputy Assistant Postmaster General, responsible for computerizing communication systems on that continent.

The administration was struggling to fit two dozen professional categories into pay scales that were reasonable for the University Hospital, in line with those of other hospitals, and in line with government policies towards the civil service. Not surprising that a collective bargaining committee, chaired by Marjorie Bowker, was made a standing committee of the board. (In Dr. Washburn's day there had been no bargaining, collective or otherwise.) Each group was represented in negotiations by a professional association.

When Rod Larsen came as Director of Manpower only Branch 23 of the Civil Service Association had union status of a sort. For some years there had been discussion with government lawyers on where the branch fitted. The lawyers said not under the Labour Act and not under the Public Service Act either. So in May 1968 the Crown Agencies Act (Chapter 17 Statutes of Alberta 1968) was passed to define the status of public employees not covered by the Public Service Act. The act named a dozen institutions — including the liquor control board, the cancer clinic, and three hospitals — the Glenrose, Foothills and University. Employees could bargain in units but were declared essential and not allowed to strike.

The president of Branch 23 was known as "The Rebel," a nickname which came naturally to this native of Dublin. Mike Oman worked 12 years as an orderly and would have gone longer if it hadn't been for the pension. When he took the job Mike said he was 43, but when he'd served the required months to go on the pension plan his birth certificate gave away his secret — he was in fact 53. The certificate showed he'd been born in 1903. In his youth he trained as a silversmith and went on the run with the Republican Army in the fight for Ireland's freedom. But as he said sadly: "What the leaders of the British couldn't destroy we destroyed later through civil war." So Mike moved to England, and worked as a grinder in an aircraft factory where, to his powers of Irish persuasion, he added the tactical skills of the British trade unionist. Eventually he emigrated to Canada and although he'd never been in a hospital got a job as an orderly at the University Hospital. Within a week he was elected to represent the orderlies in Branch 23 and quickly discovered the branch wasn't being run in a proper way at all — like a social club, not a union, and the president took no interest in grievances. At the first opportunity Mike got himself elected president of the branch. Doug Wallace, who enjoyed Mike's Irish company, gave him a private office where he could entertain grievances and relay those he considered worthwhile — about one in ten, the other nine being personality conflicts. Mike found Doug Wallace and his successor helpful and receptive. "Mike Oman? A fine man," says Bernard Snell.

Nurses still bargained through their professional body, the Alberta Association of Registered Nurses. Although some union feeling was evident the United Nurses of Alberta was not established till 1977. In this period a scarcity of nurses drew attention to their importance, most particularly in 1966 when three wards of the Mewburn pavilion had to be closed because of a shortage. All remedies were tried. Nurses were recruited in the United Kingdom. Students in the senior year were allowed to work for overtime pay. Staff nurses were allowed to work in their holidays. A day care centre was provided — the first in any Alberta hospital. A portable school classroom where 50 children could be cared for at $2.25 a day, was opened in October 1967.

Within the hospital the director of nursing was waging a determined campaign to ease the shortage by having members of the nursing team restrict their time to duties which were actually nursing-related. In this effort Geneva Purcell was bucking entrenched tradition but she opened the campaign shortly after coming to the job in 1962. She set up an in-house survey — by two senior nurses — of procedures in the wards. They documented that members of the nursing team (whose salaries were charged to the department of nursing) were assigned a lot of work which belonged in the housekeeping and dietary areas.

Their contention drew valuable though unintentional corroboration from an outside study commissioned by the board in 1965. Woods-Gordon, with a reputation for helping Ontario hospitals save money, was engaged to study the housekeeping service. Woods-Gordon found 97 housekeepers and 103 ward aides in patient care areas, and reported that actual nursing functions could be performed by 37 ward aides with other functions (and charges) transferred to housekeeping.

Further corroboration came in 1968 when KPM, which was surveying hospital administration, recommended a "nursing activity study." KPM recommended itself for the job at $25,000, but the board decided that Charles Chamberlain, the hospital's work study officer, could do it for $10,000 less, which he did. He documented the situation in the dietary area where ward aides

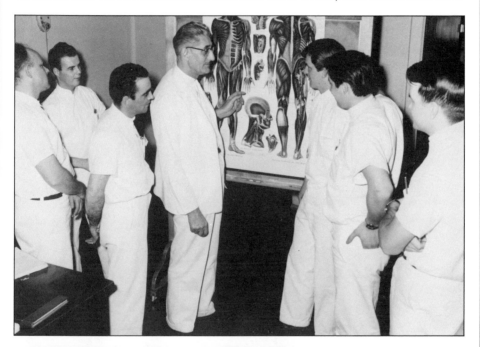

1966 — a proud day for "Slim" Lefebvre, centre, conducting a course for orderlies. In his 40 years to the day at the University Hospital "Slim" did the most to raise the orderly to professional status

May 1968 — things comfortable and familiar may be disappearing, but not where Fanny Hooson has anything to say about it. She is in her 40th year as night cook in the staff cafeteria. The cash drawer is for those who insist on paying, a hospital policy of which she does not approve

and student nurses were acting as porters.

The result was a "unit management program" serving four nursing stations. As Bernard Snell stated in his annual report for 1969: "The objectives of this project are to determine the feasibility of transferring non-nursing work from the nursing staff to others, and to maintain or improve the quality of care given to patients at no extra cost. The development of this concept is important to the future of the Centennial Hospital . . ."

The Centennial Hospital was the vision sustaining all those tossed on the sea of complexity. They plowed on through every vexation buoyed by the knowledge that they were achieving something splendid — a health sciences centre with the Centennial Hospital as the jewel in the crown.

But in September 1971 the vision was abruptly yanked away.

# Chapter 26

# 1971—1977
## Health Sciences Centre — the Grand Design

*We had to start all over again.*
*Gordon Wynn, Chairman of the Board 1965—1978*

The abrupt freeze on construction put morale in a deep chill as well. Six years uphill slogging lay ahead before sod would be turned for another design. The first fine careless rapture of planning the Centennial Hospital was never recaptured.

For a whole year the board tried to interest the new government in the problems of the hospital. Then at the end of the year the government announced a review to take 18 months!

This announcement was discouraging as the one which quashed the Centennial Hospital and it introduced a new consideration — the Calgary factor. "In order for the government to consider more fully the options open to it," the statement read, "the study will look into physician training needs including specialist training . . . and what proportion of those needs should be supplied by the University of Alberta and the University of Calgary."

The Calgary factor came on very rapidly. The southern university opened its doors in 1966. A Faculty of Medicine was established the following year and in 1970 the first class convened on the top floor of the Foothills Hospital. The school started with an arresting premise. It was to be a first-class specialist school for family practitioners. While first-year students took classes in makeshift quarters their permanent home was going up nearby. It had the confusing name of health sciences centre, confusing because it bore so little resemblance to the development of the same name being proposed in Edmonton.

In Edmonton the name was to signify something more than a hospital, while in Calgary it meant something more than a medical school. And to pile further confusion on the term *health sciences centre*, in other places it meant different things entirely. There was to be one in Hamilton, dominated by McMaster, which didn't involve the regional hospitals. In Winnipeg the regional hospitals proposed a centre which didn't involve the University of Manitoba. And in the United States the term was understood to mean a free-standing institution.

In Calgary was a single building, of half a million square feet, owned entirely by the university, containing all medical offices and research facilities with a large ambulatory care department to attract "teaching material" for students.

In Edmonton was to be a building of one-and-a-half million square feet owned by the hospital, in a complex with others owned by the university and provincial government.

And there was an important difference in funding. In Calgary half the cost was paid by the federal government because the school was set up in response to recommendations of a federal medical commission.

In September 1972 construction was far advanced in Calgary, while in Edmonton there was good news and bad news. The goods news was that the *Medical Sciences Building* was finished and occupied. It was the second piece in the grouping planned around the cancelled Centennial Hospital, complementing the first piece, the *Clinical* Sciences Building which had opened in 1969. All undergraduate students of the Faculty of Medicine were then located in CSB, south of the present Mackenzie Centre, or MSB, visible if not architecturally memorable, on the north. The handsome old medical building on 88th Avenue, erected with Rockefeller money in the '20s, was left vacant and soon occupied by the faculties of Dentistry and Pharmacy.

The bad news was that the province decreed a further 18-month hiatus in continuing development of the Edmonton health sciences centre. And thereby hangs a tale — of neglect. No upgrading had been done for a number of years in expectation of the Centennial Hospital. The year following cancellation had been a vacuum. Now the hospital faced another year-and-a-half of drift. Some renovation was required to bring the plant back to a reasonable standard for its current role. A committee identified the needs, which were whittled down to essential needs and then further to *immediate* essential needs. With a list of immediate essential needs the board went to Neil Crawford, minister of the department now known as Health and Social Development, and $920,000 was provided to renovate two nursing stations and part of the Mewburn. A concrete floor in the stores department was in danger of falling into a corridor below, but $10,000 was found in the operating budget to fix that.

The 18-month review period was not a happy time. It would hardly have been so anyway, but was exacerbated by the style and method of the special advisor brought in by the government to conduct the review. To put the case gently, many natives of Glasgow have been associated with the long history of the University Hospitals and all have been more popular than Graham Clarkson. Dr. Clarkson's medical specialty was epidemiology, but his career was administration and he had been a Deputy Minister of Health in both Saskatchewan and New Brunswick. Planning the Centennial Hospital had been an exercise in collegiality, a strong unifying force among the medical staff, but the doctors felt distinctly left out of the Clarkson process. As Bob Fraser states in his history of the Department of Medicine: "He examined the floors occupied by medicine in the Clinical Sciences Building and thereafter we saw him no more until the fall of 1973. No plans (were) requested of the staff until two months before the report was due and that . . . was unreasonable."

Dr. Clarkson assembled an expensive team. The planning leader, according to legend, was plucked from an airliner carrying him from England to a job in Australia. A young hospital administrator came from Ontario. There was a local architect, Jock Bell, who, some years afterwards, became a member of the board of the hospital. He recalls having to attend "the most rancorous meetings" with the medical staff, but points to a Clarkson concept which became an important fact of the eventual Mackenzie Centre — emphasis on ambulatory care with a transfer of some patients from expensive hospital beds to hostel accommodation.

Dr. Clarkson sent frequent requests for data, but invited no perceptions. The board saw little of him and the rare occasions weren't successful. At one meeting he complained that they seemed cynical and pessimistic about the weight his recommendations would carry with the government and in effect challenged them to seek a meeting with the minister and find out. He made clear what his recommendation would be — that the entire hospital be demolished section by section and rebuilt exactly where it was.

The report was submitted April 30 1974, after Dr. Clarkson took the precaution of having it typed in England. It was accepted by the government. The hospital board, which had no real choice, accepted it as the *program* for *regeneration* of the hospital. Regeneration was the designated word.

The *program* decreed a reduction in beds — from 1,039 to 943 — and there was nothing the board could do about that. Space allotment for each medical specialty was set, and nothing could be done about that. The board accepted the fact that inadequate space was allowed for academic research, although the government seemed unaware of the deficiency, and there was apparently nothing the board could do about that either. Also inadequate was the price tag of $86½ million, which was quickly disowned by the Department of Public Works. The board had to abide by *the program*, but balked at the order to achieve it by demolishing and rebuilding the hospital section by section. It was able to convince the government that this course would cause major disruptions of service, with an end result unsatisfactory and costly. The government agreed that the hospital could submit its own design plan, staying within limits of *the program*.

All concerned found themselves back where they had been eight years before, in a condition of *déjà vu* so intense that it was almost a medically-classifiable condition. The medical staff had been bitterly disappointed by rejection of the Centennial Hospital and increasingly soured by the Clarkson encounter. It could be expected, in this wearied cynicism, that when a brisk cheerful stranger appeared before a desk in the Clinical Sciences Building and announced "I'm the new planner — we're going to plan a hospital" his reception might lack cordiality. A senior member of the medical staff, a courtly fellow by nature, told him to shove off (or words to that effect) and not come back till he had a building showing and never say he had "the promise of the premier."

Any other keen-eyed planner would have been disconcerted, but Victor Jackson knew what to expect. Victor was a son of the granite city of Aberdeen who had gone out to India in 1939 as a lance-corporal in the British army and ended as a captain on the staff of Lord Louis Mountbatten planning the invasion of Burma. With that business settled he proceeded to Liverpool, which, before the Beatles, was better known as the source of a fresh view of architecture emanating from its university. "An architect disguised as an engineer" Victor Jackson had a academic planning appointment at Sheffield University where he learned how to live with "intertribal warfare" in the groves of academe. He came to Canada and had charge of development of the health sciences centre at the University of Calgary, so he knew all about the Edmonton situation and the intense personal factors involved. It would take diplomacy to rekindle the enthusiasm of the medical staff for collegial planning and extend collegiality to the non-medical departments as well. So he did shove off as directed, but returned to happier receptions.

*Victor Jackson selling the concept. Armed with a model of the mega-building which will become known as the Mackenzie Centre the Vice President (Planning) argues its advantages. In the unseen audience will be a degree of skepticism about this, or any, plan*

Dr. Don Rees recalls Victor Jackson's first appearance at a board meeting. It was September 4 1974. On being introduced he announced that he had just driven around the block and thought the regenerated hospital would fill nicely the space between the *Clinical* Sciences Building on the south and *Medical* Sciences Building on the north. Imposing obstacles stood in the way of this logical concept. The provincial lab was on the site and it was not in the jurisdiction of the hospital board. There was also a big laundry-and-kitchen building shown on the Clarkson plan. Eventually these and a catalogue of troubles were overcome and the Mackenzie Centre rose exactly where Victor saw it while driving around the block.

In addition to the salary of $28,000 from the hospital, Victor asked for an academic appointment to the Faculty of Medicine. He explained to Dr. Tim Cameron, the new dean, that from his experience in the groves of academe planners are suspect outsiders and should members of the medical staff (who were also members of the faculty) find it necessary to criticize him it would be as a colleague. The appointment was easily arranged. Each year Dean Cameron sent a nice letter advising Victor that in line with approved policies there would be an increase of such-and-such a percentage in the honorarium and since the honorarium was zero the increment would also be zero.

The year 1974 brought some new faces to the board and established the crew which would push the project to the next historic milestone. That was June 6 1977 when excavation began.

The most obvious change was clearly the departure of Walter Mackenzie himself, who retired as Dean of Medicine after 15 years as a driving, motivating force. His retirement marked the end of a career and also the end of an era. Never again would one strong personality exert such influence. The passing reminds Dr. Garner King of a cartoon in the English magazine *Punch*. A father and young son are in Trafalgar Square. Off in the background Lord Nelson stands atop his lonely column, but the father is directing the lad's attention to a carving of two dozen human figures. "You see, son," he says, "there are no great men anymore, just great committees."

On the hospital board the dean's chair was taken by Tim Cameron. The chair reserved for the president passed from Max Wyman to Harry Gunning. The chair allotted to the medical staff went to Don Rees, and then to popular Joe Dvorkin who died before completing his term. Among lay members there was traditionally a place for a chartered accountant. Elvin Christenson left, but Bill Astle came in. Newcomers were Dr. Morris Weinlos, former alderman, who'd been on the staff of the Misericordia for years, and Mrs. Thelma Gregg, a former nurse. Continuing members were Eric McCuaig, Ken Campbell, Marjorie Bowker, and chairman Gordon Wynn.

Board secretary Bernard Snell was the bridge with the administration, which also saw changes in 1974. George Sherwood, the business administrator, retired after 36 years in the hospital. In the '60s natural evolution had split the business administrator's responsibilities three ways. In the '70s continuing evolution brought them together again under Joe Newhouse with the title

Director (Administration). Other directors were John Read (Medical), Mary Murphy (Nursing) succeeding Geneva Purcell in 1975 and Victor Jackson (Planning). In 1976 directors were made vice-presidents as the executive director became president.

This was the company of adventurers which was handed the Clarkson report in April 1974 and pushed to ground-breaking its own version of what the report allowed. They geared up for a vexing contest, though not like a football game in which one plays against opponents, but a golf match in which one pits wit and stamina against the course. Their course was fraught with traps and

*Here's the situation in August 1974 as the search resumes for a health sciences centre plan. Almost all the structures of history still stand. The Clinical Sciences Building, first unit of the plan that was cancelled, is in the foreground. The site of the proposed Centennial Hospital is still open on the left. The second unit of the abandoned plan, the Medical Sciences Building, has risen in the northwest. Below it at left a temporary building loaned by the university houses Victor Jackson's new planning group. And alongside is the Provincial Laboratory. Removing the lab will be the key to clearing the site for the Mackenzie Centre*

hazards to peace of mind.

The money, of course, was to come from the provincial treasury and as the planning team took aim the government announced a major change in its approach to funding health care. On January 11 1975 the Department of Health and Social Development vanished and reappeared as two separate ministries: Hospitals and Medical Care — Social Services and Community Health.

The first was to concern itself with hospital-based health programs, the second with those defined as "community-based" though including mental hospitals. The minister in charge of hospital spending was to be Gordon Miniely, a chartered accountant with teen-age memories of landing in the University Hospital's emergency ward and of summers working for Bob Sherriff the Scots gardener. Gordon Miniely would eventually turn the sod for the health sciences centre and explains the government's perception:

"We had two problems, the commissions we'd inherited from the previous government. They were the Alberta Hospital Services Commission and the Alberta Health Care Insurance Commission. They were islands unto themselves. They implied an arm's length relationship with government, but this was not consistent with reality. Government has to be in full control of how money is spent and health was getting to be the biggest expenditure — close to a third of our annual budget. That was the reason I abolished the commissions."

The University Hospital board had been working through the AHSC — the Alberta Hospital Services Commission — which was soon to disappear. Like the medical staff of the hospital the board was made up of specialists. Certain members took the lead on problems in their areas of expertise — legal, financial, labour relations. In sorting out a procedure for design the lead was assumed naturally by the chairman, although it meant that Gordon Wynn's own firm was barred from the work.

He adopted a route pioneered in 1911 by the hospital committee of Strathcona city council — a local team working in consultation with an architect of international renown. He nominated two local men steeped in the facts, and subtle nuances, of the case. Tommy Groves' firm had just finished the Medical Sciences Building. Bernard Wood's firm had participated in planning the ill-fated Centennial Hospital. For the consultant he went to Toronto for Eberhard Zeidler.

As of 1986 Zeidler's national showpiece was Canada Place, the sail-topped cruiseship terminal in Vancouver harbour. In 1974 the showpiece was the Eaton Centre in Toronto, and though the glassed-in courtyards were echoed in the Mackenzie Centre, courtyards were not what attracted Gordon Wynn. Eberhard Zeidler had just published a book, *Healing the Hospital*, in which he told about designing the health science centre at McMaster University in Hamilton, and his use of interstitial space — a walk-in service floor between each working floor. By current definition an interstice is "a space between parts." By an older Latin definition it means "to stand in the middle of." In the interstitial space developed by Zeidler, workmen could stand between two floors and replace all the pipes and ducts and wiring many times over without disrupting service to patients. Zeidler had designed interstitial floors into the health science centre at McMaster University in Hamilton, and hospitals at Moncton and St. John, New Brunswick. The local ideal was a building which would be usable for one hundred years. Being able to replace machinery as it wore out or became obsolete would be an important factor. So Gordon Wynn arranged a partnership of the firms of Zeidler, Groves and Wood.

The arrangement was described to a board meeting on January 15 1975 at which members of the medical staff spoke and the secretary noted: "All outlined the problems faced in their own areas and the feeling of disillusionment which is general throughout the hospital."

By April 1975, a full year after the Clarkson report, a planning group was at work in a "Butler Building" lent by the university. It sat near the present 114th Street entrance to the Mackenzie Centre. Under one temporary roof were gathered the architectural group, the mechanical group, the electrical group and the construction group.

In addition to an innovative design concept the project was using state of the art developments in construction. One was fast-tracking, which enables work to start on excavations and foundations while drawings are completed and tendered on the superstructure. The most visible local example of fast-tracking is West Edmonton Mall, all built on that scheme. To a commercial developer fast-tracking is attractive because he may get his building a year earlier. He gets revenue a year earlier, and saves a year's interest on borrowed money and the percentage of inflation. To the University Hospital it was attractive for morale reasons. Proceeding through conventional channels no new space would have been provided for seven years, added to the eight years which had elapsed since start of planning of the Centennial Hospital.

Going hand-in-glove with fast-tracking was "project management." In olden times, when all other construction was done on the hospital buildings, the builder didn't get involved till all plans were drawn and irrevocable. Under project management the builder is involved in the planning, where his expertise may suggest the most feasible way to attack a problem. The chosen manager was PCL Construction, which, like the University Hospital, started from very small beginnings in 1906. PCL assigned Bill Ramore to the hospital and his advice was taken early. The ideal way to achieve a building to last one hundred years was with reinforced concrete. However, Bill pointed out that a project of that size would require three to four hundred concrete form workers and there weren't that many. So the choice was structural steel. Victor Jackson says: "We had to provide a design that would carry out Dr. Clarkson's program in a physical form acceptable to the hospital, to the Faculty of Medicine, and capable of being built at a cost palatable to government."

Although planning went on a fast track it was by no means a clear track. Planning had to go ahead in the optimistic belief that the line would be cleared eventually. One obstacle, strangely, was the University of Alberta. While the Clarkson reoport had been accepted by the government, the hospital, and the Faculty of Medicine, the University Board of Governors was holding back. News was filtering west about the financial impact of the McMaster health science centre on the entire university system of Ontario. The governors, quite justifiably, wanted assurance that if they committed support to a teaching hospital for their Faculty of Medicine that other programs would not be crippled. This assurance could only come from the government, through the Minister of Advanced Education and Manpower. Not till December 8 1975 did the university acquiesce in the Clarkson report "providing full financial funding is made available by the provincial government and other university capital projects are not affected . . ."

Six days before Christmas 1975 the hospital board met a cabinet committee of five ministers concerned and presented a brief called "a response to government questions." The ministers were receptive, but another full year went by before approval was obtained for the siting and configuration of the project being planned on the fast though cluttered track. The site had to be cleared of two buildings — one existing and another which showed large on the Clarkson plan.

The provincial laboratory was in its own free-standing building, erected in 1947, right where the planners saw the main entrance to the Mackenzie Centre. The hospital had a unique historical kinship with the lab going back to the early days of the campus, when the lab was the first unit in Dr. Tory's dream of a medical school with a teaching hospital. Moving it was complicated by its vague jurisdictional position, but in May 1976 word was received that the government would resolve the complications if the lab were included in Phase I of the centre.

Equally troublesome was a laundry-dietary facility proposed by Dr. Clarkson for the exact spot where the Jackson group saw the hub of Phase I of the Mackenzie Centre. While they were plotting to get rid of it, in February 1975, the government sent word that money to build it in the Clarkson loacation was being made immediately available. The offer was diplomatically declined while the board pursued with the Royal Alex the idea of a joint laundry-dietary building located off both sites. In August 1975 the government announced it would support a joint facility. Six months later it announced it would *not* support a joint venture, but the University Hospital could go it alone. Which is what happened. An American study had shown that once laundry was loaded on to a truck the cost was little different whether the truck drove around the corner or out to Mill Woods. So the search for a site led to Mill Woods, where demographic studies indicated there would be a pool of workers to draw from. Another government agency purchased the land. Printing and warehousing were added to the complex and the University of Alberta Hospitals Industrial Service Centre was in full operation in 1982.

This episode offers a good example of a problem which beset the planners as they persevered on the fast track. They were receiving confusing signals. At a meeting with the Alberta Hospital Services Commission (shortly before it was abolished) Victor Jackson was told by the chairman that on no account must he propose tearing down any existing buildings. This was certainly a signal for a sidetrack study. Based on a new provincial rule that hospitals must be air-conditioned, the cost of raising the 1914-1957 buildings to code standard come to $62-$69 per square foot, while costs of the new centre were showing $75 per square foot. Eberhard Zeidler adds the comment: "When you air-condition old buildings the humidity makes them fall apart."

At one stage Premier Lougheed offered a way out of the complexities which was attractive on many points. He suggested informally that the government would be willing to provide an entirely new site for a fresh start. The location had historic overtones. It was farm land between Grandview and Lansdowne, south of 62nd Avenue, west of 122nd Street, once the farm of Hugh Calder, Chairman of the Strathcona Hospital Committee in 1910. The advantages were enticing and the site would have been ideal except for one consideration. This was a teaching hospital. Accepting the offer would have required a separation — either the hospital from the Faculty of Medicine or the Faculty from the main campus. The hospital's mission would have been compromised. The offer had to be declined and the planners continued to wrestle with the traditional site.

On August 30 1976 the planning group presented their schematic concept of the health sciences centre. The sketches of things to come were dramatized by a show with scale models. While Victor Jackson narrated, a "magician's assistant" silently stole away old components and brought in the new. The show was put on for the boards of hospital and university and the cabinet, to help them imagine what they would wait 10 years to see in gleaming reality.

The high-rise courtyards have caused the most comment, suggesting to some observers the luxury of the hanging gardens of Babylon. However, as Tommy Groves likes to point out, if they were not warm pleasant indoor courtyards they would be the outdoor kind, windswept, rained-on or snow-packed according to season. The tradition of hospitals held that the patient should have a window for outside light and air, and because of it hospitals spread out along endless corridors. Tradition was formalized eventually in the national building code, in which the patient's window had to be a percentage of the floor space in his room with a certain percentage of that window opening for air. By the '70s the code accepted air-conditioning as equivalent to an open window and light from a skylight as natural, so courtyards could be glassed over to let in light but keep out the weather. Eberhard Zeidler adds: "They created additional space and a special atmosphere. They alleviated the oppressive feeling you get in most hospitals, especially in winter. And they were cheaper too. We didn't have to provide all outside walls."

German-born Zeidler is a graduate of the Bauhaus, at Weimar, a famous school of art, design and architecture which advocates functionalism and use of experimental materials. Tommy Groves cites the open bridges across the courtyards as a personal Zeidler touch. They were achieved by removing conventional flooring and panels enclosing the vertical "wet pipes" which extend the full height of the building.

The architects worked from the most economical measurement for a steel-truss building — based on a truss with a span of 72 feet. This allowed a maximum space free of columns of 24 by 24 feet. On these modules they created a nursing unit of 54 beds with three sub-units of 18. Zeidler comments: "Each nursing station is a self-contained small hospital with its own entrance and food service. Each station should be like a village."

Another result of the module approach caused unrest among the medical staff, producing a standard doctor's office 12 feet square, which most deemed short of adequate. Unrest was a condition the planners lived with. To counter some of it the scale model of the concept was brought into play. Victor Jackson recalls: "The model was used in 'gaming sessions' based on chess. We invited all the user groups, medical staff, nursing staff, administrators, serving staff — and that was very important. The poor sods who have to clean up the place and look after the wiring seldom get an opportunity. We asked each medical group to go to the model and mark which locations would be most appropriate for their departments. Of course lots wanted to be in the same place. But we couldn't change the number of beds. If the Clarkson Report said a department was to have 26 there was nothing we could do because the government had accepted it."

The gaming sessions established the relationships of departments and produced one significant change in design. The architects had allowed extra ceiling height on the first or second levels for the operating rooms, but consensus held that they should be on the third level, and the opinion was met by borrowing some interstitial space.

Although the government remained committed to the bed counts of the Clarkson report there was movement on other things, notably the medical library. The Faculty of Medicine argued successfully that three times the space was required and the result has been the John W. Scott Memorial Library. And the auditorium, which sparked the first interest in a health sciences centre, is close by. It became Bernard Snell Hall.

These and other contentions still lay ahead in August 1976 when a schematic concept was presented to the cabinet. In October the government annouced approval of Phase I, about half the total project. In January the siting and configuration were finalized. On June 6 1977 perseverance was rewarded with the start of digging.

The health sciences centre did not have a name. A month previous the board, upon deep deliberation, decided that components of the centre might be named for individuals, but not an entire building. No one anticipated naming the centre for Walter Mackenzie. And there were other things they didn't anticipate.

# Chapter 27

# 1971—1977
*Business as Usual at the Old Stand*

In the meantime there was that other hospital, the one which had accumulated since 1914, the old bottle into which the new wine of medical progress and social expectation had to be poured while awaiting the ideal replacement. New wine places severe strain on old bottles but progress could not be put on hold for that. Board, staff and public were caught in a situation faced by their counterparts of 60 years before.

The costs, however, were stratospherically different. In 1971 the annual expense of operating the old bottle was $23 million. By 1977 the bill shot up to $63 million, and it was increasingly difficult to grasp what the public was getting for the money. In the '70s there emerged a new gauge for understanding the productivity of the institution. From the beginning and for many years after it was simple. The work of the hospital could be measured in beds — and days spent in beds by patients. In the '50s and '60s when specialization caused competition for beds and other resources the work of the hospital might be grasped through an understanding of each division and what it did with its allocations. But with the '70s, effectiveness was measured in programs, difficult to express in rigid terms. Programs overflow the watertight compartments shown on organization charts. They involve a matrix of divisions and services, patients, families and special-interest foundations. Programs have as an objective treating the patient with every applicable resource of the hospital except the bed — the one concrete which everyone can understand.

Most obvious of all is the kidney program. By 1986 it could certainly provide the most attention-getting statistic. Some 400 patients were on the program — without it all would be dead or facing imminent death. And the program was flourishing with the dedicated use of only 22 hospital beds. Some 200 were on dialysis and 120 were achieving it in their own homes.

The outreach aspect got its start in 1970, with the impetus coming not from the hospital but the patients, two in particular. Some 25 were coming in for scheduled dialysing. One patient had to be brought from Wetaskiwin, another from Westlock. They decided they could handle the technology in their own homes, with instruction from the hospital and participation of their families. This added a further dimension to the role of the teaching hospital. In addition to doctors and members of the nursing team it was to teach patients. The communities of Wetaskiwin and Westlock raised money to buy the equipment, and a two-year demonstration was enough to sell the government. Two dialysis regions were organized, one in the south based on the Foothills, the other on the University Hospital with a mandate from Red Deer north, to the Arctic if necessary. Order-in-council 131/72 funded a training program, with equipment and follow-up supplies.

The program began with hemodialysis, in which poisons are removed from the blood — and the patient remains attached to a machine for four hours. Then in 1979, from a Toronto doctor, came an option, peritoneal dialysis, which removes the poisons from the peritoneum, surrounding stomach and intestines. The patient retains freedom of movement so the procedure is known as CAPD — Continuous Ambulatory Peritoneal Dialysis. Four times a day two litres of solution are inserted through a catheter and then drained off.

In 1986 this writer was introduced to a team training for home dialysis. The patient was a housewife of serene upper-middle-age. Her husband, an automobile serviceman, was learning to maintain and operate the equipment. The instructors were a nurse and a technician. After six weeks the entire team was to move out to the couple's home and work as a unit until the procedure was running smoothly on location. The nurse and technician would then return to become part of a new team and life-saving dialysis would go on in a home 400 miles from the University Hospital and a hospital bed.

With this distance in mind the cost of the bed offers some telling dollar comparisons. A bed in a new general hospital such as the one in Mill Woods may be taken as $200,000. But in a tertiary care hospital such as the university the capital cost may be considered $400,000 with an annual operating cost 40 percent of that. Once the equipment is in place the only expenses of home care are the dialysing solutions, $6,000 a year for hemodialysis, $20,000 for CAPD. The solutions are provided on contract by medical supply houses and delivered direct to the patients' homes. By 1986, with 120 patients on the home program, 70 had chosen CAPD. But not all can cope with the procedure on their own, and for them there is a custom-designed ward in the Mackenzie Centre, running 16 dialysis stations on three shifts a day, four hours each, morning, afternoon, and early evening for those holding jobs. Of this group many will be elderly or suffering other complications of renal disease.

From the beginning the program has had the benefit of strong continuity among the medical staff. John Dossetor was head of the division of immunology and nephrology until 1985. Others who came with special interests stayed on: Kelvin Bettcher (home dialysis), Frances Harley (paediatrics and nephrology), Ted Kovithavongs (transplants), Mrinal Dasgupta and Richard Grynoch. The only permanent loss was Donald Silverberg who moved to Israel after 10 years. Ray Ulan was away for a time at McMaster but Dr. Dossetor says "it was a fortunately reversible migration" and he became next head of the division.

In the office of the nursing team there has also been consistency — along with other assets such as enthusiasm. Phyllis Kalynchuk joined the program in 1972 and 14 years later was Assistant Director of Nursing (among eight all together) for nephrology and medicine. She became involved personally when one son became a donor to another son. She also joined the board of the Kidney

Foundation — and thereby hangs an important factor.

Within the moving fabric of a typical hospital program will be found a lay organization raising money for research and patient comforts, and promoting public awareness. In 1969 the Northern Alberta Kidney Patients Association was formed by the early participants in the program, patients and doctors. Coincidentally, the Kidney Foundation of Canada was chartered that year. In 1971 the local group formed the Alberta branch of the foundation, and the next year the Edmonton chapter. The chapter is the fund-raising arm. The operating sector of the Edmonton chapter coincides neatly with the regional dialysis area

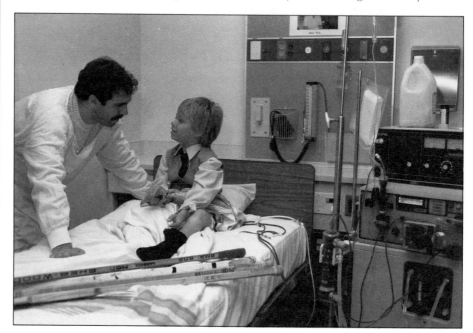

*Jumping ahead in time . . . it's March, 1986 and hockey star Charlie Huddy, honorary chairman of the Kidney Foundation's home fund-raising campaign, meets a popular patient on the dialysis program. Eddy McNalley is 11. Two transplants have failed, but he makes his cheerful way with dialysis, coming to the University Hospital three times a week for three-and-a-half hour sessions. Eddy has learned to attach his blood system to the cleansing machinery. The equipment is expensive, but at this moment probably seems of less value than the autographed hockey sticks on the bed*

established by the province in 1972 and based on the University Hospital.

Foundation dollars come from the public only, and as of 1986 50 cents of each dollar went to research, 20 to patient services, 13 to public awareness and 17 to administration. A typical patient "extra" might be seen in the Mackenzie Centre where people come for dialysis and have four hours of immobility to put in each time. The government has provided the medical equipment. The chapter's touch is the TV monitor above each of the 16 beds. In summer children are sent to a dialysis camp near Toronto at a cost of $2,000 per child. Three motor homes have been bought and equipped so patients can go travelling on extended holidays.

Dialysis is a trauma! Each individual copes with it in his or her own way, with whatever resources of personality can be summoned for the challenge. Memorial funds honour two men who coped in remarkable ways. One was Jack Guignon, who dialysed as he had lived. Jack was a bachelor farmer of the Westlock district, self-sufficient in all things, who hated going to the city for any purpose, and when he had to go on the program rejected the conventional wisdom that he needed a helper to run his machine. Jack did it his way, extending his ruggedly-independent life by several years, and at the end willed his farm and bachelor shack to his fellow patients, who benefit by the income from $90,000.

Research fellowships commemorate Warrant Officer Len Grasley, whose 28-year career with the Princess Patricia's Canadian Light Infantry was ended by kidney disease in 1970. He had a painful affliction in which the kidneys enlarge and rupture and dialysis was very trying for him as it is for some, but he bore it with military stoicism for seven years and with his army experience at recruiting and organization he was a co-founder of the Edmonton chapter. In 1985 two grants of $35,000 each were made in his name for work on immunology in Dr. Dossetor's transplant research laboratory.

From its inception this component of the program gained steadily an international reputation. And it gave "the patient of the '70s" an extended role. By long tradition patients were considered teaching material, participating voluntarily in teaching programs for medical students and members of the nursing team. On the same basis they became *research* material, with each case monitored in a research context. From observation the Dossetor group was first to report the significance of blood transfusion in facilitating acceptance of a foreign kidney. Through 15-plus years the lab contributed some 150 publications to medical literature, including widely-read reports on tissue typing among the Inuit of the High Arctic and Hutterites in colonies in Alberta.

The lab is part of an information network, which in 1981 carried news of an important advance in immunology — the application of cyclosporine, which minimized rejection factors with fewer side effects. A successful transplant is obviously the best treatment for failing kidneys. For other failing organs it is the only treatment and advances in immunology related to the kidney have cleared the way for other transplants, eventually even hearts.

These are side effects of the kidney program, a phenomenon of such complexity it could not have happened in any age before the '70s. Understand the kidney program and understand what's going on in the institution symbolized by the Mackenzie Centre. Counts of beds and patient days, though kept neatly as in 1906, convey little. Some 150 programs are at work there. In the period from 1971 to '77, while the planners were struggling towards the future, these forces were gathering strength, rattling the cage of the old hospital.

Unchecked medical progress was not the only force jolting the time-worn structure. A strange public attitude was an unwelcome surprise. Long characterized by grateful acceptance of any hospital service, public expectations were rising faster than operating costs — which tripled in this period. A general impatience stirred up by the '60s was given a biting edge by Medicare. The benefit of universal medical care, conferred in 1969, was showing unsettling side effects. These effects have been noted by all doctors. Perhaps Ron Wensel may speak for all as he observes:

"In essence the government gave a warrant to everyone on health. People began to feel they were entitled to medical care on demand, and on time. They insisted on the best — now. They became adversarial and we had to practice defensive medicine."

Peter Owen enlarges on the matter of litigation: "When I became legal counsel for the hospital in the late '40s my time was spent mostly in trying to collect from patients. By the '70s the situation had reversed and my time was taken by patients trying to collect from the hospital."

A restless impatience among clients of the hospital was extending to the workers whose number continued to increase — from 2,910 in '71 to 3,517 in '77. In 1973 the first-ever strike of Alberta nurses occurred at the Royal Alex. Provincial law banned strikes by employees of the University Hospital, but 1975 saw two walkouts by kitchen, laundry and maintenance workers. They made a surprise exit on April 23 and again on June 13. The disruptions involved 1,700 members of Branch 23 of the Civil Service Association, though not all took part. A notable exception was the greenhouse keeper who knew his plants would expire of neglect.

The second episode lasted 10 days, and despite the tensions was surprisingly good-natured. The hospital decided to take the union to court, but needed evidence of the strikers receiving notice that their walkout was illegal. So Rod Larsen, the manpower chief, went visiting along the picket line with a camera, and a number of pickets agreed to be photographed accepting the notices, a sporting gesture unusual in labour strife. The court case resulted in a $5,000 fine for Bill Broad, provincial president of the Civil Service Association, and there was satisfaction from that, but more from the post-strike atmosphere. "There was no aftermath," recalls Joe Newhouse, whose destiny it was to be acting chief executive during the commotion while Bernard Snell was on sick leave with a heart attack. "There were no penalties. Some of the men shook hands with me when they came back to work." But the greatest satisfaction came during the strike itself. "We couldn't believe the support from the community. Housewives, doctors' wives, my wife. They kept the housekeeping and dietary services going amazingly well. Our biggest problem was finding ways to use all the volunteers."

1975 — the hospital kitchens. Service workers are outside on the picket line but volunteers make sure patients get their meals on time. There are no recorded complaints from patients

The following year the organization which had taken the service staff on illegal strike applied for a significant change of name. On May 19 1976 Branch 23 of the Civil Service Association became Branch 54 of the Alberta Union of Provincial Employees. (Statutes 1976 Chapter 9.) The change showed the temper of the time, a time in which the Mackenzie Centre was coming together in trial and tribulation. When excavation actually began almost all salaried employees of the hospital were represented by a union, or a body with a union label on its approach to management.

Even the house staff, those fun-loving fellows who had laughed off poverty and Hong Kong style housing with the midnight lunches of Fanny Hooson and fruit juice redeemed by alcohol pinched from the pharmacy, formed the Professional Association of Interns and Residents of Alberta. It is probably coincidental that this occurred in 1972, when Fanny retired after 43 legend-filled years of late suppers and chiding lectures. Whatever the truth, the association gained a wage increase — $5,200 to $7,900 for residents in the first year, $7,500 to $10,000 for those in the fourth.

In 1973 the hospital found itself across the table from yet another new entity, the Health Sciences Association of Alberta. This body brought together for bargaining purposes most of the skilled occupations created in the '60s by high-technology diagnostic and laboratory equipment. It was a field once thought of mostly in terms of George McMillan the x-ray technician and Tommy Robson the physiotherapist. It had grown to several hundred people in some two dozen specialized occupations — some graduating from NAIT programs, some from degree courses of the university, some from programs within the hospital. Each occupation had its own professional organization, mainly interested in education. The HSA took over the bargaining. Eventually the nurses went the same route. The AARN — the Alberta Association of Registered Nurses — continued to work the educational side but the United Nurses of Alberta was formed in 1977 as bargaining agent. Nurses of the University Hospital did not join the UNA, but bargained through their own staff association.

Excavating the Mackenzie Centre began June 6 1977. On the twenty-second of the month the UNA called out the nurses of the Royal Alex and the General and the walkout cast an unscheduled burden on the University Hospital, $50,000 cash, plus uncountable human costs to patients denied treatment, and nursing staff, prohibited from striking by the act governing the hospital.

By this time the hospital was also bargaining collectively — along with other institutions — through the Alberta Hospital Association. The government was sympathetic. It accepted late and retroactive wage agreements as amendments to approved budgets — notably in 1976 when a ruling that Certified Nursing Aides and Certified Nursing Orderlies must be paid the same cost the University Hospital another $551,000, the entire cost of running the hospital for a typical year in world war two. Though supportive the government was nervous about upwardly mobile expenses. Deputy treasurer "Chip" Collins warned that health costs, if allowed to grow unchecked, would consume all the revenue. Apprehension was to increase when the bills started coming in for the Mackenzie Centre.

---

While these unionized happenings attracted outside attention a quiet revolution was changing a fundamental labour practice within the hospital. Unnoticed, the era of the apprentice student nurse came to an end. The demise may be deemed a *fait accompli* as of January 1 1973, when the School of Nursing admitted the first course for whom there would be no "service" component. It was a victory for those who argued that a nurse should be a product of *education* and perceived *training* as a word to be shunned in polite conversation. Helen Penhale had fought to put the idea across a generation-of-student-nurses earlier and failed. The opposing view, strong among doctors and stronger among practicing nurses, had lost no vigour, but enough key people were inclined towards accepting — if not exactly welcoming — the Penhale perception.

Several persuasions were in force. In 1969 the university withdrew its BSc students from the hospital's program. Nursing courses were starting in community colleges while long-established hospital programs were closing, to leave eventually only four in Alberta — The Foothills, Misericordia, Royal Alex and University. Then in 1971 came one of those catalyst events. Ruth Thompson, Director of the School of Nursing for seventeen years, was retiring. Naming a successor was an opportunity for something completely different.

Geneva Purcell carried a message to all willing to listen, and others not so willing. "We have plenty of nursing expertise. What we need is an educator. This person need not be a nurse and need not be a woman." The idea had the disadvantage, as well as the attraction, of having never been done before. Perhaps the most important approval came from the national executive of the Canadian Nursing Association. A call went out for an educator who need be neither a nurse nor a woman and the lot fell on Hal Chalmers.

He developed a program shortening the course from three years to two-and-a-half, the missing six months being the "service" component. Students would still participate in ward programs, but not as apprentices, a far cry from the 1920s when a member of the first class had her graduation set back because she "owed" the hospital service time. The deletion was controversial, raising vigourous dissent from doctors and nurses who believed *practice* was essential to development of the complete nurse.

Geneva Purcell comments: "The curriculum was built around the family — from birth to death — all sequences in the context of human experience. Some major changes were required to do this. From our association with the university we were able to develop courses in psychology."

Hiring a non-female, non-nurse educator as Director of a School of Nursing was a pioneering gamble, but returned a profit. And when Hal Chalmers moved on he was followed by Les Lewchuk, in the same category.

One of the pleasant traditions of student nursing disappeared at this time — the pink uniform patterned with small UAHs in white — woven at one time, later printed. It gave way to plain pink, symbolic perhaps that the hospital and school of nursing were no longer the same entity.

Heather Montgomery has viewed the changes continuously since 1965, latterly as assistant director of the school. She notes a major side effect of the quiet revolution: "It ended the old hospital spirit in which the nurses and residents were the cohort. They lived in the hospital. They were in it twenty-four hours a day. They worked together and they protected each other from the supervisors."

Gradually the students abandoned the nurses home and lived in their own homes or Lister Hall or apartments like students of any educational program. And across 114th Street the residence of the house staff was being eyed for another purpose by planners of the Mackenzie Centre. They saw it as a hostel — for patients of an expanded ambulatory care service in the hospital of the near future.

———

Reflecting a condition in society, the hospital had a drug problem, though not with abuse. The problem was trying to keep some handle on the legitimate use of drugs. Prescriptions are said to be "compounded" in the pharmacy. Here was a compound of public expectations, ingenuity of researchers and clinicians, in a teaching centre and hospital of last resort.

In 1961 the pharmacy spent $333,000. In 1971 it spent $964,000, en route to $1,825,000 in 1977 and $5.5 million in 1986. There are some inner figures which don't match those exact years but illustrate some of the upward forces. In 1946 the total inventory required to be kept on hand was worth $13,000 — by 1981 it was $500,000. In 1956 the pharmacy dispensed $40,000 worth of antibiotics and steroids — by 1981 that figure had multiplied twenty times.

The pharmacy is a measure of activity in the hospital's medical service. In the early '70s it responded to several leading-edge requests from intensive care, as Dr. King and his associates sought improvements to conventional intravenous feeding. A high-protein oral system developed for astronauts was brought in from the United States, and like any space-age technology was expensive. For patients requiring help in the long term there was developed TPN, or Total Peritoneal Nutrition. TPN replenishes elements in the system which become depleted through extended intravenous treatment. The specific need of each patient for extra amino acids, vitamin complexes and other useful things had to be calculated by the laboratory, the indicated solution made up in the pharmacy, and injected by the doctors into the patient — where it was absorbed through the peritoneum or stomach lining. TPN was expensive, but worth it.

The hospitals' therapeutics committee limited the prescribing of certain drugs to certain doctors but that was more a way of keeping track than keeping a lid on. Keeping track was the best that could be hoped for. In 1976, one of Walter Maday's last projects before retirement was creating a new-style formulary. The dictionary defines a formulary as "a book containing the names of pharmaceutical substances and their uses." Formularies had been compiled in 1936,

'44 and '56, but this was more than a book, extending to the computer. The pharmacy didn't have one but obtained cards which could be processed on a university machine. For this effort Mary Wholey Bell came back and devised a symbol code of seventeen digits, to record what drug, what patient, what doctor. The system was designed to provide information for treatment and research, meet requirements of the hospital's accounting department, and ease the anxieties of government officials watching the dollars go by.

---

On April 28 1971 the board took a firm stand taken against a popular trend. "While we recognize that social values are in a state of flux, outsiders should not be able to dictate what hospital policy should be." A reply was sent to a city lawyer advising him "that the hospital board has duly considered the matter and feels that its present position is fully justified." However, before the lawyer's baby was two years old the fully justified position had been fully reversed. The father had requested permission to attend the birth and been refused, but since July 1 1973 the father in the case room has become as traditional as the pacing, chain-smoking cartoon character out in the waiting-room with his fellow sufferers. By 1986 special suites designed into the Mackenzie Centre allowed whole families to be with the mother until the time to go behind the screen. And 90 percent of deliveries were attended by husband, friend, mother, or coach — the "breathing" coach — a de facto member of the obstetrical team undreamed-of in Dr. Vant's era.

In 1973 fathers were not a problem for Peter Beck, head of obstetrics — he'd invited a few into the case room at McGill — but they were for some of his colleagues, especially anaesthetists.

Dr. Beck comments: "A family-oriented obstetrical service is not a bad thing as long as people abide by protocol. My difficulty was keeping a lid on so that medical standards were maintained. Medicine experienced a wave of *consumerism* in the '70s and in no area was there more consumerism than in obstetrics. It was not so in gynaecology. No one ever asked to be present at a hysterectomy, although liberalization of this procedure was much more important to women than family births. Prior to the '70s it was almost unacceptable except when disease was present in the uterus, and was denied to women who had uncontrollable problems after the child-bearing years. Notably, there are no laws against removal of gall bladders or appendices, but we have two safeguards against unwarranted hysterectomies. Provincial law requires a consultation — or second opinion in the popular term — and a hospital rule requires a consultation if the woman is under 40."

---

A decision taken April 7 1976 may be flagged with a big "sign of the times." On that date the board authorized a high-risk obstetrical unit. Seen primarily as a protection for mother-and-baby this unit was subject to several other perceptions. It was also perceived as a protection for the hospital's doctors, the practice of obstetrics having emerged as one of the high-risk categories for litigation — along with anaesthesia, orthopaedics, neurosurgery and cardiovascular surgery. The government, which played a persuasive role in creating the unit, had its own perception. It was to be part of a broader scheme linking "problem" obstetrics with continuing intensive medical support for the infant. The government perception, with funding attached, was incorporated in the Northern and Central Alberta Perinatal Program, a regional concept analogous to the kidney program.

Dr. David Schiff has an autobiographical insight into the story, commencing in 1972 when he arrived from McGill with an appointment to both participating departments, obstetrics and paediatrics. It meant leaving his home town of Montreal where he had grown up in "Duddy Kravitz Country" and attended the same high school as the mythical Duddy. His coming was made possible when a doctor with a university appointment in paediatrics left to be married and her salary was freed. Juggling salaries, and stacking partial salaries to create a full one, became characteristic of the period as departments strove to do their duty as they saw it in patient care, teaching and research. Dr. Schiff's major assignment was upgrading the premature nursery — a significant advance of the '60s — to a neonatal intensive care unit current with the '70s. The nursery was treating about fifty infants a year. With more staff and new monitoring equipment, within two years it was treating 400. And many were arriving from country points by air ambulance as use was made of a new emergency charter service made available by the province.

These numbers gave a proven base on which to approach the province for a regional program, with the benefits of earmarked funds and political fondness for high-tech equipment. The Alberta Hospital Services Commission was sympathetic, but withdrew to neutral gound when a rival claimant appeared. The Royal Alex, with the second-largest obstetrical unit in Canada, argued that the state-of-the-art neonatal ICU should be located there. The Alex was then second to Toronto's East General Hospital, though the two are now about even at 5,500 deliveries a year, compared to 2,400 for the University.

Feelings were intense. The AHSC offered a mediator to help achieve a compromise which could be lived with by all parties, and after months of contention the compromise was that each should have an ICU — with the University Hospital the high-risk referral centre.

Air ambulances became extensions of the hospital as the neonatal and general intensive care units made increasing use of the provincial charter offer. Saskatchewan had a well-publicized government service, but Alberta shied away from the socialism of that, preferring to leave the flying to private enterprise. The system worked, and still does, the government supplying the aircraft through three main charter companies, the hospital the equipment, and the ICUs the staff. "We take the ICU to patients," says Dr. Garner King, head of the general unit, who got the flights going in 1972. A resident, a nurse and a technician or therapist are sent to meet the patient and referring physician at the home airstrip. There are about 150 flights a year, with some 25 to the

Northwest Territories. Dr. King estimates that 25 to 40 percent save lives. Over the years, only two patients have been lost en route. On occasion a surgical team is sent to operate in a local hospital. Air ambulances save valuable time, and for the patient they also save valuable money. If he is brought in by ground ambulance he is responsible for the bill.

While planning teams wrestled with the design of the Mackenzie Centre, mercy flights, so recently leading news stories, became hospital routine. Some 300 babies a year now begin life with an airplane ride to the Centre's neonatal ICU. There is a red telephone in the unit which won't accept outgoing calls, the hotline connection with all hospitals in Alberta. The unit accommodates forty babies at a time, struggling to overcome congenital defects or prematurity. Of all the scenes inside the Centre there is none quite so appealing as forty tiny human beings, helpless but squirming with determination, being assisted by skilled people and high technology in its most humanitarian application. They stay an average seventeen days. In the early '70s they were surviving at two months premature; they now survive at three months and more. The unit follows its graduates — in the interests of patient care, teaching and research. A big reunion party was being planned for August 1986. And it was bound to be big. The number of young lives saved by the unit could be 8,000!

There are two signs on the door. One reads *Neonatal ICU*. The other reads *Northern and Central Alberta Perinatal Program*. The ICU has run more smoothly than the other component of the program, the high-risk obstetrical unit. David Schiff has been head of the ICU since inception, while the high-risk unit has seen four directors come and go. Clinicians have seen it as a consulting service rather than a care unit, a latter-day example of what can happen to best-laid plans.

---

The neonatal unit was only one of several paediatric initiatives taken in the chairmanship of Dr. E.E. McCoy (1971-1983). To the admirable clinical service established by Ken Martin (1957-1971) he added the research component, which doesn't show results in counts of beds and patient days, but exerts an influence like the pull of the moon on ocean tides.

Ernie McCoy came into the department through a process that would have been unimaginable a dozen years before. It began in the Department of Educational psychology at the University of Alberta, which, with the interest of specialists in genetics, neurology and the like, set up on paper a Research Institute into Mental Retardation. The institute was given life with a grant of $250,000 from the Canadian Association for Mental Retardation, and the search for a qualified director brought back Ernie McCoy. Though a graduate of the U of A, class of '49, Ernie was not an Albertan. A Victoria boy, he studied here because the People of the Rain Forest felt no urge to spend money educating doctors when so many MD's wished to practice in British Columbia. The UBC medical school did not come to pass until McCoy was far along "the classical route" to higher research. He specialized in St. Louis, practiced in Burnaby, returned to academe at Vanderbilt, became the fourth Alberta grad to win a Markle scholarship, and was at the University of Virginia when the call came to return to his alma mater to head research in mental retardation. He agreed to come if given the same facilities he enjoyed at Thomas Jefferson's university, which meant scraping together $100,000 for laboratory equipment and a clinical metabolic unit. He was appointed professor of paediatric research with part of his salary coming from Ken Martin's budget and the following year he succeeded Ken as chairman.

A major thrust of the McCoy regime was bringing into paediatrics specialists from the Department of Medicine — with a subspecial focus on children. For example, a cardiologist treating adults is concerned with failing hearts, while the paediatric cardiologist deals with new hearts developing. Among adults the immunologist treats acquired immune system deficiencies — among children these deficiencies are congenital. An oncologist-haematologist deals with all cancers but the most prevalent among children is leukemia. In gastroenterology adults have encountered most viruses while children are in the process. The same applies to infectious diseases, which was gaining a subspecialist as this was written. With the help of direct government funding regional programs — akin to nephrology and perinatal care — were soon set up for oncology, hemophilia, and genetics which gave advice to prospective parents.

In a period when time was severely rationed no one was ever compelled to waste any wondering what Ernie McCoy was thinking. He thought paediatrics should have a perment seat on the powerful medical staff advisory board, equal to "the so-called major departments of surgery and medicine" and waged a six-year campaign crowned with success.

Of the biggest issue of the mid-'70s he recalls: "An awful lot of time was diverted from service, teaching and research by the Mackenzie Centre. Departmental space allotments were frozen at 1974 level by the Clarkson report. The planning committee had an endless chain of architects to supposedly assist us. They usually lasted a few months and then disappeared with little continuity. I remember one meeting with a cigar-smoking architect from Toronto who wouldn't listen to us and I told the project chief we would not be back to another meeting with him."

Construction began in June 1977 and the following April Dr. McCoy took away a strong opinion from a meeting at the home of Dr. Neil Duncan. Fellow paediatricians Henry Pabst and Sam Cox were there, along with lawyer Bob Graessor and Mrs. Dimmer, mother of a sick child. The result of the meeting was incorporation of the Northern Alberta Children's Hospital Foundation. The Chairman of Paediatrics thought it should be built and said so, though many colleagues thought otherwise because of implications for existing institutions, and provincial leaders were thinking mostly about dotting the countryside with ten-room cottage hospitals. The controversial proposal refused to go away or be swept under and in the provincial election campaign of 1986 the leader of the winning party announced that he too thought it was a good idea.

The research component for the Department of Psychiatry was added by Bill Dewhurst, who came from England in 1969 and succeeded the admirable clinician Keith Yonge as chairman in 1975.

Dr. Dewhurst observes: "The best patient care is received where teaching and research are going on. You have students asking awkward questions. There's an enthusiasm about the place.

"I was at the Institute of Psychiatry at Maudsley Hospital, London," he recalls. "I had no money and no space and thought of Lord Rutherford's remark: 'We have no money, therefore we must think.' So I thought of coming to

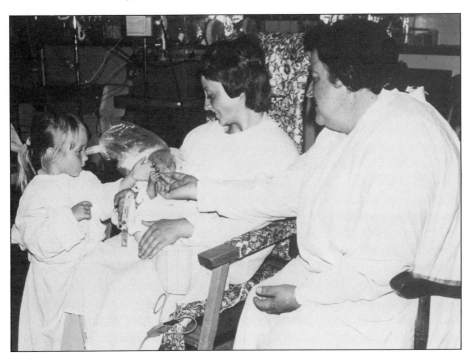

*1977 — a family visit to the neonatal intensive care unit. Three generations: grandmother, mother with patient, patient's older sister*

Canada. Two places were open — McMaster, which was still a hole in the ground, and here, where I was told the Clinical Sciences Building had three empty labs.

"After the rigidities of the United Kingdom two things amazed me. I actually met a Minister of Health. And when the university made a decision something was actually done."

The Dewhurst special interest was neurochemistry, investigating the premise that major depressions have a chemical base. By 1986 the research team numbered twenty, including organic chemist Ron Coutts, synthesizing molecules for specific projects. An inquiry with which the layman could identify was into the psychology of sleep. Although human beings spend a third of their lives in this activity it has been largely taken for granted. Under investigation were *nocturnal apnoea* — in which the victim may stop breathing while asleep; *mioclonus* — jerking of the muscles in sleep; and *narcolepsy* — which appears in early adolescence and makes victims fall asleep during the day, with the potential of devastating effects on careers.

The residency program, in the treatment-teaching-research triangle, had grown to twenty-five, with support from the province, the Alberta Heritage Fund for Medical Research, the federal government and the Medical Research Council of Canada. The Canadian Mental Health Association, the lay group to be found in any such matrix, had little money, but contributed a public information service.

In the early '70s the department was on the leading edge of the greatest change in direction symbolized by the Mackenzie Centre, establishing an *external* psychiatric service. This experiment brought in Dr. Hassan Azim, a cheerful graduate of the University of Cairo, who admits to having never heard of McGill until an Egyptian pal got a job as squash instructor at a Montreal racquet club. The friend wrote about the Allan Institute, psychiatric department of the Royal Vic, a former mansion high on Mount Royal where CPR magnate Sir Hugh Allan had enjoyed a commanding view of company ships steaming up the St. Lawrence. In Sir Hugh's old drawing room there had opened in 1954 the first "psychiatric day hospital" in Canada. Young Dr. Azim was accepted as a resident in 1960 and was there when (as he says) "it was decided that ambulatory care was the way to go — psychiatry should be *out*patient service with *in*patient backup, the exact reverse of tradition." He stayed to run the institute's external service and in 1971 was invited to Edmonton to develop a pilot project on the same model.

The cancelled Centennial Hospital had included a large psychiatric day centre, augmenting the 59-bed inpatient ward on Station 14. Dr. Azim added an evening equivalent and a walk-in-clinic to the proposed service, and the only opposition came from within the hospital, where tradition, though a strength, may not facilitate innovation. Doctors objected that patient care would be compromised because they saw psychologists, nurses and social workers treating and prescribing. On the other hand, non-medical departments objected to their psychologists et al. being selected, supervised and evaluated by the psychiatric service. Dr. Azim argued that the project could only succeed with people specially suited who wouldn't be moved in and out to meet needs in other areas. The administration gave support to this departure from the norm, then the board, and eventually the province. And in funding the project the government, for its own satisfaction, built in a unique feature — a permanent four-man evaluation team of PhD psychiatrists and research assistants. While most evaluators come from outside and are seen as "the enemy" this group has come to be viewed as the fourth component of the outpatient service.

The first component in action was the day hospital, in February 1973, in

*The Aberhart — by 1971 the yellow-brick institution on University Avenue, built as a special treatment centre for tuberculosis, stands half-empty. It becomes part of the University Hospital complex, adding 220 beds and 250 staff*

the former laundry of the Aberhart TB wing. An evening hospital opened in October, offering the same service to patients able to work or attend classes in daytime hours, and overcame some initial problems when it was viewed as a holding tank for alcoholics and other unfortunates. The walk-in clinic opened its doors in November '75 in the former nurses residence of the Aberhart and "ended the waiting list" for people feeling a need of mental help. They see a therapist immediately and are channeled to the level of treatment required — psychiatric, psychological, nursing or social service. By 1986 1,500 people a year were walking in.

"The main thrust of my chairmanship has been organizational, defining and putting in writing people's jobs and relationships." So says George Molnar, fifth Chairman of the Department of Medicine, who followed Bob Fraser in 1974 and served to 1986. Maintaining the '70s trend Dr. Molnar came with a research background. A U of A grad, he came back with it after twenty-three years on the academic staff of the Mayo establishment, working on thyroid and diabetes.

"When I came back we were seeing the turning of the tide of excessive subspecialization. The American College of Physicians and the Royal College in Canada were fighting it. I felt the whole patient should not be lost sight of. It was bad for the patients and the students too. No new divisions have been created, but we've seen the growth of interdisciplinary services such as critical care medicine, geriatrics and oncology.

"I've tried to structure things to give our clinical and research people as little administration as possible. A lot of paper shuffling and money handling is a restraint on scholarly activities. We've developed our research component so we have PhD's in equal numbers with clinicians, but I would think it worrisome if the scale tipped too far. In a hospital like this there is always a possibility that people could be so full of zeal they would forget about teaching students and taking care of people. Maintaining direction will always be a problem. Mayos has developed a philosophy that continually renews itself."

In the early '70s the effects of the Hall report (1965) and Alberta's version of Medicare (1969) were being felt throughout the hospital. The effect on the Department of Surgery is noted by Dr. Tom Williams, who was named Chairman in 1974 when Bob Macbeth went to the Canadian Cancer Society.

Medicare put a virtual end to a socio-medical tradition — going to the Mayo Clinic for major operations. "If you were going to spend your own money you might as well spend it at Mayos. Alberta Health Care made that choice very difficult. Anyway, by this time we were doing everything Mayos were doing. That wasn't the case when I came here from Liverpool in 1957 to do research with Walter Mackenzie."

Responding to provincial support of one recommendation in the Hall report the university virtually doubled the number of medical students. This had implications for the teaching hospital, and for surgery created a problem in clinical instruction because surgeons cannot be taught in large groups. But the problem had a helpful side-effect. Clinical teaching was extended to the Royal Alex and gradually to other hospitals easing town-and-gown tensions.

Dr. Williams notes another effect of Medicare. With health care taking a third of the provincial budget an enhanced government presence was inevitable. "Civil servants are a problem. They have access to figures that support their misconceptions. Governments like to see hospitals operating as efficiently as possible, which means the shortest possible intervals between admitting, operating and sending the patient home. This may be efficiency in a general hospital, but for proper teaching students have to talk, listen, examine and reflect on patients."

The operating rooms were busy — 20,590 surgical procedures in 1971, 23,682 in '77. About a third were cystoscopies. From then on these were reported separately as major surgical procedures declined slightly in numbers, but increased substantially in hours required and staff involved.

---

In anaesthesia, the outrider of surgery, monitoring devices were the thrust of the '70s. This is the judgment of Dr. George Moonie, who succeeded Ted Gain as chairman in 1975. He adds: "When I joined the department in 1951 the only tool we had was literally a finger on the pulse."

Each decade features its own advance. In the '50s bulbar polio brought improved respirators, with which the anaesthetist could actually breathe for a patient. Before that the best that could be done was to keep the patient breathing on his own.

In the '60s the advance was non-explosive anaesthetic agents — halothane, enflurane, isoflurane — "after we spent a lot of money putting copper strips under the carpets of the new operating rooms to carry off static electricity."

The '70s brought machines for continuous, simultaneous monitoring of vital signs — up to a dozen at a time. "You can imagine how important that is in organ transplants, multiple trauma and severe burns." The technology applied the same principles developed for monitoring gas pipelines and telecommunication networks, and resulted from private enterprise. "When the profession starts asking, the companies develop."

These devices cost a modest $3-5,000 each. A more expensive advance, which came later in the '70s, was the *mass spectrometer*, which analyzes the patient's breath, every few seconds giving readings of oxygen, carbon dioxide and the anaesthetic agents themselves. But advances in aid of anaesthesia offered no challenge to hospital budget makers. Advances in support of radiology were a different matter.

---

Jack Miller was Chairman of Radiology in the period when technology was being most lavishly supportive. Dr. Miller arrived with a useful extra in his résumé. He started out as a mechanical engineer in his native south Africa, then took an MD in Johannesburg, specialized in Chicago and joined the Department of Radiology in Edmonton in 1963. At that point traditional x-ray service had been enlarged by nuclear medicine — the use of radioactive agents for diagnosis and treatment.

His appointment as chairman in 1970 (till 1983) coincided with a technological explosion. First came ultrasound, based on the SONAR with which Allied navies tracked submarines in world war two. Ultrasound analyzed sound waves reflected back from the inside of a patient, and found quick use in obstetrics and cardiology.

At the same time budget controllers were grappling with what Dr. Miller calls "the most striking advance in radiology since the discovery of the Roentgen ray in 1896." This was the CAT scanner, or CT scanner, or Computer Tomography Scanner, which linked the art of tomography — any of several techniques for making x-ray pictures — with the computer. The first scanner came to the University Hospital in 1974. One of Walter Mackenzie's last promotions, it cost $250,000 and acquisition was complicated by the new *Calgary factor* — the government had to buy another for the Foothills Hospital.

The CAT scanner resembles the hoop which the stage magician passes around the body of his reclining lady assistant to show there are no wires and the performance of the scanner seems magic too. The hoop slides along the patient's body to the point where the physician wants an inside view. It then rotates to send pictures from hundreds of projections and the computer puts the information together.

While the CAT scanner was on the leading edge of technology it was also leading the push towards ambulatory care, causing more confusion for the poor fellow trying to "get the picture" on the hospital from counts of beds and patient days. Neurology offers a good example. The scanner can do on an outpatient basis what used to take four or five days in bed.

Within ten years ever-higher technology produced a CAT scanner costing $1.3 million, but the old one was not wasted. It found a home at the Alberta Research Council — testing core samples.

Technology had other mortar shells to lob among the budget controllers. New dimensions were added to the time-honoured fluoroscope, a device by which a diagnostician could observe on a fluorescent screen shadows within a patient caused by x-rays. Technology of television screen and motion picture film, added to fluoroscopy, resulted in machines costing a hundred times as much as the monitoring devices which meant so much to anaesthesia. For the budget makers there was not only the cost of equipment to consider, but space, training programs and wage agreements for new categories of employees. And as Wayne Strudwick (Director — Human Resources) observes: "Technicians in the leading edge always feel they should be paid more than other people."

Specialization in medicine and surgery worked its way into fluoroscopy with units specially-designed and equipped for gastro-intestinal, genito-urinary, paediatric, bone-and-joint, and heart-and-chest work. The machine in the cardiovascular catheterization unit is the most expensive at a million dollars and is the most spectacular. Consider angioplasty, in which the surgeon inserts a balloon to try to enlarge a congested artery. The surgeon can see what amounts to an artist's impression of the artery. He can observe its action. He can run the film back as often as he likes to study the case. And he can watch the effect as the balloon is inserted. The "image" factor became such a reality that in 1982 the name of the department evolved to Radiology and Diagnostic Imaging.

The influx of new hardware was well-timed. The radiology section of the Mackenzie Centre could be designed around it, and in this effort radiology enjoyed a productive relationship with the consulting architect assigned to the department, which was not always the case. Among the features worked in by Holland-born Dik Arendsen of the Zeidler group was a system to standardize quality of x-ray pictures. A team from Kodak came up to help on this one. As a result the three developing fluids are held in basement tanks and piped to fifteen stations in the hospital.

In the early '70s the four-year residency program became a "farm system" for radiology as for other departments. Dr. "Giri" Rao was chosen to set up the ultrasound program and sent to Colorado Medical Centre for the most advanced training then available. However, new currents flowed around established tradition. The veteran Dr. "Curly" Holmes was a tradition all to himself, still coming to work at four a.m. so he could be free by seven and leave as his colleagues were arriving. George McMillan had retired but the frail orderly who had been the first x-ray technician in the hospital still came to visit. In his time George had been the entire staff of radiology. By 1986 the staff had grown to 150, including a PhD physicist, radiation safety officer and some sight-impaired people working in the dark room. "We carry on the tradition of George McMillan," says Dr. Miller.

---

Hospitals are rich with human interest stories and there is a special kind of interest when a former patient returns after a long interval. When Allan Froehler came to convert personnel records to the computer, he came in a wheelchair. In 1957, 12 years old, he had been in Rehabilitation and was a particular charge of Dr. Mike Carpendale because most of the patients were polio victims. Allan was different. His spine had been shattered in a gunshot accident. After several months he was able to leave determined to get on with life, eventually earned a degree in business administration, found a career in the developing field of computers and in the early '70s, when hospital personnel records were automated, returned as a computer software consultant.

His presence was tonic for the staff and for the patients as well, especially those permanent residents of the hospital in the polio ward. And thereby hangs another human interest story. With Allan Froehler's expertise they incorporated a data processing firm called *Datamation*. Bob Johnston was firm president, shareholders included Gary McPherson, Clayton May and Marion Chomik. Directors meetings were held in the polio ward which was also registered head office. Employees of the company worked in a rented office across 112th Street. Datamation existed for 15 years and at the best of the oil boom did an annual business of $1½ million.

_____

Since Allan Froehler's patient days there'd been an enormous decline in the Department of Physical Medicine and Rehabilitation. In 1957 rehabilitation was a booming activity involving up to 300 beds in the designated provincial centre for polio recovery. But by the early '70s, with polio a thing of the past, the service had dwindled to 22 beds, and they were in the Aberhart, three blocks from the main hospital. It was in danger of losing accreditation for postgraduate training.

So in 1975 a search was made for a full-time chairman and found Clyde Nicholson. He had been in family practice at Stony Plain for 15 years and had gone to specialize in Seattle where (as his successor Rubin Feldman notes) "rehabilitation was beginning to develop a scientific method, comparable to other specialties."

The chairman of this department wears more hats than the conventional two, with responsibilities in other schools, hospitals and organizations with an interest in rehabilitation. Dr. Nicholson reclaimed six beds in the main hospital, got six residents, and introduced some innovations like all-day "retreats" on which other departmental activity was cancelled to permit a meeting of minds and pooling of experience. A multidisciplinary approach was taken. A good location was assured in the Mackenzie Centre.

With polio long past a new focus was needed and rehabilitation became, in effect, a spinal cord injury service. But in the '80s a strange historic twist brought back the original raison d'être. Post-polio syndrome appeared, a deterioration of muscle strength in people who had weathered the disease 30 years before. As this was written the department was treating 60 patients and was the largest post-polio centre in the country.

_____

Salk vaccine also affected the role of the second-oldest surgical specialty. Orthopaedics had grown with the aftermath of polio epidemics of the '20s and in the '60s 30 percent of the work was related to the final epidemics.

But Dr. Salk directed orthopaedic attention to effects of other diseases, notably arthritis. Replacement of hip joints came first, then knee joints. And by the 1980s orthopaedics would be concerned with cancer and replacement of entire bones. A malignant tumor in the bone or surrounding tissue once meant removal of a limb. But with a procedure developed by the Mayo Clinic and the Sloane-Kettering Institute the leg can be left and a bone implanted. The procedure has the name *limb sparing*. By 1986 four to six a year would be done at the University Hospital, each a thing of joy.

Orthopaedics would have developed a strong research capacity in the '70s — if Dr. Mike Emery had lived. That's the judgment of Dr. John Huckell, who in

1976 became chairman of the division his father headed for 12 post-war years. "Mike showed real leadership," he says. "He also had a unique tie-in with the hospital. The family firm, the Emery Company, supplied uniforms for our operating rooms for many years. Mike started a program of bioengineering research on muscle diseases. He died young of a blood disorder related to leukemia, but if he'd lived he would have made quite a mark in the world."

In the Mackenzie Centre a state of the art teaching facility known as the R. Graham Huckell Motor Skills Laboratory and Library commemorates the second chairman of orthopaedics who was long ago exiled from the hospital for the unconscionable act of marrying one of the nurses without permission. It is a well-equipped room in which postgraduate students can practice operations in a controlled setting and doctors on staff can try innovations — using plastic models and synthetic bones known in the trade as "Sawbones."

The lab was financed by ingenuity, an interesting example of how good things can happen. Rotary Clubs raised $8,000. Ex-patients and others gave to a total of $25,000. To this the provincial Department of Advanced Education added a matching grant. Such grants are not available to hospitals for patient care, but teaching programs can qualify. John Huckell laughs: "I got thinking in terms of matching government grants in the '70s, when I was President of the Edmonton Symphony Society."

---

Plastic surgery, long linked in public perception with lifting the faces of celebrities, made news of deeper local significance with an important step towards involvement with trauma. In 1975 a team was formed to provide microvascular surgery. Not a self-explanatory term it is the art of reattaching a severed limb. The microvascular dimension was added when Dr. Gary Lobay returned from study in San Francisco, and as Dr. Mac Alton says, he was called on for a demonstration on his first day back.

"I could hardly believe it. It was Gary's first day on the job. I'd gone to Pigeon Lake and when I turned on the TV for the 11 o'clock news there was Gary standing in front of the Camsell Hospital with (Dr.) Henry Shimizu. A farmer near Rimbey had been running a machine. His three-year-old daughter was lying in the grass and the machine went over her and sliced off her arm. She was brought in to Gary. Our operating rooms were closed so our first reattachment had to be done at the Camsell.

"There's an interesting story about the suture Gary used. It's so fine it has to be put in with a microscope. We didn't know we had any but Gary had brought some back from San Francisco. Let's say he 'acquired' it.

"Many of our cases come from the farms," he continues. "In the west, a common injury is losing a thumb in a power takeoff in farm machinery. Patients usually arrive in the evening and the operation will take four to eight hours."

Plastic surgery's trend towards trauma work continued and led to the burn unit, of which more later.

---

While administrators grappled with problems of a scale unknown to their predecessors they were distracted by trifles which the oldtimers would never have encountered or countenanced. A typical trifle, unthinkable before the '70s, is cited by Joe Newhouse:

"One day Pam Allan came into my office and said a (member of a visible minority group) woman was going to Eddie Keen — the crusading broadcaster on CHED. It seems she was in a room with three other women and a (member of the same visible minority group) man came in and climbed into bed with her. The other patients raised a hell of a row and the nurses and orderlies came and threw him out. The woman claimed it was only because he was a member of a visible minority group and she was going to Eddie Keen and tell him about discrimination in the University Hospital. I thought for a minute and said: 'Tell her to go to Eddie Keen'."

It was a teapot tempest of which nothing more was heard, but it revealed a new public attitude, come to bedevil hospital administrators as they tried to plan the future and rationalize the past.

———————

It was a time rife with occasions for peptic and cardiac upset and one of the victims was Bernard Snell in an incident which occurred after a long union meeting. He went directly to a social function at a friend's home and while talking to another guest realized that all was not well. The next he knew he was in company with Dr. Joe Dvorkin, obviously in an ambulance. He'd suffered a cardiac arrest and was en route to intensive care. Before he could leave the hospital as a patient he had open-heart surgery performed by Dr. John Callaghan. Back at work he circulated a reminder of something all hospital staff are taught — that even if a patient appears to be unconscious he may be aware of everything going on about him. They all laughed at his story, but they got the message. As his stretcher was being removed from the ambulance he heard a concerned female voice say: "That's Dr. Snell. What's the matter with him?" And a jovial masculine voice replied: "Oh, he's drunk!"

———————

The period 1971-77 is perceived justly as one of dynamic dislocation, but another important perception sees it as one of consolidation. This view is held by Donald F. "Tim" Cameron (known as Tim because unaccountable nicknames are a tradition in his family), Dean of Medicine from 1974 to '83.

By law the dean holds a seat on the board of the University Hospital. Dr. Cameron observes: "The Dean of Medicine is in a strange position. The Dean of Education operates no schools, the Dean of Law has no connection with courts, but the Dean of Medicine spends 90 percent of his time in hospital-related affairs."

In affairs of the University Hospital the dean has been a man for his time: Rankin from the beginning to 1945, Ower to '48, Scott to '59, Mackenzie to '74, Cameron to '83, Douglas R. Wilson through '86. But the Cameron influence covers a wider arch of years. From 1962 he was assistant dean and alternate on the board and attended many meetings. "Walter Mackenzie loved living out of a suitcase," he recalls. "Whenever something interesting was going on in the world he'd start packing. And while he loved international conferences he hated meetings and would sometimes arrange for a secretary to knock on the board room door and announce an emergency in surgery." Meetings and reports were an increasing burden for all medical staff. When Bill Taylor, as acting head of paediatrics, was required to suffer through seemingly endless debates of General Faculty Council he improved the non-shining hours writing a biography of

Bernard Snell
Chief Executive Officer
1966-1984

Dr. D. F. (Tim) Cameron
Assistant Dean of Medicine
1962-1974
Dean 1974-1983

fellow Scot J. Norman Collie, the mountaineer.

In the late '60s and early '70s growth in the medical staff was slanted strongly towards research, building up the third dimension to patient care and teaching. The research establishment "just growed," but unlike the legendary Topsy who obviously "growed" on sound principles, it developed on the flamboyant recruiting of Walter Mackenzie, handshakes, and "soft" money, that is, funds obtained through the hospital system of the province. Although research is an academic exercise (and people held university appointments) most were paid through hospital funds because university budgets were tight and the provincial hospital system was accommodating. A researcher might hold a tenured university appointment tagged "subject to continued government funding."

There were strategies for providing positions. A composite salary might be created — so much from a hospital department, so much from the faculty, so much from an outside foundation. It was a fun way to build but did not offer a secure base for the future or a means to compete for top people.

The Cameron chronicle resumes: "When the crunch came there was an attempt by hospital and university to rationalize what had grown up from enthusiasm and put it on a sound basis. After years of good intentions we had a mishmash of the hospital paying people to serve the Faculty of Medicine and the university paying people to work in the hospital. And another complication had worked its way in. The hospital would want to hire someone to run a special unit, but people put great stock in academic appointments and he wouldn't come without one. This cost the university nothing, but having nominal academics with no commitment to the faculty caused friction."

Another view of the same problem from John Read, Vice-president — Medical in the hospital: "When I first heard about the place the relationship between hospital and Faculty of Medicine was put as a model. However, when Walter Mackenzie left we found it was based on his personality — a marvellous fellow, but a kindly dictator. We had to recognize that an ongoing institution must depend on mechanics rather than personalities which inevitably change. Everything had to be formalized, even to job descriptions and evaluations. And that doesn't always work well either. Marriage may break up a beautiful relationship."

Then there was the historic anomalous position of the provincial lab. By tradition the staff worked for the hospital, were appointed by the university and paid by the province. Pathological service, a major budget item for other teaching hospitals, was thus reduced to zero.

There seemed no urgency about rationalizing a comfortable anomaly when the sector most critically in need of consolidation was the research establishment, operating year to year on "soft" funds. The federal government supported research, but on a population basis, which sent most money to institutions in Ontario and Quebec. Large corporate support was an Americanism which had not penetrated Canada. Unwittingly the OPEC oil ministers took a hand in the solution. In 1973 they made the first of many price hikes which increased the revenues of all oil-producing states, including Alberta. The government of Alberta responded to the windfall with the Alberta Heritage Trust Fund, formally proclaimed on May 19 1976. Observing the process, Dean Cameron and his University of Calgary counterpart Lionel McLeod were proposing a medical equivalent, which they called "An Alberta Heritage Health Research Fund." With the writing skill of Dr. Ernie McCoy, whose paediatric research staff was built almost entirely on "soft" funds, they developed a brief based on the following argument:

"Throughout the world those health care institutions with a strong re-

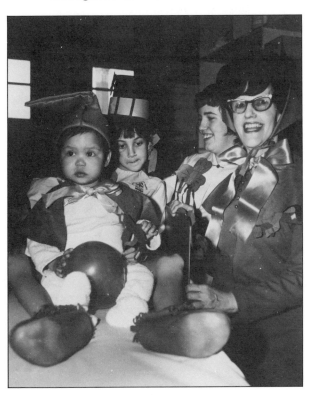

*1977 — St. Patrick's Day*
*comes to the children's ward*

search base have provided the highest levels of health care. Research programs provide resource individuals conversant with the latest advances in specialized areas of medical knowledge and technology. The interaction between these persons and the medical teams involved directly in patient care is an essential prerequisite to the development of new health care techniques and concepts."

Cameron, McLeod, McCoy and Co. assembled a vigorous brief in support of the argument, but then found they didn't know where to go with it. No one could tell them what minister of the crown was responsible for medical research. Premier Lougheed said he didn't know either, but would send word and shortly after advised them it would be his personal responsibility.

He had been pursuing his own initiatives on the subject, reportedly after the experience of a friend who went to Mayos for an operation because it was not available in Alberta. He convened think sessions of medical and business people to decide how much money should be put in the fund to make it effective. Eventually the figure $300 million was identified, and legislation creating the Alberta Heritage Foundation for Medical Research was proclaimed March 26 1980. Income from the fund supports basic investigation on a secure ongoing basis.

Though the period 1971-77 is perceived with justice as one of dynamic dislocation it was also one of consolidation for research, third dimension of the mandate of the University of Alberta Hospitals.

# Chapter 28

# 1977—1986

*The Mackenzie Centre*

O n June 6 1977, when construction crews fenced off the employees' softball diamond and the big diggers began shaking adjacent buildings the health sciences centre did not have a proper name. In May the board had received a well-reasoned argument that rooms or facilities within the complex might be named for appropriate individuals but not the building itself. The proposition was made official policy, but then Walter Mackenzie died.

He succumbed quickly to cancer in January 1979, only weeks after completing his final assignment, a study for the Alberta Medical Association which recommended seatbelts in automobiles.

In March the board rescinded the no-name policy, as Dean Cameron advanced the convincing argument: "Dr. Mackenzie was one of the few Canadian physicians of truly international reputation and the man who was in no small measure responsible for the development of this medical centre from a purely provincial one to one of national and international stature."

On March 7 the board agreed that the mammoth complex be designated the Walter C. Mackenzie Health Sciences Centre. This pleased almost everybody, but raised concern about identity, fear that the traditional University of Alberta Hospital might be shuffled out of public awareness. It was obvious that the hospital had become plural. To retain tradition and recognize the acquisitions the board proposed that the name be pluralized. This course was accepted by the government. The University of Alberta *Hospitals* Board was to be recognized as owner of the University of Alberta Hospital, the Aberhart Hospital, the Edmonton Veterans Hospital (the Mewburn acquired officially December 31 1979) and the Walter C. Mackenzie Health Sciences Centre.

Pluralism was achieved through Chapter 51 Statutes of Alberta 1980, but by the time the act received royal assent on May 22 concerns about identity were dwarfed by urgent worry about costs of the Mackenzie Centre.

When the fence went up around the site in 1977, all assumed that the struggles were over, and apart from days when the contractors would be asked to keep the Franki earth packers quiet until noon so lab procedures could be carried out free of vibration, they could forget about the health sciences centre and get on with patient care, teaching and research. And so it seemed till early 1980 when unexpected news of serious problems with financial and other controls heralded a new age of anxiety. There are conflicting perceptions about the reports and what went wrong, if in fact anything did go wrong, but the government's perception was so vivid that Phase II was in severe jeopardy.

The board's perception of what happened on Phase I led to a lawsuit naming all the principal suppliers of service. As this was written the case (with all matters pertaining) was before the courts and therefore off limits, but the process should eventually add a rare judicial dimension to an epic case study of a public project unique in size, scope, innovation, complexities born of human desire for the latest in excellence, and emotion generated.

There is an important human factor to be noted about the unwelcome surprise. The people who had fought so hard and long to get the project underway were largely gone. They had stepped aside with satisfaction in the belief that the centre was coming up not only steel and concrete, but roses as well, and a new set of people had taken over in the same belief.

At government level Dave Russell replaced Gordon Miniely as Minister of Hospitals and Medical Care.

At project level Victor Jackson went to the Alberta Research Council, and his place was taken by Gordon Pincock, formerly assistant to Bernard Snell, who had made a study for the board on problems with the work.

At board level Gordon Wynn retired after 14 determined years and Peter Owen, the hospital's solicitor since the post-war, became chairman. The senior member of the board was Bill Astle, who had joined only in 1976. Newcomers were Mrs. Dorothy Horton, Mrs. Nancy Lieberman, Don Sprague, Les Mabbott and Ivan Finlay. (Bill McMullen, a chartered accountant, died suddenly in 1979 and an art gallery in the Mackenzie Centre is named for him. Jock Bell came in '81). From the university Tim Cameron was still dean, but Myer Horowitz had replaced President Harry Gunning. Dr. Peter Allen represented the medical staff.

The new people, serene in the belief that the project was on time and on budget were caught in a situation fraught with dismay for them and danger for the hospital. Phase I was bound to be completed, whatever the cost, but Phase II hung twisting in the wind.

The prospect of Phase II being cancelled was daunting. The hospital would be stranded half-in half-out of the future, in a mishmash of buildings dating from the ages of the Model-T to the space ship, which would have worked as a general hospital but could never become a "world-class" medical centre. An opportunity which would come this way but once was in danger of slipping away. Phase II and the designation "more than a hospital" hung in the balance from mid-1980 to early '82.

The government had to be convinced all over again, and this time not only that the project was valid, but so were the figures. There was a distrust of figures showing costs — future, current, even past figures seemed to grow if not watched. And the press wasn't helping. In making the medical centre a demonstration project of the Heritage Fund the government had attracted media attention to the project and to itself. On the principle that "good news is no news" the press ran horror stories based on leaked figures under such banners as Extra Millions for Hospital Raise Questions, Health Care Construction Costs

Double, Triple-Cost Nightmare. By the time ex-cabinet minister Roy Farran got to it in his newspaper column it had quadrupled. "Hospitals are notorious money eaters," he wrote, "but the (Mackenzie Centre) takes the biscuit. Its cost is now expected to be four times the original quote. . ."

The hospital board labelled the stories "distortions," but the denials drew little notice compared to the charges.

"It was a traumatic time," observes Peter Owen, chairman of the ambushed board, "but Bernard Snell was the very best chief executive officer we could have hoped for. He was a dynamo and he was a man of so many parts. He is recognized worldwide for his skills as a hospital administrator. He was a storehouse of knowledge of what the board should know about its own hospital and others in the health care scene."

Every persuasion had to be employed — in voluminous documents describing changes in management and reporting procedures, in official meetings without number and in unofficial personal appeals. Bernard Snell and Peter Lougheed, who were personal friends, had a compact never to jeopardize the relationship by discussing the hospital. But the president broke the treaty to plead the cause. Eventually, in April '82, the board staked its reputation on a brief to the cabinet asserting that (in 1981 dollars) Phase I had cost $126 million and Phase II could be built for $207 million.

In May, as the Department of Radiology became the first to move into Phase I, the government authorized Phase II. "The best news we had in the entire nine years," says architect Tommy Groves.

Anxiety was to rule for some time yet, but when all the bills were in, "after all the howling and hollering" as architect Eberhard Zeidler describes it, the overrun on Phases I and II was 27 percent, which compared rather well with overruns on such public buildings as the Edmonton Convention Centre, Montreal's Olympic Stadium and the National Centre for the Performing Arts in Ottawa.

A detailed table showing the cost progression from 1975 to '86 will be found as an appendix. Here is a capsule summary:

In December 1975 the board presented to the cabinet a proposal to build the centre in two phases, total cost 135 million in 1975 "constant" dollars. The "constant" dollar is an invention of the economist, one which is adjusted annually, in this case to include the rate of inflation in construction costs. Because of the large amount of high-tech equipment which had to be purchased in the United States, it was also to include the exchange rate of the American dollar. When the board met the cabinet on December 19 1975 the U.S. dollar was worth $1.0154 Canadian. By 1986 it was running near $1.40. Between 1975 and 1986 135 million "constant" dollars became 332 million. The actual final cost was $412 million, leaving a difference of $80 million, or 27 percent.

The project went through three separate management structures and philosophies — directed by Victor Jackson to 1980, Gordon Pincock to 1985, and Bill Lavender to the final occupation, known as the commissioning. This term was a personal touch of Dr. Snell, wartime ship's surgeon with the British

Merchant Navy, who likened the process to commissioning a ship.

Among the 700 or so people who worked on construction there is played a private in-joke version of Trivial Pursuit, in which questions and answers are intelligible only to them. Questions are based on what Ian Stewart, project manager for PCL Construction, calls "the rich tapestry of events." How many contracts were issued on Phase I? How many amendments were issued? What department needed four inches of concrete shaved from the floor because the space was designed for the Mark II version of high-tech equipment and the leading-edge Mark IV version didn't fit? The answer to question one is 400. Ian

A glass crown for the Mackenzie Centre. The helicopter becomes an airborne crane to place a steel truss across an atrium. A new breed of cleaning staff will be needed to match the high-tech construction technique. Cleaning once meant floors mopped by orderlies. In the future it will include high-rise ceilings and people with the skills to get up there and let the sunshine in

Stewart plays the game well, which comes of being on the site seven years to the finish. Les Albert, the general superintendent, was there the entire nine years, a quarter of his career with PCL. Surveying the finished product from across 114th Street Les observed: "People think they see a five-storey building but there's actually twelve storeys, with the interstitial spaces and two underground levels. And there's forty-seven acres of floor space. It takes an awful lot of fellowship and understanding to put a project like this together."

Year after year they put it together, with steel, concrete, brick, tile and glass, acres of glass, raising a structure that is like many things other than a hospital. It's like the Crystal Palace of Victorian London, like the hanging gardens of Babylon, like three high-rise apartments, like a flow of Mediterranean plazas, like an H.G. Wells version of the future, a place in which pipes and elevators are visible, but so are the corridors — transformed from endless clattering tunnels to free open balconies.

It all went up smoothly. While the board was enduring a kind of hell the only incident setting back the builders was an encounter with high water. It came at the close of a day when Phase I was down to finishing touches. A plumber testing a fire-hose cabinet on an upper level neglected to set a plug back on the line. By the time a security guard noticed water on ground level and the flow was stemmed a three-inch pipe had spewed water under 80 pounds pressure for thirty-five minutes. On floors below carpets were soaking and drywall no longer dry.

The nine-year job is commemorated by a welter of statistics. Les Albert likes the one about "date of substantial completion" on Phase II. It was ready on February 10 1986, eighteen days ahead of schedule. But his favorite figure is one that doesn't exist. "There's a rule of thumb that a project like this takes half a dozen lives. We didn't lose a soul."

There've been some welcome awards to display on the soft-toned walls. In 1984 came an award of merit for graphic design from the National Design Council of Canada. In 1986, as commissioning neared completion, the hospital received a Governor General's Gold Medal for architecture — in a competition sponsored by the Royal Architectural Institute of Canada. And the hospital also appeared to be in line for an unofficial but immensely significant "pharmacy" award. When the first group of 300 patients moved to the garden environment of Phase I the pharmacy noted the demand for analgesics and tranquillizers going down sharply — perhaps by a third. With the transfer of patients to Phase II the discovery was to be the subject of a scientific study by the nursing research team. A hospital report predicts: "The findings of this research project could well have far-reaching impacts for the future of hospital design and architecture of public facilities."

*John W. Scott
Health Sciences
Library*

# Chapter 29

# 1977—1986
*More Than a Hospital*

As the fence went up around the Mackenzie Centre a pilot project was starting to test a major premise of the design and of the Clarkson report on which it was based. It involved surgery. The premise was that outpatient service could be extended to surgery in sufficient volume to offset the required reduction in surgical inpatient beds. The design showed a day surgery ward of 40 beds with a hostel in backup.

The premise applied to all medical services. Having been adopted by the provincial government the Department of Ambulatory Care was being set front and centre in the architect's rendering.

The pilot project on surgery started exactly nine years after the board, acting on the best information available in 1968, had made the total disappearance of the outpatient department a future hospital policy. Circumstances have forced many a change in direction but this was 180 degrees.

The pilot project on surgery was directed by Dr. Andrew Masson, Chairman of Ambulatory Care, who apologizes for the word ambulatory. Ungainly, inaccurate and confusing. A patient once complained that a member of the Ambulatory Care staff had cut the sleeve off his coat. Investigation showed it was an ambulance driver, and nothing could be done about that. "But I'm afraid we're stuck with the name," he says, "it's a universal North American term."

Dr. Masson was perhaps the last man to come from the "negotiation list" of Walter Mackenzie. They met in the early '60s when a Mackenzie world tour touched down in the Caribbean and young neurosurgeon Andrew Masson showed the visitors around the University Hospital of Jamaica. For thirteen years he received a Christmas card and then an invitation to come to Edmonton to assist Lloyd Grisdale, whom he succeeded as chairman in 1976.

"I've just followed Lloyd Grisdale's plans," he says modestly. "He deserves all the credit. People generally aren't aware of Lloyd's many contributions because he's so low key. The man who stirs things up gets attention and you need him, but at certain times you want someone with a slow smile to calm things down. I was made Chairman of Ambulatory Care because they wanted Lloyd to take over the project committee for the entire health sciences centre.

"Another who deserves a lot of credit is Dik Arendson, the Zeidler architect. He had a real feel for hospitals. He did our department, in addition to radiology and the operating rooms."

The pilot project in day surgery stayed on live status until March 1985 when outpatient service moved to the Mackenzie Centre, completing the evolution from a distant outpost across the river to an auxiliary station on the northeast corner of the main building to the front entrance of the hospital of the future.

"Being an inpatient is an unnatural feeling for anybody," he observes, "and even more for children. We operate one shift a day, starting at six-thirty in the morning and closing at three to give people time to recover."

It seems to a layman, such as this writer, that with the power in the computer someone might create a software program to calculate the equivalent in beds, patient days, and associated costs like nursing, saved by day surgery. Perhaps the most dramatic example would be a cataract operation. When the Clarkson Report came to the board in 1974 cataract surgery required that a patient spend ten days in a darkened hospital room with a cloth over the eye. By 1986 the same patient might be in and out the same day and be driving a car two days after that. 45 percent of gynaecological surgery is done in the day ward. So are operations on the nose, tonsils and adenoids, and surgery to correct strabismus (or squint) in children. Day surgery has also shortened the waiting period — in some things from nine months down to three.

Surgery is well-served. On the medical side almost any procedure ending in *oscopy* can be done in the day environment. Visitors strolling the plazas of the new centre see frequent works ending in *oscopy* — derived from the Greek word meaning "to look inside." Arthroscopy is perhaps most identifiable because of its constant appearance on the sport pages. With an arthroscope a doctor can make a small hole to look inside a knee and remove cartilage if necessary.

Gastroscopies take a load off the emergency service. "Here we've been able to separate out true emergencies," says Dr. Masson. "The corridors of the old place used to look like a conglomeration of stretchers in the Crimean War. Of course a true emergency is a matter of perception. If you have a bad stomach pain in the middle of the night that's a true emergency for you."

---

There is a gauge for measuring the effectiveness of an ambulatory care program. It's one of those "impossible dreams" but if totally successful there would be no Level 1 patients filling up hospital beds. Each morning of the hospital day every bed patient is assessed on a scale of 1 to 5, with the sickest placed in Level 5. The routine is called Patient Care Classification and rates each inpatient from the viewpoint of how much nursing care is required.

It was an important innovation of 1979 set up by a consulting firm rejoicing in the name *Medicus Canada* working with nursing unit supervisors and general duty nurses of the hospital. On a daily basis it determines the quantity and quality of care required and translates the information into numbers of nurses.

Hospital care is labor-intensive. The system appealed to administrators as a means of ensuring adequate care with justifiable expense. It also appealed to the funding source, the government, which feels comfortable with things which can be put in numbers.

It establishes ratios in effect twenty-four hours a day. At Level 1 one nurse might look after ten patients; at Level 5 two nurses are assigned to each patient. Each day's total is translated into "workload units" and staffing is done accordingly.

In the heroic past matrons Jessie Dickson, Margaret McCammon, Ethel Fenwick and Helen Peters had a rather primitive way to establish a ratio. They could total up all the nurses (staff and student) the board could provide and somehow spread this force over the patient population whatever it happened to be. Sunnier moneyed times gave Jeanie Clark and Geneva Purcell more resources. Patient Care Classification gave Mary Murphy and her successor Loretta Ytterburg (and *her* successor Pam Allan) a scientific base on which to satisfy the patients, the administration, the board and the government.

Bonita Price, who has been with Classification since the beginning, notes two other uses of the system. "Assessing the work of a nursing unit used to be all retrospective. We would analyze a sampling of patient's charts after discharge. Now that's done currently. The system has also proved itself in emergencies. During the nursing strikes at other hospitals in 1979 and 1982 we were able to move out Level 1's to make way for sicker patients."

Patients in the lowest category are independent of nursing support except for tests and medical procedures. Although in theory a tertiary care hospital would restrict itself to more serious needs the diagnostic skills in such a place attract people from afar. On a typical day 8 percent of beds will be occupied by Level 1 cases with one nurse serving ten patients.

Thirty-four percent, able to do some things for themselves, will be on Level 2, with one nurse able to serve about six.

Forty-nine percent with moderately-high dependency will be in Level 3, with one nurse to three. Examples might be children and people recovering from major surgery.

Eight percent will need one-to-one attention for all activities. Sick babies and obstetrical cases will be found at Level 4.

Level 5 was added atop the four Medicus categories by the University Hospital, to include people in intensive care units, the burn unit, or in for a heart transplant. A patient at this level needs two nurses in constant attendance monitoring all body support systems. About one percent will be judged Level 5.

---

Meanwhile a quiet revolution was occurring among the work patterns of people who delivered nursing service. In 1979 the board ratified a policy called Modified Work Week, which was already in effect in about a quarter of the nursing units. Modified Work Week was in fact a return to the twelve-hour day which nurses of previous generations had fought to escape. However, there was a difference. The old-time nurse worked it six days a week, while nurses of the '80s worked three shifts one week and two the next. An apparent step backwards it suited contemporary lifestyle, leaving a nurse long stretches free for family, and suited as well the hospital's new style of staffing to changing requirements rather than the greatest conceivable disaster. By 1986 the hospital employed 500 nurses full-time and some 900 part-time and casual.

---

Under the system which classifies patients according to the amount of nursing they require, the highest level is given to those in the burn unit. Formed in 1978 this unit became the best-publicized in the hospital and is significant beyond its service to humanity because of the unique involvement of the public.

Dr. Mac Alton, Chairman of Plastic Surgery, recalls how it happened:

"One day I got a call from the Shriners. They have burn institutes for children in Galveston, Boston and Cincinnati. The boss of the Cincinnati hospital was being brought to Edmonton to speak to a convention of physiotherapists. Would I like to meet him? We met and discussed what we could do in our hospital. Station 49 was empty. We thought we could convert it for $30,000 and the local Shrine said they could give us the money. Then something happened which I think of as an example of *serendipity* — an unexpected pleasant occurence. The firefighters came along and said they wanted to support the unit. They put on an annual magic show and through 1985 gave us three million dollars. And when the firemen finally came and told us they were through — it always happens with volunteer things, they start with enthusiasm and end with a few people doing all the work — serendipity struck again. The Shriners came back in.

"There's no better-equipped burn unit in North America. We used the money to buy equipment and for training the burn team. We set up a team of plastic surgeons, residents, nurses who have the most involvement with patients, physiotherapists, dietitians and social workers.

"And we expanded into research. With the firefighters' money we endowed a chair at the university. We put in $500,000, we persuaded the hospital to add $300,000 and the province matched the whole thing so we have that income for research.

"There are two financial advantages to this kind of funding. It takes a burden off the rest of the hospital and we get to use it *now*. In the normal budget process we might get what we need three years from now. And those are only the financial advantages. The greatest is having the public directly concerned with a phase of hospital operation."

---

Coincidental with the burn unit a service appeared which dramatized, and depended on, all medical progress since the first sufferer was boosted through the window of the Strathcona cottage hospital. The HOPE program — Human Organ Procurement and Exchange — came in October 1979. Growing out of the work of the transplantation laboratory it was funded by the province as a regional program (like dialysis) with a southern counterpart based on the Calgary Foothills.

Pauline McCormick, a nurse who did intensive care at the Royal Alex and dialysis at the University, has been in charge since the beginning, working under a HOPE committee. This is a multi-disciplinary committee, like so many in the hospital, which make it easy for the layman to get best medical care but hard for him to get a clear picture of how the hospital functions.

With her Liverpool-Irish lilt, Mrs. McCormick observes that success has depended on education — of the public and also the professions.

We used to need 50 offers to get 15 organs but now we seldom turn one down. The doctors know what can make an organ unacceptable. High blood pressure, diabetes, biochemistry, the AIDS virus. Age is also a consideration.

*371*

*1977—1986*

*1982 — "last rounds" are made at the Colonel Mewburn Pavilion. Patients move to the Mewburn Veterans Centre on University Avenue and this portrait of Frank Hastings Mewburn goes with the territory. Late in the '20s the University Hospital's crusty colonel made a fabulous subject for Noel Grandmaison*

There are no hard-and-fast rules, but we believe that a person can be a heart donor up to age 40, livers to 45, kidneys to 65 and corneas any age.

"We are dealing with death and dying. Many donors are accident victims. A time of sudden death is the wrong time to approach a bereaved family, but it is the only time. From the death of the donor to completion of surgery can be only 24 hours.

"To spare the family the additional trauma we promote signing the HOPE donor endorsement on the back of the driver's license. Surveys indicate that 80 percent of people *would* sign but only 50 percent *have* signed.

*Walter C. Mackenzie*
*Health Sciences Centre*
*main entrance*

Midway in 1986 HOPE had a waiting list in all categories.

After 1500 cornea transplants since 1965, 170 were waiting. After 434 kidney transplants since 1967, 96 were waiting. After six heart transplants since 1985 the list was growing. Livers have been accepted for centres where those transplants are done. Pancreases are accepted for research. Skin is often needed for plastic surgery following accidents. And with the limb-sparing program, in which whole cancerous bones are replaced, bone banks were starting in the University Hospital and across the country. Bones can be frozen and used when needed.

Pauline McCormick concludes: "As long as there is a waiting list there will be a HOPE program."

Heavy public support of this leading-edge service of the hospital was one of many signs of a new environment, a new mood, apparent to trustees of the University of Alberta Hospital Foundation. The Foundation has its own board, separate from the board of the hospital, but working in contrapuntal harmony with some interlocking. It had been chartered back in 1962 (Statutes Chapter 96) and empowered to "seek and receive" gifts for "advancing the position of the University of Alberta Hospital as a progressive treatment, teaching and research institution." But there had been no seeking and little receiving, with the fund of some $3 million coming in two lumps — the old Rockefeller grant of the '20s and the operating surpluses built up by Angus McGugan and his successors. For years there was fear the province might get its hands on these hard-won surpluses and then when the province agreed they could be transferred from hospital accounts to the Foundation fear arose that the federal government might seek to get its hands on them. Eventually these perils were skirted with diplomacy and finesse and by legislation of 1979 the money was locked away safely in the Foundation's vaults, where the income went to support hospital projects. But the Foundation had been created in a defensive mode and remained so until March 1984 when signs of a new environment in health care financing brought a sharp turnaround. The Foundation "came out of the closet," hired a full-time manager and went on record as being the fund-raising arm of the hospital.

The Chairman of the Foundation at the time was Elvin Christenson, who'd been a member of the hospital board for many years. He explains the new initiative:

"In Alberta hospital funds had all come from the government purse, but we could sense it wasn't without a bottom. We had an awareness of large fund-raising in Ontario where dependence on government had never been allowed to take hold. We also had an awareness of huge budgets to operate the Mackenzie Centre. The hospital had to have those extra things to attract leading medical people and realize its full potential. We thought we could play a role to make it happen. It would be a small role in dollars, but a leading role just the same. It's not sound or wise to look to government for everything. If we do we lose our independence."

The initial effects have been modest public awareness events. A ten-kilometer neighbourhood road race ending at the nurses residence was co-sponsored by the *Edmonton Sun*. A Festival of Trees, a one-night success at the hospital in 1985 was to expand to four days at the Convention Centre. The festival is a competition in the decoration of artificial Christmas trees ending with an auction. For direct fund-raising there was to be an approach to the corporate sector, asking help for health along with recreation and the arts. Also forming was a concept of an alumni association of hospital patients. About the ultimate size of the fund, Elvin Christenson observes: "We aren't sure what our target is, but if you're not talking millions you've missed the point."

1986 offered two good examples of those extras the hospital needs. A lithotripter, which dissolves kidney stones without surgery, cost $60,000. A boon to ophthalmologic surgery was a YAG laser machine. It cost $123,000 and $20,000 of that was a gift from the downtown Rotary Club.

———

Ex-patients have shown encouraging financial support. 1986 brought the first annual Open Heart Open. Organized by Tom Miles and Waldo Ranson in appreciation of a service which has allowed them to go on experiencing the triumphs and tragedies of golf, it was in aid of John Callaghan's Heart Surgery Research Foundation. Some 60 open-heart cases paid $150, including curling great Hec Gervais, who has a commercial as well as medical connection with the hospital. In the 1950s, when the barter of vegetables for health care mercifully ended, hospital potatoes were bought on contract and a major supplier was Gervais' St. Albert farm. And thereby hangs a reminder that a questionnaire filled in by the contestants confirmed an observation of Dr. Vant in Chapter 19. Asked what they remembered of their surgery they loved the quality of the staff but knocked the food.

———

Of course a person in hospital is out of tune psychologically when supper trays appear. If board vice-chairman Margaret Andrekson were to fly to Paris and bring back all the chefs from La Tour d'Argent there would be spectacular tantrums over trays rejected by patients as inedible. There is a widely-held misconception that the dietary service is a giant "meals on wheels" with everything trucked from Mill Woods. Actually the Patient Support Centre is a first-step production centre, first step in a process which takes advantage of deep-freezing and cry-o-vac packaging of individual portions and ends in 17 pantries, one for each nursing station, where components are assembled to individual order. In the pantries, an integral part of Eberhard Zeidler's "village" concept, cooking is completed on some items. Eggs, toast, coffee and tea are done on the spot. Tomatoes, which go limp and lifeless if sliced too soon, are also done on the spot. The service got a three-star review from columnist Larry Tucker of the *Edmonton Sun*, a surgical patient. He wrote: "I can't for the life of me imagine how any hospital could be more pleasant — for staff, patients and visitors. (None of ) those long gloomy corridors that make you feel like you're on the way to the gallows when you go for a stroll. This was too good to be true, I kept telling myself. Just wait till they bring round the dinner trays. Well I had a terrible time with supper. Not eating it, selecting it. A choice of seven appetizers, eight salads, four dressings, four cold salad plates, four sandwich plates, 10 vegetables — and get this, 17 hot entrees. It was unbelievably good."

---

All such reviews are gratefully accepted. The dietary service also nourished a growing staff. In 1977, when giant machines started shaking the earth along 114th Street the hospital had 3,517 employees. By 1986, with the Mackenzie Centre entering full operation, the payroll showed a total of 6,146. 3,226 fulltime employees, 2,124 part time, 846 medical students and residents, 120 third-and-fourth year medical students in clinical instruction. And personnel work had progressed to a new emphasis. From recording hours of work, to negotiating contracts, the emphasis for the '80s was on training programs for high-technology teams.

---

As the end of the construction era loomed brighter the board found itself in a process akin to post-war planning. When the stapling guns had fired their last volleys, when the last workman had packed his tools and cleared out, what then? This is a situation in which a board earns its money, though members did not take their honorariums, but turned them over to various comfort funds in the hospital. And the honorariums were for board meetings only. Under the provincial act committee sessions weren't recognized. As chairman Peter Owen expressed the problem:

"We had to define the role the hospital was to play, what use was to be made of the $425 million facility? We were being pressured by various users, all pushing in different directions. I identified four pressures:

---

1.   From members of the Faculty of Medicine who had offices in the hospital and treated some patients but whose main interest was teaching. They regarded the hospital as an adjunct of the medical school.

2.   From the attending staff, doctors with admitting privileges, who said 'nonsense, the medical school needs *us* — we don't need *it*.' They wanted a patient care institution and were incensed that the number of beds was being reduced.

3.   From researchers, who objected that the building was inadequate to serve a function equal in importance to 1 and 2.

4.   From a large constituency, inside and outside the walls, who felt that we should continue to be a community hospital serving the south side.

"We tried to reconcile these legitimate but conflicting interests. I think our feeling was that patient care, teaching and research are not conducted in isolation and patient care must never be overtaken or undermined."

As many minds grappled with philosophical problems of the future two concrete decisions had to be made which would affect the future profoundly. Both Peter Owen and Bernard Snell were preparing to retire, doubtless with some of the feelings of men who have been paddling a kayak through the Fraser Canyon and see a chance to come ashore. The board chose the new president. The new chairman was chosen personally by Peter Lougheed. It happened in 1984 when all sorts of terrible things were supposed to happen, but the Oilers won the Stanley Cup and Ross Vant celebrated his eighty-third birthday.

In April, Edge King was in his president's office at Canadian Utilities, preparing to retire after 17 years when an invitation came from the Premier's office — to breakfast on Friday the 13th. He checked to see how many others would be at the breakfast and was advised there wouldn't be any others.

"I tried to think of all the boards where there might be a vacancy," he laughs, "and was determined not to accept. But the hospital job came right out of the blue. Peter Lougheed told me the government was concerned about the costs of the Mackenzie Centre and they wanted a business person as chairman. There were still problems with construction. As an engineer I'd been involved in some big power and gas plants. I'd never even been a patient in the hospital so I jumped in cold. On May 31 I retired as president of Canadian Utilities, Northwestern Utilities, Alberta Power and Northland Utilities, and the next day I was chairman of the hospital board, at considerably less remuneration. And the last advice I got was from a friend who'd just read an article maintaining that 'Nobody Runs A Hospital!' "

With the departure of Bernard Snell it was the board's obligation to the community to not merely provide a replacement but ensure a succession. Somewhere out there was someone with the right stuff to enlarge the tradition. How would they recognize this person? They concluded that with the Mackenzie Centre near complete they needed someone with skills in operating rather than developing a major facility. This person would be recognized by a proven track record in running a large health care complex resembling the University of Alberta Hospitals. By tradition the chief executive officer, except for brief breaks, had been a medical doctor and the medical fraternity wished very much to see this continued. However, the current trend in the health care field was contrary to tradition. The final instruction to the selection committee (chaired by Nancy Lieberman) was simply to identify the best person available.

The quest led to several places, most notably Columbus, Ohio, home of Ohio State University Hospitals, the largest university-owned teaching hospital in the United States for half the time. Half the time? How could that be? Because bed counts fluctuate as wards close and reopen for renovations or seasonal adjustments and the rest of the time more beds would be active at the State University of Iowa.

The explanation amused the President at Ohio State, a Canadian.

Donald Cramp had grown up in Ontario on a farm near Owen Sound. In 1960 he took a degree from Ivey School of Business at London. Then he went on to Columbia for a master's in hospital administration, serving administrative residencies in New York City, Kingston, Ontario and Waterville, Maine. He was made a Fellow of the American Public Health Association in 1965. He joined the faculty of Ohio State's School of Allied Medical Professions in 1980, at age forty-one, was named President of the Hospitals, a complex of health care units — for active treatment, long-term care, cancer and psychiatry — bonded by the benefits and complications of clinical-academic-research entwinement. The selection committee made Donald Cramp their choice to run the University of Alberta Hospitals. He came to work on August 1 1984.

Meanwhile the vigourous retirement of his predecessor was being kicked off by a series of functions arranged by groups with which he had been associated. One was the air reserve, where he had served with the medical unit. 418 "City of Edmonton" Squadron laid on a bird's eye view of the scene of twenty-seven years' work — in secret conjunction with the hospital staff. As the Twin Otter flew low towards the buildings, big letters on a roof came in sight spelling out — *Good Luck Dr. Snell.*

However, as the flight continued, he found that his past luck had not all been good. The route included the Snell home in Quesnell Heights, where the pilot pointed out damage to the roof, caused by some forgotten hail storm and visible only from the air. Repairing the roof was a priority retirement project.

While Dr. Snell attended to his roof, Mr. Cramp was relearning the art of "working Canadian." After years south of the border he found that his timing was off. In the United States action and response have a *bang bang* quality. In Canada they have a distinct national characteristic, softer and slower. He was reminded of the old axiom of vaudeville performers expecting applause: "Wait for it! Wait for it!"

Positive response was essential if he was to put across the Cramp concept of what was meant by "more than a hospital." More than a hospital, it was a large and dynamic corporation handling $200 million a year.

From this concept he effected a major reorganization in just six months. It aimed to separate clinical and administrative functions, shorten lines of reporting, and emphasize "corporate research and strategic planning."

The revised structure took effect February 1 1985 and drew from Dr. Ross Vant the prized comment: "Young man, when I ran the hospital I had three assistants."

"We were on the airbus flying down to Calgary for a meeting at the Foothills," Edge King recalls, "and Don Cramp proposed his idea that we have an operations review. It was a big thing. The province agreed to share the cost and we hired Kellog and Stevenson to examine every operation of the hospital in detail. We were told that 25 percent of provincial hospital spending was on us and we knew we'd be hitting a new plateau of cost with the Mackenzie Centre, but no one had a handle on how much it would be. The review told us it would take an extra $28 million."

The inside view, second level
looking south. Construction
complete, people are about to
bring it to life

The operations review fastened a solid grip on the present, but what about the future? With the Mackenzie Centre an assured fact in terms of bricks and mortar what was its potential? And how was that to be achieved? Answers were sought through a process called *Vision 2000*, which attempted to codify the future — in five-year segments — to the turn of the century. It was a simulated round table discussion on a very large scale. Many people were approached for advice on where the hospital should be — in five years, in ten years, in the year 2000. Where should components be in relation to the hospital, the hospital in relation to others across North America? Where should it rank? Among 1,500

*From the air looking northeast 1986. Almost the same perspective as the aerial view of 1928 in Chapter 8*

acute hospitals in Canada, 8,500 in the United States — 15 teaching hospitals in Canada, 62 in the United States? In the view of Donald Cramp, who initiated Vision 2000, the process should reveal how it can be among the top ten teaching hospitals in North America. Tradition and capital having provided a facility second-to-none, how can exceptional people be attracted to it, and how can the roles of the hospital be so defined that individuals and institution reach full potential?

The process was organized by Gordon Pincock, who moved to Policy Advisor (Corporate Affairs), a new position in the mode of the large corporation. Staff work was done by Olga Szafran. The process needed a starting point, which was provided by the operations review and also by the hospital philosophy, written in 1968 but still valid. To these "givens" were added the proverbial "future considerations." What advances in medicine would be available at hospital level? What changes in the structure of society — an aging population for example — would affect demand for health care? What would be the government's capacity to respond?

These and other considerations were then put to the staff of the hospital. "The field managers at supervisory level really know the ability of the hospital to do things," Gordon explains. "We identified 150 areas of responsibility and asked the coordinator for each area to provide answers from the shared values and experience of their people. The report will make 400 recommendations, but the overriding answer will be: 'Where should be put our resources?'" Edge King adds: "Once Vision 2000 is agreed to, future budgeting will be tied to it." Budgeting means not money alone, but all needed resources. Dr. Tom Ward, Assistant Vice-President (Medical) comments: "In the past, everything could continue to grow. It can't any longer."

In Dr. Hepburn's day the only question was: "Can this hospital do it?" Capability is now taken for granted in almost any proposal. The hard question will be: "Should some other hospital do it?" Inevitably the hardest question of all will be posed: "Should some existing program, some popular program creating warm feelings and goodwill for the hospital, be shifted elsewhere?" There, as the beleaguered Hamlet said, will be the rub. But with wrong answers to the hard questions the vision of the year 2000 could be missed.

---

In 1985 heart transplants were the big hospital news story. In the community Dr. Dennis Modry became a household word, along with Khursheed Mellick, Dale Robinson and Wayne Yee who received the hearts. But behind the headlines was a case study of how decisions must be made in search of the future proposed in Vision 2000. It's the study of a *process*.

An essential forerunner to the process occurred in the summer of 1968, when first attempts at a local transplant program were foundering on the shoals of rejection. Dennis Modry, nineteen years old and hoping to be admitted to medical school, was transplanting animals in the lab at the invitation of Dr. Cec Couves, promoter of the program that faded. With an MD in 1973 Dennis was away to McGill, for five years general surgery followed by five more years of cardiovascular research and surgery. After that it was hard for a married man with four children to be a student again, but he felt deficient in immunology and was accepted at Stanford. "The most richly-endowed university in the world," he notes. "Twelve Nobel laureates were working there. When I stepped on the campus I could almost feel the cerebration." In his third year he was picked to head the transplant division, an appointment sought by 50 well-qualified specialists. Then, late in 1982, began "the process."

Dr. Elliot Gelfand made the first move. A paediatric specialist in car-

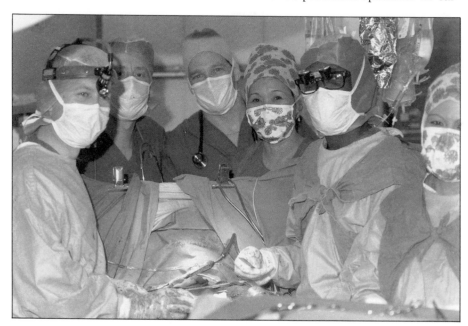

*July 28 1985 — smiling behind surgical masks, the team which has just completed the University Hospital's first heart transplant. From the left, Dr. Dennis Modry (surgeon), Dr. Daniel Vincent (anaesthesiologist), Dr. D. Duval (technician), Elma Arndt (cardiovascular operating room supervisor), Dr. D. Drakes (resident), Merna Najor (nurse)*

diovascular surgery was leaving. Would Dennis Modry be interested in coming home to take that place? He would be interested if he could do unlimited open-heart surgery — and could implement a transplant program.

Step two in the process was a meeting in Edmonton in January 1983 with representatives of three key constituencies: Bob Fraser, Chairman of the hospital's Future Roles Committee; Tim Cameron, Dean of Medicine; and Lloyd Grisdale, Deputy Minister of Hospitals and Medical Care. They agreed that he should carry on at Stanford and write a proposal for a transplant program.

The proposal took 200 pages, and most of 1983, in which time the nucleus of a transplant team was forming. Daniel Vincent, cardiac anaesthesiologist, spent six months at Stanford and worked on operations. Roger Amy, pathologist, took a course on transplants. Judy Boychuk, a Canadian nursing instructor, heard about the program and wanted to be part of it.

The process moved up a notch in March 1984 when Dr. Modry returned to Edmonton to join the division of cardiovascular surgery and begin selling the 200-page program. At this point he had done 25 heart (and three heart-lung) transplants, more than had been done in all of Canada. Seventeen months were to go before he would do another, and that was only because the process was speeded up.

The heart-lung program was competing with 17 others seeking to be added to the service of the hospital, all worthy, all seeking three steps of approval — from medical staff, board of the hospital, and government which has the money.

The Medical Staff Advisory Board relates to the board of the hospital as the Eskimos coaching staff relates to the club directors. Coaches work under chronic pressure of deciding among competing priorities within intractible limits. Club directors have influence but must rely on the judgment of the coaches. The board of the hospital has influence, which it used to accelerate the heart program, but must depend ultimately on the collegial wisdom of the medical staff to identify forces conducive to Vision 2000. For years the football club had to drop popular players to bring in new ones. The hospital was spared this unhappy aspect.

Dennis Modry attended 100 meetings, selling his program to every board and committee with a role in the decision. Eventually the advisory board made its recommendations on the 18 proposals, trying to place them in priority.

That was in March 1985. In the normal course of the process there would have been no transplants until 1987. Programs accepted by the hospital board would have been submitted to the government at the end of *calendar* year 1985. Fifteen months would then have elapsed — till the end of *fiscal* year 1986-87 — while the Department of Hospitals evaluated them and decided which it would fund.

But the board accelerated the process, with a pilot project of three operations, financed within the budget of the division of cardiovascular surgery. It was done with the understanding of Dave Russell, the minister, that it could be the basis for a permanent program.

In June the hospital sent 17 members of the transplant team to Stanford to work four days with their counterparts in nursing, physiotherapy, respiratory therapy, pathology, anaesthesia, social service and infection control. Dr. Modry circulated his book on transplant management. Judy Boychuk conducted seminars for the nursing team. Prospective recipients were identified by Dr. Jeffrey Burton. The HOPE program put out a call for donor hearts. On July 28 Khrusheed Mellick was wheeled into the operating room.

Mellick died later of pneumonia and a brain hemmorhage, but the first donor heart beat strong to the end. For Dale Anderson, operated on August 11, and Wayne Yee, November 5, life returned to normal.

In 1986 only this scale model existed of the Heritage Medical Research Building but on July 8 sod was turned for the real thing. It was to rise along 87th Avenue and provide research facilities comparable to those for teaching and patient care. Designed by the Woolfenden group of architects the services are set on the outside walls to allow for maintenance or replacement without disturbing work in the labs

With data from the pilot project the hospital requested money for a dozen operations in fiscal year 1986/87 — double the number later. With some needed reconstruction the start-up cost $2-1/2 million.

The decision faced by government was bigger than it looked. Alberta would, in effect, be providing a transplant centre for western Canada in a period of economic decline. Government was also venturing where ethics and economics were on collision course, an area where society might have to make ethical choices between a seeming-miraculous procedure benefiting one person and a less costly procedure helping 10. There were indications the decision would be put off till after the May 8 election, but in the last week of the campaign Premier Getty committed the government to the program.

Thus was "the process" completed on the question of whether the University Hospitals should do heart-lung transplants. But that was one question. Many others await the process.

---

1986 was declared a year for history, with events and projects to celebrate "80 Years of Caring." Within the anniversary year historic dates were programmed in advance, each date calling for another department to move into the Mackenzie Centre. Familiar things were left behind in older buildings including some A's. In keeping with current spelling custom in North America the painters made signs directing visitors to departments of Pediatrics, Orthopedics, and Gynecology.

The process was called *commissioning*, as of a great ship, and with each move steam built up leading to the completion ceremony. That event was programmed for September 16, 80 years after the first patient was boosted through the window of the Strathcona cottage hospital, 20 years after the board of the University Hospital took up the idea of a health sciences centre.

---

As history made measured advances on days scheduled by the hospital, a date of enormous significance was interjected by the Alberta Heritage Foundation for Medical Research. On July 8 sod was turned for a research building to match the capacity for teaching and patient care in the Mackenzie Centre. The seven-storey building along 87th Avenue was to correct a deficiency in the Clarkson plan which the hospital recognized in 1974, but the government remained unaware of till 1982 because the university didn't make an issue of it.

"Peter Lougheed was not happy to learn that further funds were to be expended," says Dr. Lionel McLeod, Executive Director of the Foundation, "but research space was inadequate. We could find only 8-9,000 square feet in the Mackenzie Centre. A unit of its size should have forty-plus people in research and that called for 50,000 square feet of assignable space."

The atrium feature of the Mackenzie Centre is in the design but displayed along the outside walls instead. This allows for a unit to be remodelled without disruption to others. It is to be named the Heritage Medical Research Building, owned by the university, but used jointly by university and hospital.

"The objective is not an ivory tower," Dr. McLeod continues. "We want clinicians from the hospital doing clinical research there, along with the people in basic research. There's a need to have at the bench the doctors actually treating patients. To make sure of the multi-discipline approach the Foundation has retained for 10 years the control of research space."

The building for which sod was turned on July 8 will be a symbol of what Bernard Snell calls "the indissoluble marriage" of hospital and university.

*The hospital has had some popular visitors in 80 years, but this is the all-time hands-down winner, with President Donald Cramp. It's July, 1985. She has come to meet the veterans in the foyer of the Mackenzie Centre, commemorating a royal occasion of 1939*

In 1986 two hospitals stood crowded on to a site intended for one, the face of the new hidden by many faces of the old. The Office of the President was sandwiched, literally and figuratively, between old and new, with a strange but compelling view of both. From the windows of his office, in a wing jutting out beside the new main entrance, the president and his visitors could observe the reddish-brown face of the Mackenzie Centre and the unadorned rear walls of buildings dated 1914 to 1960.

The president has entertained many visitors, domestic and international. A Winter Cities Conference was held in Edmonton and delegates applauded the

*What a site — 1986. The new hospital behind the cocoon of the old*

idea of "doming" applied to health care in a sub-boreal climate. A touring group came from the Soviet Union and their thoughts were the proverbial riddle wrapped in a mystery inside an enigma. "But the Chinese delegation was marvellous," says Donald Cramp. "They were here for the twinning of Edmonton with Harbin. I met them at the old hospital and showed them around. They were complimentary about the arrangements and the courtesy of the staff and wished they could have something as nice in Harbin. Then I took them into the Mackenzie Centre and they were speechless. And when I told them the old place they had admired was going to be demolished and the equipment sent to hospitals in Mexico, Columbia and India there was total disbelief. One said: 'Oh to be a Canadian.' Another wished it could be taken apart brick by brick and assembled in China."

There have been many local visitors. The Mackenzie Centre tends to leave them at a loss for words — the old red walls staring through the windows of the president's office have the opposite effect.

The visitors have worked within those walls, or their mothers worked there, or a friend was a long-time patient there, or their babies were born there. They tell the president, who is a latecomer, things he ought to know about those old buildings which have served their time, and served exceedingly well, things everyone ought to know if the hospital of the future is not to lose its humanity in high technology. They tell different stories, but on leaving make the same request. When the walls come down they want a brick, a common brick to have and to hold as a reminder of an institution that was always more than a hospital.

# Appendix 1

Annual Operating Cost of the University of Alberta Hospitals

Calendar year/Dollars

| Year | Dollars | Note | | Year | Dollars | Note |
|------|---------|------|---|------|---------|------|
| 1906 | 4,148.66 | *(09 months)* | | 1945 | 668,658.99 | |
| 1907 | 6,689.69 | | | 1946 | 897,429.43 | |
| 1908 | 5,708.75 | | | 1947 | 1,111,054.27 | |
| 1909 | 8,088.00 | | | 1948 | 1,277,616.10 | |
| 1910 | 10,148.64 | | | 1949 | 1,419,316.48 | |
| 1911 | 10,000.00 | | | 1950 | 1,712,656.13 | |
| 1912 | 14,732.56 | | | 1951 | 1,866,605.92 | |
| 1913 | 21,600.00 | | | 1952 | 2,276,101.47 | |
| 1914 | 43,500.00 | | | 1953 | 2,449,284.29 | |
| 1915 | 45,500.00 | | | 1954 | 2,718,303.29 | |
| 1916 | 45,800.00 | *(10 months)* | | 1955 | 3,085,729.00 | |
| | | | | 1956 | 3,362,624.00 | |
| 1917 | | | | 1957 | 3,696,200.00 | |
| 1918 | | *To March 31* | | 1958 | 4,729,341.00 | |
| 1919 | Military Hospital | *To December 31* | | 1958 | 3,881,123.00 | *(09 months)* |
| 1920 | No record | *To December 31* | | 1959 | 5,784,827.00 | |
| 1921 | | | | 1960 | 6,283,500.00 | |
| 1922 | | | | 1961 | 6,650,000.00 | |
| | | | | 1962 | 7,177,900.00 | |
| 1923 | Not separated from | | | 1963 | 8,004,800.00 | |
| 1924 | University accounts | | | 1964 | 8,821,100.00 | |
| | | | | 1965 | 9,774,000.00 | |
| 1925 | 245,908.17 | | | 1966 | 11,261,200.00 | |
| 1926 | 252,557.63 | | | 1967 | 13,162,600.00 | |
| 1927 | 267,224.69 | | | 1968 | 15,500,500.00 | |
| 1928 | 67,708.60 | *3 months to March 31* | | 1969 | 17,251,808.00 | |
| 1929 | 323,291.38 | *To March 31* | | 1970 | 18,757,000.00 | |
| 1930 | 332,197.15 | | | 1971 | 23,074,000.00 | |
| 1931 | 454,335.03 | | | 1972 | 26,289,000.00 | |
| 1932 | 487,251.85 | | | 1973 | 29,845,000.00 | |
| 1933 | 462,562.63 | | | 1974 | 37,426,000.00 | |
| 1934 | 436,742.23 | | | 1975 | 50,361,000.00 | |
| 1935 | 470,413.93 | *To December 31* | | 1976 | 57,461,000.00 | |
| 1936 | 515,257.65 | *To March 31* | | 1978 | 78,889,000.00 | *(15 months)* |
| 1937 | 498,892.44 | *To March 31* | | 1979 | 72,228,000.00 | *(12 months)* |
| 1938 | 520,272.76 | | | 1980 | 85,798,000.00 | |
| 1939 | 536,785.04 | | | 1981 | 104,969,000.00 | |
| 1940 | 528,584.89 | | | 1982 | 130,132,000.00 | |
| 1941 | 520,027.62 | | | 1983 | 157,271,000.00 | |
| 1942 | 572,357.54 | | | 1984 | 167,246,000.00 | |
| 1943 | 587,342.69 | | | 1985 | 178,572,000.00 | |
| 1944 | 610,443.05 | | | 1986 | 193,671,000.00 | |

# Appendix 2

*Walter C. Mackenzie Health Sciences Centre*

| Year | Phase I | Approved Changes Phase I· | Total Phase I | Phase II |
|---|---|---|---|---|
| 1975 Implementation Report | $ 86,394,800 | $ — | $ 86,394,800 | $ 49,162,600 |
| 1977 May 1 Base Budget | 99,100,320 | — | — | 6,046,000 |
| A Library Expansion | — | 3,825,200 | 102,925,520 | — |
| 1978 August 24 Cabinet Approval | 110,585,158 | — | — | — |
| A Planning Office Costs | — | 3,289,565 | — | — |
| B Escalation on Planning Office Costs | — | 291,200 | 114,026,683 | 62,691,840 |
| 1979 August 27 Cabinet Approval | 128,489,247 | — | — | — |
| November Phase II Approval | — | 1,807,829 | 137,297,076 | 83,659,000 |
| A Phase II Planning Office and Utility Relocate 2,250,000 | — | — | — | — |
| B Phase II Equipment Approval 83,659,000 | — | — | — | — |
| 1980 April Inflation Adjustment | 148,341,554 | — | 148,341,554 | 93,266,757 |
| Re-estimate to Completion March 1981 (April 1980 Dollars) | 188,448,000 | — | 188,448,000 | 126,880,000 |
| 1981-1986 Inflation Adjustment | — | — | — | — |
| 1986 Budget to Completion | — | — | — | — |

·*This does not include the recommended $4,000,000 Hospitals Board Contingency for a total budget of $415,473,499*

| Approved Changes Phase II | Total Phase II | Estimated Changes | Approved Inflation | Total Approved Changes | Total Project |
|---|---|---|---|---|---|
| $ — | $ 49,162,600 | $ — | 14% $19,588,920 | $ — | $135,557,400 |
| — | — | — | — | — | — |
| — | 56,046,000 | — | 8% 14,575,478 | 3,825,200 | 158,971,520 |
| — | — | — | — | — | — |
| — | — | — | — | — | — |
| — | 62,961,840 | — | 12.68% 35,149,724 | — 3,580,765 | — 176,988,523 |
| 2,250,000 | — | — | — | — | — |
| — | 83,659,076 | — | — | — | 220,956,076 |
| — | — | — | 11.57% 20,652,235 | — | — |
| — | — | — | — | — | — |
| — | 93,266,757 | Phase I: 40,026,446 Phase II: 37,872,243 | — | — | 241,608,311 |
| — | 131,139,000 | — | — | — | *319,587,000 |
| — | — | — | 91,986,499 | — | — |
| — | — | — | — | — | 411,573,499 |

# Appendix 3
*The University of Alberta Hospitals*

**The Board**

Egerton W. King
*Chairman*

Margaret Andrekson
*Vice-Chairman*

J.B. (Jock) Bell
Donald Brandt
Ivan G. Finlay
Dr. James Fischer
Ross J. Harris
Dr. Myer Horowitz
E. Lanny Mann
Gerald R. Pearson
Dr. Douglas R. Wilson
Norman Witten

**Senior Administration**

Donald A. Cramp
*President*

Dr. Peter B. Allen
*Vice-President (Medical)*

S. Pam Allan
*Vice-President (Nursing)*

Richard G. Bennett
*Vice-President (Finance)*

Donald Schurman
*Vice-President (Operations)*

J. Gordon Pincock
*Policy Advisor (Corporate Affairs)*

Douglas G. Fletcher
*Assistant Vice-President (Operations)*

H. Douglas Hooper
*Assistant Vice-President (Operations)*

Dr. T. Ward
*Assistant Vice-President
Medical — Administration*

Dr. A.F. Masson
*Assistant Vice-President
Medical — Outpatient*

Dr. W.B. MacDonald
*Assistant Vice-President
Medical — Academic*

Peter J. Portlock
*Managing Director
Corporate Affairs*

**Medical Staff Executive**

Dr. J.G. Purdell-Lewis
*President*

Dr. R. Wensel
*President-Elect*

Dr. M. Beaudry
*Secretary*

**Medical Staff
Advisory Board**

Dr. K. Walker
*Chairman*

Dr. J.G. Purdell-Lewis
*Secretary*

**Medical Departments
Chairmen**

Ambulatory Care
*Dr. A.F. Masson*

Anaesthesia
*Dr. W.B. MacDonald*

Dentistry
*Dr. B.K. Arora*

Laboratory Medicine
*Dr. H.E. Bell*

Medicine
*Dr. E.G. King*

Obstetrics and Gynaecology
*Dr. K. Mitchell*

Ophthalmology
*Dr. H.T. Wyatt*

Pediatrics
*Dr. P.M. Olley*

Physical Medicine
and Rehabilitation
*Dr. R.M. Feldman*

Psychiatry
*Dr. W.G. Dewhurst*

Radiology and
Diagnostic Imaging
*Dr. D.B. Russell*

Surgery
*Dr. B.K. Weir*

**Senior Nursing Personnel**

Dorothy Meilicke
*Director Nursing Service
and Systems*

Mary Pat Skene
*Director Nursing Research
and Education*

Donna Lynn Smith
*Director Nursing Service*

*Assistant Directors of Nursing*
Donna Armann
Nellie Beatty
Linda Buzzell
Louise Davis
Phyllis Kalynchuk
Ann Martin
Kathy Oberle
Elvira Pain
Marian Skidmore
Marilyn Wells-Annarilli